Exercises and Experir

Modern Chemistry

Teacher's Edition

H. Clark Metcalfe
John E. Williams
Joseph F. Castka

HOLT, RINEHART AND WINSTON, PUBLISHERS
New York • London • Toronto • Sydney

H. Clark Metcalfe

P.O. Box V2, Wickenburg, Arizona, 85358; formerly teacher of chemistry at Winchester-Thursten School, Pittsburgh, Pennsylvania, and Head of the Science Department, Wilkinsburg Senior High School, Wilkinsburg, Pennsylvania

John E. Williams

Formerly teacher of chemistry and physics at Newport Harbor High School, Newport Beach, California, and Head of the Science Department, Broad Ripple High School, Indianapolis, Indiana

Joseph F. Castka

Formerly Assistant Principal for the Supervision of Physical Science, Martin Van Buren High School, New York City, and Adjunct Associate Professor of General Science and Chemistry, C. W. Post College, Long Island University, New York

---

Editorial Development   William N. Moore, Roland J. Cormier, Pamela Hirschfeld, Betsy Mastalski

Editorial Processing   Margaret M. Byrne, Regina Chilcoat, Anne Drouillard

Art, Production, and Photo Resources   Vivian Fenster, Fred C. Pusterla, Robin M. Swenson, Russell Dian, Annette Sessa-Galbo, Beverly Silver, Anita Dickhuth, Louise Hannibal

Product Manager   Laura Zuckerman

Advisory Board   Rhenida Bennett, John W. Griffiths, David J. Miller, Douglas A. Nash, William Paul, George Salinger, Jean Slankard, John Taggart

Consultant   John Matejowsky

Researchers   James R. George, Erica S. Felman

Safety Consultant   Franklin D. Kizer, Executive Secretary, Council of State Science Supervisors, Inc.

The topics in *Exercises and Experiments in Modern Chemistry* are arranged to follow the order of presentation in *Modern Chemistry,* 1982 edition. *Exercises and Experiments in Modern Chemistry* may be used with any current high school chemistry textbook by adjusting the sequence of topics.

The exercise section is divided according to the unit organization of the 1982 edition of *Modern Chemistry.* The exercises supplement the work in the textbook. It is recommended that the assignment from the textbook be studied before the corresponding exercise is undertaken. Regular use of an exercise book helps students to establish good work and study habits. Complete answers to the exercises appear in the *Teacher's Edition Exercises and Experiments in Modern Chemistry.* On the completion of a chapter and/or unit, the class may be given the appropriate test from *Tests in Modern Chemistry,* 1982.

Users of past editions of *Modern Chemistry* will recognize a complete revision of the experiments section of *Exercises and Experiments in Modern Chemistry.* A research study has revealed that such a revision was desirable and timely. A smaller number of workable laboratory assignments was chosen and presented in a different format adaptable to the time requirements of any current chemistry course in secondary schools. Tighter safety regulations were incorporated in rewriting and redesigning the experiments. These new features are completely described below.

How the Experiments Are Organized

Title and Introduction. An opening paragraph sets the theme for the experiment and reviews major concepts that are pertinent to the experiment. Each experiment in turn is correlated to a chapter in *Modern Chemistry,* 1982. This allows students to interrelate their laboratory experience with what they learn from their textbook. A *Correlation Chart of Experiments with Chapter and Text Sections in Modern Chemistry, 1982* appears on pages T15–T16 and provides the teacher with an overview of the laboratory program.

Objective. The objective at the beginning of each experiment helps the student to understand what is to be learned or accomplished by performing the experiment.

Apparatus and Materials Lists. These lists enable the students to organize all apparatus and materials needed to perform the experiment. Knowing the concentrations of solutions is vital information needed in calculations and questions at the end of the lab. *Experiment Notes* on preparing for each experiment begin on page T17. The notes also provide instructions on preparing reagents. A list of *Chemicals and Apparatus Used* begins on page T38 and will help the teacher when ordering supplies for the year.

Safety. The SAFETY paragraph is placed at the beginning of the lab to alert the teacher and students to procedures for which special caution may be necessary. Stress the importance of adhering to the safety symbols and the safety material covered in the student's manual, pages 97 to 110. Important material on *Safety in the Science Classroom* is featured in the *Teacher's Edition Exercises and Experiments in Modern Chemistry,* pages T1–T14. We suggest that all science teachers review the safety material in this section prior to beginning the school year.

Recording Your Results—Observations—Data. A simple directive is given to the student stating where to record results, data, or observations during the course of an experiment.

Procedures. When following the procedures of an experiment students are performing concrete laboratory operations that duplicate the fact-gathering techniques used by professional chemists. The students learn the "chemist's skills" in the laboratory.

Data and Calculations Tables. The data the student should accumulate during the progress of an experiment is organized into a separate and distinct table. The entries in turn that the student will make in the Calculations Table emphasize the mathematical-physical-chemical relationships that exist among the accumulated data. Both tables help the student to think logically and to formulate a broad generalization as to what occurred during experimentation. The teacher is provided with a set of typical student data for each experiment.

Calculations. Space is provided for all math work and computations based on the data gathered by the student. All student answers should be entered into the Calculations Table. The solutions to all problems are found in the *Teacher's Edition Exercises and Experiments in Modern Chemistry.*

Questions. Based on the data and calculations the student should be able to develop a plausible explanation for the phenomena observed during experimentation. Questions are asked, and the student must draw conclusions that are pertinent to the objective of the experiment. Answers to all the questions appear in the *Teacher's Edition Exercises and Experiments in Modern Chemistry.*

Further Experimentation and Correlating Your Facts. These sections help to stimulate and guide project activity or serve as a review of major concepts covered in the lab experiment and textbook.

The authors and publisher wish to acknowledge the work of Mr. Dean M. Hurd, chemistry teacher at Carlsbad High School in Carlsbad, California. Mr. Hurd served as a writer and consultant to the editor in selecting, revising, and rewriting the present list of experiments. We also wish to acknowledge helpful suggestions from Mr. Stanley Starr, Chairman of the Science Department at Briarcliff High School in Briarcliff Manor, New York, and Mr. William P. Stuchell, Chairman of the Science Department at Punxsutawney Area High School in Punxsutawney, Pennsylvania, for corrections and amendments to the contents of previous editions of *Exercises and Experiments in Modern Chemistry.*

Table of Contents

SAFETY IN THE SCIENCE CLASSROOM

EXPERIMENTS

Safety in the Science Classroom

It is important that students learn how to think scientifically and solve problems through the use of scientific processes. Students should be given the opportunities to engage in scientific work through laboratory and other "hands-on" activities. However, unless safety precautions are taken to protect the students and others during the performances of certain science activities and experiments, science programs could become dangerous to the student and teacher.

The responsibility for safety and the enforcement of safety regulations and laws in the science classroom and laboratory are those of the principal, teacher, and student—each assuming his or her share. This means that proper attitudes toward safety should be developed from the outset. The safety material featured in the front sections of the Teacher's Edition and Pupil's Edition of **Exercises and Experiments in Modern Chemistry** was designed to aid all participants in accomplishing this end. This information on safety is not intended to be all-inclusive, for no publication could possibly list safe practices for every science classroom situation. Nor should the information be read as legal requirements, but as suggestions and recommendations for the establishment of a safety base upon which to build.

It is important that teachers and students study and review the safety sections featured in this edition of **Exercises and Experiments in Modern Chemistry** prior to performing experiments or working in the laboratory (see pages 97–110). In addition, the safety techniques and skills emphasized in Experiment 1, *Laboratory Procedures,* should be practiced and adhered to by everyone participating in the *Modern Chemistry* laboratory program. By following the recommended safeguards and precautions written in this lab course, you will be fostering good safety habits.

OSHA

The Occupational Safety and Health Act of 1970 established two agencies, one of which has issued a wide range of safety and health regulations and has the authority of enforcement.

During its first two years, OSHA was obliged to issue many regulations quickly. As a result, it seldom went through the lengthy procedure of drafting its own rules. Instead, it adopted many voluntary "consensus standards" previously developed by such groups as the American National Standards Institute, National Fire Protection Association, Compressed Gas Association, American Conference of Governmental Industrial Hygienists, and American Society for Testing and Materials.

In more recent years, OSHA has drawn up many regulations on its own, often based on recommendations forwarded by the National Institute for Occupational Safety and Health (NIOSH). This practice is expected to become more and more the norm in the future.

OSHA and the States

Federal OSHA regulations apply only to those states which do not have their own OSHA-approved plans for protecting safety and health. In states with OSHA-approved plans, the safety and health rules are enforced by state OSHA officials rather than by federal compliance officers. To be OSHA-approved, a state safety program does not have to be identical to OSHA's program. It must, however, be "at least as effective as" the federal OSHA program.

As of early 1977, twenty-three states had an OSHA-approved plan that enables them to adopt and enforce their own safety and health regulations. These plans regulate employers in both private organizations (such as companies and private universities) and state organizations (such as state universities, hospitals, and laboratories). Teachers who are interested in determining whether there is a plan in their state and what provisions are required, should contact their district safety officer, or phone a regional or area office of OSHA.

In the remaining twenty-seven states (along with six other jurisdictions, such as the District of Columbia, Puerto Rico, and the Virgin Islands), federal OSHA regulations control the safety and health practices of all private organizations. Each of these states, however, enforces its own rules governing state and local organizations (including school systems).

It is recommended that teachers be aware of this federal act that was passed to provide health and safety standards primarily for private industry. Many of the states with an approved state plan have extended these standards to public agencies, including schools. Questions that may arise regarding a particular safety practice should be referred to one of the ten regional or 121 area offices of OSHA.

Inspection of Workplaces

OSHA has an expanding staff of compliance officers who inspect work sites to see whether they meet the agency's safety and health standards. Almost always, these inspections are made without advance notice. However, advance notice may have to be given if, for example, the inspection is in response to an employee complaint about a possibly hazardous condition that occurs only during certain phases of an operation.

In-Service Training Programs

A State Science Supervisor may elect to design a detailed program to manage and implement safety training for the high school teachers in that state.

Such plans can be geared to the special needs and requirements of the particular state. Reference documents include the Federal Occupational Safety and Health Act 1970 and corresponding regulations, state laws, and regulations of this type, and other similar or related standards from private industry and agencies.

Science teachers are encouraged to initiate and participate in an In-Service Training Program on safety in the science classroom. Contact your regional OSHA office or State Science Supervisor concerning such safety training programs.

Laboratory Safety Guidelines

The following is a list of some of the safety guidelines that teachers should follow in the science laboratory.

1. All science laboratories should have and use the *Safety Control Equipment* listed and described on pages 100–102. Review the use and location of each piece of equipment with your students.

2. Teachers should know the location of and how to shut off utilities. Label or color code all master shut-offs clearly.

3. Always perform an experiment or demonstration prior to allowing students to do the activity. Look for possible hazards. Alert students to potential dangers. Safety instructions should be given each time an experiment is begun. Review all safety symbols and cautions specified in the experiment. See pages 99–100, *Safety Symbols.*

4. It is recommended that teachers receive certification from the American National Red Cross in First Aid. Every science laboratory should have a properly equipped First Aid Kit. One copy of the Red Cross book, *Standard First Aid and Personal Safety,* should be kept with each First Aid Kit. It is also recommended that a chart showing proper treatment for specific injuries be prominently posted.

5. Demonstrations involving hazardous chemicals must be so arranged as to shield both pupils and teachers from mishap. Even when there is no likelihood of an accident, pupils should be asked to evacuate seats directly in front of the demonstration table whenever there is any possibility of injury to them by the spattering of a chemical, an overturned burner, inhalation of fumes, etc.

6. The following phone numbers should be posted right next to the telephone for use in case of an emergency.

Rescue Squad _____

Fire _____

Police _____

Hospital _____

Duke Poison Control Center _____(919) 684-8111_____

The **Duke Poison Control Center** is open 24 hours a day. Its purpose is to advise physicians and individuals on procedures and treatment relating to any type of poisoning.

7. Make accident reports promptly, accurately, and completely. A standard report form, as shown on page T13, can be used to report such incidents and ensure that all necessary information is recorded.

8. Teachers should dispose of dangerous waste chemicals and materials as prescribed by appropriate standards and the laws for your community. See page T8, *Chemical Disposal,* for further information.

9. Teachers should have a thorough understanding of the potential hazards of all the materials, processes, and equipment that will be used in the school laboratory. See page T5, *Storage Facility for Chemicals,* and page T7, *Storage of Chemical Reagents,* for further information.

10. Teachers should excuse students having medical problems that could be aggravated by certain conditions or prevent the student from being able to safely perform certain activities. Teachers should prohibit the wearing of contact lenses in the laboratory unless certified written permission is obtained from the student's doctor and parents.

11. It is recommended that an ongoing safety audit of classroom and laboratory facilities be conducted by teachers, students, and administrators. A form, such as the one on page T14, could be used to indicate areas needing attention by maintenance staff, teacher, etc. As conditions are corrected, a notation could be made on the form which would be kept on file for future reference.

12. Teachers should keep an inventory of all chemicals stored in the laboratory. A list of all chemicals should be kept on hand along with the amount of each chemical purchased and the date it was obtained (see the example on page T9). Additions to and deletions from this list should be made whenever necessary.

13. All reagent bottles should be prominently and accurately labeled with labeling materials not affected by the reagent. See page 103, *Labeling,* and review the safety material with your students.

14. Laboratories and storage facilities should be locked at all times when not under direct supervision of a responsible person. See below, *Storage Facility for Chemicals,* for further information. Students should not have indiscriminate access to the laboratory stock room and should never be permitted to study, work, or experiment without competent supervision in the laboratory.

15. Extra precaution should be taken when handling volatile liquids such as ether, gasoline, alcohol, carbon disulfide, etc. These chemicals should be used in very small quantities and in a well-ventilated room. **NEVER** allow open flames from burners, matches, or lighters near such volatile liquids, for they are highly flammable. Before undertaking the use of such hazardous materials in the laboratory, teachers should ask themselves, "Is the educational objective valuable enough to warrant the risk and precautionary measures?" Teachers should also caution students about the use of these chemicals outside the school.

16. Special precautionary measures should be taken by teachers when cleaning up mercury spills. See page T8, *Chemical Disposal,* for further information.

17. All laboratory equipment and apparatus should be free of asbestos material. Many safety supply companies offer ceramic-fibered materials that serve as an excellent replacement for asbestos.

Storage Facility for Chemicals

A proper storage facility is essential to the safe operation of any science laboratory. Provision should be made for an inside central storage room of chemical reagents. An inside storage room allows the use of an inventory control system and provides fire protection and security. There are three critical elements that must be dealt with when siting, designing, and constructing an inside storage facility. They are fire protection, chemical exposure protection, and protection against criminal and careless acts.

Fire Protection

1. The walls, floor, and ceiling should be constructed of fire-resistive materials.
2. The storage room should be liquid-tight where the walls join the floors.

3. Provide for a drain in the floor and a water tap so that spilled materials can be flushed away. The floor should be at least four inches lower than the floors of the surrounding rooms, especially where flammable liquids are stored.

4. All doors should be approved, self-closing fire doors.

5. A fire extinguisher should be immediately accessible. The multipurpose type covers class A, B, and C fires. Class D type fires include fires of combustible metals. They require a special extinguisher powder. Dry sand applied with a scoop may also be used to extinguish small class D fires. Contact your local fire department for additional information and demonstrations on how to extinguish fires.

6. Storage rooms should be well-ventilated and have explosion-proof lighting.

7. Flammables and highly dangerous chemicals should be locked in a fire-resistant cabinet with proper ventilation when a central storage facility is not available.

8. All electrical outlets and equipment must be properly grounded. The switch and light fixtures should also be of the sparkproof variety.

9. Refrigerators used to store chemicals should be of the explosion-proof design. **NEVER** use a standard household or commercial refrigerator.

10. No source of heat or fire, including open flames and smoking, should be permitted in the storage area.

11. Gas cylinders should be secured against falling over and stored away from heat sources.

Chemical Exposure Protection

1. Be aware of the types of chemicals stored. Keep an inventory of the contents of the storage room.

2. All chemicals should be adequately labeled.

3. Preparing solutions or mixing chemicals should not be permitted in the storage area.

4. Laboratory chemicals and student equipment should not be stored in the same room.

5. The condition of stoppers, caps, and containers should be checked regularly to see that fumes, liquids, etc. are properly contained. Old paper containers or containers with metal caps are hazardous, and you should dispose of them. Only use containers approved by safety supply companies.

Exercises and Experiments in Modern Chemistry, Teacher's Edition
Holt, Rinehart and Winston, Publishers

6. Reagent shelves should be equipped with a ledge or restraining wire to prevent slipping or sliding of bottles or glassware.

7. Emergency instructions of procedures for fires, explosions, chemical reactions, spillage, and first aid should be conspicuously posted near all storage areas.

Protection Against Criminal and Careless Acts

1. The chemical storage area should have a sturdy door with a good lock.

2. The chemical storage area should be secured at all times when not in use, with access only to authorized personnel.

3. Students should **NOT** be admitted to the storage room. Nor should any student be allowed in the preparation area without supervision.

Storage of Chemical Reagents

Many science laboratories store reagents on the shelves in alphabetical order to facilitate retrieval of individual chemicals. Although it is a convenient system for storage and retrieval, it may result in incompatible chemicals being stored close to one another and create a potentially hazardous condition. For example, strong oxidizing materials should not be stored next to organic materials. In fact, all potentially hazardous chemicals should be segregated from the less dangerous. This does not mean that they have to be stored in another room or cabinet. They can be stored on another shelf or on the other side of the room.

A suggested Chemical Storage Pattern is found on pages T10 and T11. It was taken from the *Chemical Catalog Reference Manual of Flinn Scientific, Inc.* However, as the note on page T10 states, "Surely this list is not complete and is intended only to cover the materials **possibly** found in an average school situation. This is not the only method of arranging these materials and is purely suggested."

Also, the teacher should particularly note that Holt, Rinehart and Winston, Publishers is not recommending that you store or use all of the chemical reagents in the list on pages T10 to T11 taken from the *Flinn Scientific, Inc. Chemical Catalog Reference Manual.* The chemical reagents needed to perform the experiments in the **Modern Chemistry** laboratory program are found on pages T38 to T40. This *Modern Chemistry Chemicals List* is meant to help you in planning purchases of chemicals solely for the **Modern Chemistry** lab program. How the chemicals are stored is completely left to the professional judgment and responsibility of the teacher.

On page T12 you will find a chart entitled *Incompatible Chemicals.* Check your storage area and make certain these chemicals do not come in contact with each other as indicated by the chart. This information was taken from the safety manual *STOP—Safety First in Science Teaching* and was developed by the Division of Science Education, State Department of Public Instruction, Raleigh, North Carolina 27611. For those teachers who regularly handle less common but equally dangerous materials, a copy of the *Manual of Hazardous Chemical Reactions* is recommended for their high school science departments. This 470-page book is available for a modest fee from the National Fire Protection Association, 470 Atlantic Avenue, Boston, MA 02110.

Chemical Disposal

Disposal procedures of chemicals are numerous, and some are complex. However, the recommended procedures listed in the *Laboratory Waste Disposal Manual,* published by the Manufacturing Chemists Association, 1825 Connecticut Avenue, NW, Washington, DC 20009, should cover most chemicals found in the science laboratory. The above publication can be purchased for a modest fee and is highly recommended for school systems with disposal problems.

Small amounts of dilute acids, bases, or salt solutions may be flushed down the drain with large amounts of water. All material should be soluble in water. Volatile, carcinogenic, corrosive, toxic, or insoluble materials should never be flushed down the drain. Chemical waste should not be permitted to accumulate. Items should be properly disposed of immediately after they are no longer needed or wanted.

Immediately contact your local fire department or police squad to safely remove and dispose of hazardous materials, such as volatile organics, explosive gases, explosive compounds, poisons, and poisonous gases that could easily get out of control or that are outdated, obsolete, or in a state of deterioration or decomposition.

You can also contact your local EPA solid waste office for information on proper disposal of surplus or dangerous chemicals. Materials that will no longer be used should be discarded by a person qualified in chemistry. Assistance may be obtained from local fire and health departments and from the local American Chemical Society.

Mercury and its compounds should not be flushed down the drain. Mercury in solution can be precipitated with a solution of sodium chloride. The precipitate can be discarded with other solid lab waste.

Exercises and Experiments in Modern Chemistry, Teacher's Edition
Holt, Rinehart and Winston, Publishers

To clean up mercury spills (from broken thermometers, etc.) the following steps can be taken:

(a) Moisten 20 mesh zinc with 0.1 N hydrochloric acid.
(b) Allow the moistened zinc to stand 10 to 15 minutes.
(c) Pour the "activated zinc" on and around the mercury spill and leave it for a little while. The spilled mercury combines with the activated zinc, making it possible to sweep up.

Special powders to clean up mercury spills can also be purchased from safety supply companies.

Inventory of Stored Chemicals

The following is an example of how to set up an inventory list for stored chemicals.

Name of School:			Page 1	
Street Address:				
City/County:			Zip Code:	
Chemical Name	Amount	Date	Comments	
Acetamide				
Acetanilide				
Acetic acid				
Acetic acid, glacial				

Suggested Chemical Storage Pattern

Storage of laboratory chemicals presents an ongoing safety hazard for school science departments. There are many chemicals that are incompatible with each other. The common method of storing these products in alphabetical order sometimes results in incompatible neighbors. For example, storing strong oxidizing materials next to organic chemicals can present a hazard.

A possible solution is to separate chemicals into their organic and inorganic families and then to further divide the materials into related and compatible families. Below is a list of compatible families. On the next page you will find this family arrangement pictured as shelf areas in your chemical stores area. The pictured shelf arrangement will easily enable you to rearrange your inventory into a safer and more compatible environment.

INORGANIC
1. METALS, HYDRIDES
2. HALIDES, SULFATES, SULFITES, THIOSULFATES, PHOSPHATES, HALOGENS
3. AMIDES, NITRATES (EXCEPT AMMONIUM NITRATE), NITRITES, AZIDES, NITRIC ACID
4. HYDROXIDES, OXIDES, SILICATES, CARBONATES, CARBON
5. SULFIDES, SELENIDES, PHOSPHIDES, CARBIDES, NITRIDES
6. CHLORATES, PERCHLORATES, PERCHLORIC ACID, CHLORITES, HYPOCHLORITES, PEROXIDES, HYDROGEN PEROXIDE
7. ARSENATES, CYANIDES, CYANALES
8. BORATES, CHROMATES, MANGANATES, PERMANGANATES
9. ACIDS (EXCEPT NITRIC)
10. SULFUR, PHOSPHORUS, ARSENIC, PHOSPHORUS PENTOXIDE

ORGANIC
1. ACIDS, ANHYDRIDES, PERACIDS
2. ALCOHOLS, GLYCOLS, AMINES, AMIDES, IMINES, INIDES
3. HYDROCARBONS, ESTERS, ALDEHYDES
4. ETHERS, KETONES, KETENES, HALOGENATED HYDROCARBONS, ETHYLENE OXIDE
5. EPOXY COMPOUNDS, ISOCYANATES
6. PEROXIDES, HYDROPEROXIDES, AZIDES
7. SULFIDES, POLYSULFIDES, SULFOXIDES, NITRILES
8. PHENOLS, CRESOLS

NOTE: If you store volatile materials (ether, hydrocarbons, etc.) in a refrigerator the refrigerator must be explosion-proof. The thermostat switch or light switch in a standard refrigerator may spark and set off the volatile fumes in a refrigerator and thus cause an explosion.

Surely this list is not complete and is intended only to cover the materials possibly found in an average school situation. This is not the only method of arranging these materials and is purely suggested.

Reproduced with permission of FLINN SCIENTIFIC, INC.

SUGGESTED SHELF STORAGE PATTERN

INORGANIC	ORGANIC
TOP	TOP

INORGANIC #10
SULFUR, PHOSPHORUS, ARSENIC,
PHOSPHORUS PENTOXIDE

INORGANIC #2
HALIDES, SULFATES, SULFITES,
THIOSULFATES, PHOSPHATES, ETC.

INORGANIC #3
AMIDES, NITRATES, (Not
AMMONIUM NITRATE),
NITRITES, Etc.

INORGANIC #1
METALS & HYDRIDES
(Store away from any water)

INORGANIC #4
HYDROXIDES, OXIDES,
SILICATES, Etc.

INORGANIC #7
ARSENATES, CYANIDES, Etc.
(Store above acids)

INORGANIC #5
SULFIDES, SELENIDES, PHOSPHIDES,
CARBIDES, NITRIDES, Etc.

INORGANIC #8
BORATES, CHROMATES, MANGANATES,
PERMANGANATES, Etc.

INORGANIC #6
CHLORATES, PERCHLORATES,
CHLORITES, PERCHLORIC ACID,
PEROXIDES, Etc.

INORGANIC #9
ACIDS, except NITRIC

ORGANIC #2
ALCOHOLS, GLYCOLS, Etc.

ORGANIC #3
HYDROCARBONS, ESTERS, Etc.

ORGANIC #4
ETHERS, KETONES, Etc.

ORGANIC #5
EPOXY COMPOUNDS, ISOCYANATES

ORGANIC #7
SULFIDES, POLYSULFIDES, Etc.

ORGANIC #8
PHENOL, CRESOLS

ORGANIC #6
PEROXIDES, AZIDES, Etc.

ORGANIC #1
ACIDS, ANHYDRIDES, PERACIDS, Etc.

MISCELLANEOUS

MISCELLANEOUS
(NITRIC ACID)

If possible avoid using the floor since a spill may cause a reaction with
the spilled product and that material stored on the floor.

Incompatible Chemicals

Many chemicals react violently, produce toxic fumes, and are fire hazards when they interact. The chemicals listed in the left-hand column should be stored in a manner that will prevent them from coming in contact with those in the right-hand column.

Chemical	Should not come in contact with
Acetic acid	Chromic acid, nitric acid, perchloric acid, ethylene glycol, hydroxyl compounds, peroxides, and permanganates
Acetone	Concentrated sulfuric and nitric acid mixtures
Acetylene	Bromine, chlorine, fluorine, copper tubing, as well as silver, mercury, and their compounds
Alkali metals (K, Na, Ca), powdered aluminum, and magnesium	Water (K & Na), carbon dioxide, carbon tetrachloride, and the halogens
Ammonia, anhydrous	Mercury, hydrogen fluoride, and calcium hypochlorite
Ammonium nitrate (a deliquescent, hydroscopic, powerful oxidizing agent)	Strong acids, metal powders, chlorates, nitrates, sulfur, flammable liquids, and finely divided organic materials
Aniline	Nitric acid and hydrogen peroxide
Bromine	Ammonia, acetylene, butane, hydrogen, sodium carbide, turpentine, and finely divided metals
Carbon, activated	Calcium hypochlorite, all oxidizing agents
Chlorates	Ammonium salts, strong acids, powdered metals, sulfur, and finely divided organic materials
Chromic acid	Glacial acetic acid, camphor, glycerin, naphthalene, turpentine, lower molecular weight alcohols, and many flammable liquids
Chlorine	Same as for bromine
Copper	Acetylene and hydrogen peroxide
Flammable liquids	Ammonium nitrate, chromic acid, hydrogen peroxide, sodium peroxide, nitric acid, and the halogens
Hydrocarbons (butane, propane, benzene, gasoline, and turpentine)	Fluorine, chlorine, bromine, chromic acid, and sodium peroxide
Hydrofluoric acid	Ammonia (aqueous or anhydrous)
Hydrogen peroxide	Copper, chromium, iron (most metals or their salts), flammable liquids, and other combustible materials
Hydrogen sulfide	Nitric acid and certain oxidizing gases
Iodine	Acetylene and ammonia
Nitric acid	Glacial acetic acid, chromic and hydrocyanic acids, hydrogen sulfide, flammable liquids, and flammable gases which are easily nitrated
Oxygen	Oils, grease, hydrogen, flammable liquids, solids, and gases
Perchloric acid	Acetic anhydride, bismuth and its alloys, alcohols, paper, wood, and other organic materials
Phosphorus pentoxide	Water
Potassium permanganate	Glycerin, ethylene glycol, and sulfuric acid
Silver	Acetylene, ammonia compounds, oxalic acid, and tartaric acid
Sodium peroxide	Glacial acetic acid, acetic anhydride, methanol, carbon disulfide, glycerin, benzaldehyde, and water
Sulfuric acid	Chlorates, perchlorates, permanganates, and water

Exercises and Experiments in Modern Chemistry, Teacher's Edition
Holt, Rinehart and Winston, Publishers

RECOMMENDED
STANDARD STUDENT ACCIDENT REPORT

(check one)

☐ School Jurisdictional
☐ Non-School Jurisdictional

Recordable ☐
Reportable Only ☐

School District:
City, State:

General		
1. Name		**2. Address**
3. School	**4. Sex** Male ☐ Female ☐	**5. Age** **6. Grade/Special Program**
7. Time Accident Occurred Date: Day of Week: Exact Time:		AM ☐ PM ☐

Injury

8. Nature of Injury

9. Part of Body Injured

10. Degree of Injury (check one)
Death ☐   Permanent ☐   Temporary (lost time) ☐   Non-Disabling (no lost time) ☐

11. Days Lost
From School: From Activities Other Than School: Total:

12. Cause of Injury

Accident

13. Accident Jurisdiction (check one)
School: Grounds ☐   Building ☐   To and From ☐
Non-School: Home ☐   Other ☐   Other Activities Not on School Property ☐

14. Location of Accident (be specific)	**15. Activity of Person** (be specific)
16. Status of Activity	**17. Supervision** (if yes, give title & name of supervisor) Yes ☐ No ☐
18. Agency Involved	**19. Unsafe Act**
20. Unsafe Mechanical/Physical Condition	**21. Unsafe Personal Factor**

22. Corrective Action Taken or Recommended

23. Property Damage
School $ Non-School $ Total $

24. Description (Give a word picture of the accident, explaining who, what, when, why, and how)

Signature	
25. Date of Report	**26. Report Prepared by** (signature & title)
27. Principal's Signature	

This form is recommended for securing data for accident prevention and safety education. School districts may reproduce this form adding space for optional data. Reference: *Student Accident Reporting Guidebook,* National Safety Council, 425 N. Michigan Avenue, Chicago, Illinois 60611. 1966. 34 pages.

SUGGESTED SCIENCE TEACHER SAFETY CHECKLIST

SCIENCE TEACHER _____   SCHOOL _____

DATE _____

Any condition in-operative is considered unsafe. Check (✔) those items and location not safe and submit copies to the person(s) designated by your local school division.

ITEM	CLASSROOM #	LABORATORY #	STORAGE ROOM #
Door(s)			
Window(s)			
Floor			
Cabinet(s)			
Shelving			
Ventilation			
Lighting			
Heat (above 25°C)			
Water			
Waste Drain			
Fire Extinguisher			
Safety Shower			
Fire Blanket			
Eye Wash			
First Aid Kit			
Fume Hood			
Student Lab Station			
Instructor Preparation Station			
Instructor Demonstration Desk			
Master Water Cut-off Valve			
Master Electric Cut-off Switch			
Master Gas Cut-off Valve			
Chemical Reagents			
Disposition of Hazardous Materials			
Disposition of Unlabeled Materials			
Disposition of Unusable Equipment			
Glassware			
Other			

COMMENTS:

Courtesy of Virginia State Department of Education, Richmond, Virginia

Exercises and Experiments in Modern Chemistry, Teacher's Edition
Holt, Rinehart and Winston, Publishers

Correlation Chart of Experiments with Chapter and Text Sections in Modern Chemistry, 1982

Experiment	Text Chapter	Text Sections
1. Laboratory Procedures	1	1.14–1.16
2. Accuracy and Precision in Measurements	1	1.13, 1.17
3. Energy and Entropy: Phase Changes	2 20	2.14 20.7
4. Developing a Logical Model	3	3.2–3.3
5. Flame Tests	4 24	4.1–4.3 24.2, 24.12
6. Tests for Iron (II) and Iron (III) Ions	6	6.7
7. Water of Crystallization and Empirical Formula of a Hydrate	7	7.9–7.12
8. Mass and Mole Relationships in a Chemical Reaction	8	8.1–8.3, 8.9–8.10
9. Boyle's Law	10	10.7–10.8, 10.12, 10.15
10. Comparing the Masses of Equal Volumes of Gases	11	11.2
11. Molar Volume of a Gas	10 11	10.5–10.12, 10.14, 11.5–11.6, 11.10–11.11
12. Heat of Crystallization	12	12.11, 12.13
13. Solubility and Rate of Solution	13	13.5, 13.7–13.10
14. Freezing-point Depression of a Solvent	13	13.12
15. Reacting Ionic Species in Aqueous Solution	14	14.5
16. Hydronium Ion Concentration, pH	16	16.6–16.8
17. Titration of an Acid and a Base	16	16.2, 16.5, 16.10–16.11, 16.13–16.14
18. Percentage of Acetic Acid in Vinegar	16	16.2, 16.5, 16.10–16.11, 16.13–16.14
19. Carbon	17	17.2–17.12, 17.14

Experiment Notes

The following pages contain experiment notes that provide hints on preparing for an experiment and for performing it. All materials should be assembled and prepared in advance of the experiment. The amounts of chemicals or materials needed to perform an experiment are listed on a per student basis or on the assumption that a pair of students are working together. By looking at the listed amounts, the teacher should be able to estimate how much of the chemical or solution is needed for all students in each class.

In making up solutions, distilled water should be used. The amount of solution to be made up will vary with the experiment in which it is used and the size of the class or classes. This is also true of the number and size of the bottles used for dispensing the solution. Consequently, no general suggestions can be given. Estimate as best you can!

For convenience, the materials list also gives the amounts of materials needed for making up one liter of each solution. The teacher can readily make his or her own adjustments when preparing smaller or larger quantities.

Unless otherwise stated, dissolve the amount of the material indicated in distilled water and dilute to one liter.

The teacher should examine the APPARATUS list found at the beginning of each laboratory experiment. The apparatus list indicates the equipment needed to perform the experiment. For example, see page 165.

Exercises and Experiments in Modern Chemistry, Teacher's Edition
Holt, Rinehart and Winston, Publishers

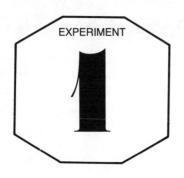

Laboratory Procedures

This experiment will take 2 periods to complete. After completing this experiment, the students should possess the lab techniques and safety skills necessary to complete the laboratory portion of the course.

Close supervision of the students is mandatory when they are working with glass tubing. Stress that tubing never looks hot. Also stress that they should never attempt to force tubing into stoppers with excessive force. Remind them that they should always wet the tubing and stopper, and always wrap the tubing with a towel.

The sodium chloride in parts 3 and 4 is reusable by each class if you designate a special container for the students to dispose of the NaCl after each part.

MATERIALS NEEDED per student or pair

Part 1 The Burner	copper wire, 18 gauge	10 cm
Part 3 Handling Solids	sodium chloride	5 g
Part 4 The Balance	sodium chloride	23 g
Part 6 Filtration	sodium chloride	3 g
	fine sand	3 g

Observing a Candle

This experiment can be completed in 15 minutes. The student gains experience in making scientific observations. Distinction is made between quantitative and qualitative observations, and between interpretations and observations. This simple experiment is an excellent way to begin the course in chemistry. Little or no prelab discussion is necessary.

MATERIALS NEEDED per student or pair

1 candle, with base   1 ruler   1 pack of matches

Accuracy and Precision in Measurements

This is an excellent experiment for demonstrating the concepts of accuracy, precision, and uncertainty in measurements. The experiment should be performed immediately after section 1.17 in the text is completed. For most students, procedure 4 will be their first practical experience with the concept of uncertainty. The wide variations in data for the identical object measured should provide convincing evidence for the need to express the uncertainty of every measurement.

Another excellent activity involving uncertainty is to have 5 or 6 stations in the lab that require each group of students to make several different kinds of measurements. Station one, for example, could make use of the

Exercises and Experiments in Modern Chemistry, Teacher's Edition
Holt, Rinehart and Winston, Publishers

balance. Station 2 could measure volume, etc. Some stations should require adding 2 or more measurements to demonstrate the additivity of uncertainty. For example, one station might require the determination of a length that is greater than the size of the ruler to be used. The variations in data under these conditions should be greater than when only a single measurement is made.

MATERIALS NEEDED per student or pair

metal shot (aluminum, copper, or lead)   around 18 g

Energy and Entropy: Phase Changes (Teacher Demonstration)

This experiment should be performed after section 2.14 in the text is discussed.

This experiment is an excellent demonstration of the energy and entropy changes that occur when a solid is heated and a liquid is cooled. It vividly shows the student that the temperature of a pure substance remains constant during a phase change.

Occasionally the acetamide will freeze at 69.8°C rather than 79.8°C. This is most likely due to overheating the liquid or allowing the acetamide to remain too long in the hot-water bath. To avoid this possibility, keep in mind to immerse the test tube of acetamide after the water bath has boiled and the flame has been lowered, and to remove the test tube when 90°C is reached. If the temperature drops below 75°C, remember to drop a few seed crystals in the test tube. Do not attempt to reuse the acetamide for this experiment. If less than 10 grams of acetamide is used, the loss of the flat portion of the melting curve may result. Also keep in mind, when cooling the acetamide, to scratch down any crystals that appear on the sides of the test tube above the liquid. This will ensure solidification at the proper temperature. Acetamide has a tendency to undercool, but if the above procedure is followed, the temperature will quickly rise back to the temperature at which crystallization begins.

MATERIALS NEEDED

CH_3CONH_2, acetamide (practical grade)   10 g
Consult a recent *NIOSH Registry of Toxic Effects of Chemical Substances*. Acetamide has been listed as "animal positive carcinogenic." Therefore, all necessary precautions should be taken by the teacher, if acetamide is used in this experiment as a teacher demonstration.

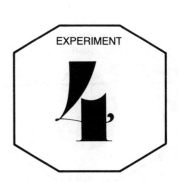

Developing a Logical Model

This experiment should take no more than 20 minutes to complete. The student is given an opportunity to develop his or her own procedure and then use inferential thinking to determine the approximate size, shape, and location of a hidden object inside a black box.

The black boxes can be inexpensively constructed using half-inch particle board shelving for the top and bottom pieces and 1″ × 2″ pine for the sides (this would be a good project for the wood-shop classes).

The unknown object can be a small piece of doweling, a small section of the 1″ × 2″ pine, etc. Make sure the object is well secured (attach with nails or screws and glue). Do not position the object in such a way that the marble could become stuck.

Emphasize that the objective is to determine the approximate size, shape, and location of the object and not its actual identity.

Flame Tests

Although the stated objective for this experiment is the development of an identification technique, it can also be used to introduce concepts that provide information about the behavior and the arrangement of electrons in atoms (sections 4.1–4.3). To emphasize this point, apply a high voltage to a gas discharge tube (helium or neon) and place a few crystals of sodium chloride on the grating of a lit Fisher burner. Then ask what the electricity did to the atoms of the gas in the tube, and what the heat did to the atoms in the salt.

Emphasize the importance of clean test tubes. At least one flame test should be demonstrated. Point out that the color lasts only briefly, and several trials are usually needed before the color of the flame can be determined.

MATERIALS NEEDED per student or pair

HCl, 6 M (516 mL conc./L solution)	60 mL
NaCl, 0.5 M (29 g/L solution)	4 mL
Ba(NO$_3$)$_2$, 0.5 M (131 g/L solution)	4 mL
Ca(NO$_3$)$_2$, 0.5 M (82 g/L solution)	4 mL
LiNO$_3$, 0.5 M (35 g/L solution)	4 mL
KNO$_3$, 0.5 M (51 g/L solution)	8 mL
NaNO$_3$, 0.5 M (43 g/L solution)	8 mL
Sr(NO$_3$)$_2$, 0.5 M (106 g/L solution)	4 mL
Dry NaCl	just a pinch for student to sample in flame

Tests for Iron (II) and Iron (III) Ions

This experiment can be completed in a single period. This is an excellent demonstration of dual oxidation numbers of a transition element.

The solution of iron (II) ammonium sulfate should contain 10 mL of concentrated sulfuric acid per liter. A substitute solution could be iron (II) sulfate. Add 10 mL of sulfuric acid and an iron nail. Either solution must be prepared fresh, otherwise iron (II) will become iron (III)!

Exercises and Experiments in Modern Chemistry, Teacher's Edition
Holt, Rinehart and Winston, Publishers

iron (III) chloride, 0.1 M (Dissolve 27 g of $FeCl_3 \cdot 6H_2O$ in water to which 20 mL of conc. hydrochloric acid has been added. Dilute to one liter.) — 15 mL

potassium ferrocyanide, 0.1 M (42 g $K_4Fe(CN)_6 \cdot 3H_2O$/L solution) — 2 mL

potassium ferricyanide, 0.1 M (33 g $K_3Fe(CN)_6$/L solution) — 2 mL

potassium thiocyanate, 0.2 M (19 g KCNS/L solution) — 7 drops (0.35 mL)

iron (II) ammonium sulfate, 0.1 M (Dissolve 39 g of $Fe(NH_4)_2(SO_4)_2 \cdot 6H_2O$ in water to which 10 mL of conc. sulfuric acid has been added. Dilute to one liter.) — 15 mL

EXPERIMENT 7

Water of Crystallization and Empirical Formula of a Hydrate

Two parts of the procedure in this experiment are critical, if satisfactory results are to be obtained. The opening must not be too large when placing the cover on the crucible, and heating should be very gentle for the first few minutes. Too large an opening or too much heat in the beginning will cause some of the hydrate to leave with the water vapor.

If you do not have a desiccator, you can use an old peanutbutter jar or similar vessel. Bend down the ends of a pipestem triangle to act as legs. The crucible will fit very nicely in the triangle. Fill the bottom of the jar with granular anhydrous calcium chloride. A substitute drying agent could be some of the anhydrous barium chloride residue.

Caution the students about using tongs at all times. Also stress that you never place a hot crucible on the balance pan.

MATERIALS NEEDED per student or pair

$BaCl_2 \cdot 2H_2O$ (C.P. crystals of barium chloride) — 5 g

If the section on Further Experimentation is to be done, then anticipate the use of 5 g for each of the crystals listed.

EXPERIMENT 8

Mass and Mole Relationships in a Chemical Reaction

This one-period experiment is an excellent demonstration of the mass–mass and mole–mole relationships of reactants and products in a balanced chemical reaction. The experiment is easy to perform and the percentage of error is low.

Caution the students about adding the HCl to the $NaHCO_3$. Make sure they know that the acid must be poured very slowly to avoid losing some of the solid through spattering. Also make sure they heat the solution gently to avoid losing any of the product. It takes at least 15 minutes for the dish to cool. Caution the students about touching the dish before it has cooled sufficiently.

MATERIALS NEEDED per student or pair

$NaHCO_3$ — 3 g

HCl, diluted (1:4); 200 mL conc./L solution — 12 mL

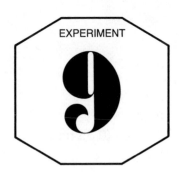

Boyle's Law

This experiment should take about 20 minutes to perform. Boyle's law is clearly demonstrated using very simple equipment.

Each apparatus should be carefully checked for possible leaks. If the apparatus leaks, the piston will not return to its original position, regardless of the number of times you twist the head. The most probable source of leakage is the bottom end of the syringe (where the needle is normally attached).

Each weight should be approximately 500 g. Less mass will provide too small a $\triangle V$. Greater mass will cause the pressure to be so excessive that air will begin to escape around the gasket. Ideally, 500-g weights should be used. However, four laboratory manuals will work, but are unwieldy.

Remind the students to give the piston several twists each time they change the force. The frictional force is quite significant, but if the piston is twisted until a stable volume is reached, reliable data should be obtained.

Emphasize that each graph should be full-page. Be on the lookout for students who may choose a size of unit that results in the plotted points only covering a small portion of the page.

You may wish to have the students plot the uncertainty of the values as well as the actual values (see sample graphs). This could lead into a discussion on uncertainty and experimental error.

MATERIALS NEEDED per student or pair

carpet thread   12 cm

Comparing the Masses of Equal Volumes of Gases

Make sure the students check the bags for any leaks or drops of water. Welding supply companies rent tanks of oxygen and carbon dioxide. The smallest tanks are good for 8–10 classes and are relatively inexpensive. Most schools have regular deliveries from a welding supply company for the shop classes. Make sure you secure the bottles so they cannot fall over. Overfill the bags and remind the students not to cap the medicine dropper until the pressure in the bag stabilizes.

If you don't have an air supply in your classroom, use a bicycle pump.

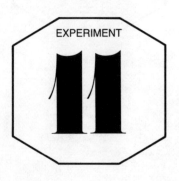

Molar Volume of a Gas

This experiment provides a simple method of experimentally determining the molar volume of a gas. In addition, students will be performing partial pressure, volume–pressure, and temperature–pressure calculations. It is important, therefore, that students review sections 10.5–10.12, 10.14, 11.5, 11.6, 11.10, and 11.11.

Exercises and Experiments in Modern Chemistry, Teacher's Edition
Holt, Rinehart and Winston, Publishers

Make sure the length of the magnesium ribbon does not exceed 4.5 cm. Longer pieces can displace all the water from the tube, and make measurement of the volume impossible.

To save time in weighing, the instructor may weigh a bright, untarnished piece of magnesium ribbon a meter or more in length (allow approximately 4.5 cm per student). An analytical balance should be used, and the mass should be determined to the nearest 0.001 g. Assuming the ribbon to be uniform, the length of sections having a mass from 0.040 to 0.045 g may be determined. Such an amount of magnesium will liberate 40 to 45 mL of hydrogen gas.

MATERIALS NEEDED per student or pair

magnesium ribbon, untarnished	4.5 cm
HCl, 6 M (516 mL conc./L solution)	10 mL
thread	25 cm

EXPERIMENT

12

Heat of Crystallization

This experiment can be completed in 40 minutes. The seeding of undercooled sodium thiosulfate provides for a spectacular display of rapid crystallization, as well as providing for a simple method to measure the heat released by a liquid when freezing.

A review of the principles of a styrofoam-cup calorimeter would be helpful to the students. Ask why they measure the change in the temperature of the water rather than the liquid sodium thiosulfate.

The sodium thiosulfate can be recovered by having the students deposit the liquid in a vessel lined with plastic wrap.

Caution the students about not allowing the temperature of the liquid sodium thiosulfate to rise above 75°C. Also emphasize that the liquid must not be stirred while cooling.

MATERIALS NEEDED per student or pair

$Na_2S_2O_3 \cdot 5H_2O$ 15 g

EXPERIMENT

13

Solubility and Rate of Solution

This one-period experiment is an excellent introduction to solubility and the factors that affect the rate of solution.

Caution the students about handling chemical solids, particularly sodium hydroxide.

MATERIALS NEEDED per student or pair

$Na_2S_2O_3 \cdot 5H_2O$	6 g
NaOH	4 or 5 pellets

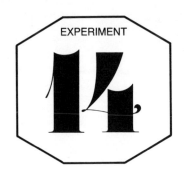

Freezing-point Depression of a Solvent (Teacher Demonstration)

This experiment can be completed in a single period. The student will be given the opportunity to determine $\triangle T_f$ and K_f, when a solute is added to a solvent.

Use granulated fine sugar (from the supermarket) for the solute. The coarse crystals supplied by chemical companies are usually so large that a great deal of time is wasted in dissolving them. Powdered sugar does not work well, because it leaves a cloudy appearance when dissolved.

Acetamide has a tendency to undercool. Keep in mind to set aside a few seed crystals in case the temperature of the liquid drops to 70°C without freezing. You may wish to discuss the undercooling effect, and the resulting dip in the plot of time-versus-temperature. This dip is observable on the sample graph (acetamide + 1.75 g curve).

An interesting supplementary activity is to make use of NaCl, $CaCl_2$, and $AlCl_3$ in place of sugar. Since these salts produce 2, 3, and 4 ions respectively per molecule of salt when dissolved, $\triangle T_f$ is doubled, tripled, and quadrupled.

MATERIALS NEEDED

acetamide (CH_3CONH_2)   10 g   sugar, granulated fine   3.50 g
Refer to the toxicity notes on acetamide in Experiment 3, p. T-19, and take all necessary precautions when using acetamide in a teacher demonstration.

Reacting Ionic Species in Aqueous Solution

This experiment can be completed in 20 minutes. The students are given the opportunity to use deductive thinking to choose the correct ion pair that precipitates out of solution. The students are also given practice in writing net ionic equations.

Each solution should be placed in 30-mL dropping bottles. Clear acetate sheets used for an overhead transparency project work very well for plastic sheets. Plastic wrap also works, but is difficult to reuse. Make sure you caution your students about not allowing the tip of the dropper to touch the drops on the plastic sheet.

MATERIALS NEEDED per student or pair

$Ba(NO_3)_2$, 0.1 M (26 g/L solution) $BaCl_2$, 0.1 M (24 g $BaCl_2 \cdot 2H_2O$/L solution)
Na_2SO_4, 0.1 M (14 g/L solution) Na_2CrO_4, 0.1 M (16 g/L solution)
$NaNO_3$, 0.1 M (9 g/L solution)   NaCl, 0.1 M (6 g/L solution)
Only one or two drops of each solution are needed.

Hydronium Ion Concentration, pH

This experiment can be completed in a single period. The students determine the pH of several acids and bases and rank them according to decreasing acid strength. The students will also perform 3 dilutions for a strong and weak acid and a strong base, and determine the resultant pH values.

Exercises and Experiments in Modern Chemistry, Teacher's Edition
Holt, Rinehart and Winston, Publishers

Best results are obtained by using "Panapeha" brand strips. Each strip contains 6 squares for color matching, and covers pH values of 1–14. Also available are "EM" brand strips which contain 4 squares per strip. "EM" paper is available in wide and narrow range.

Carefully check your distilled water for pH. Occasionally, the pH may be 1 less or greater than 7. This can result in erroneous readings for the weak acids and bases.

You may wish to demonstrate the use of a pH meter to complement the use of the indicator and to obtain more exact readings.

MATERIALS NEEDED per student or pair

HCl, 0.10 M (9 mL conc./L solution)   5 mL
$HC_2H_3O_2$, 0.10 M (6 mL glacial acetic acid/L solution)   5 mL
NaOH, 0.10 M (4 g/L solution)   5 mL
H_3PO_4, 0.033 M (2 mL conc./L solution)
NH_3, 0.10 M (7 mL conc. ammonia-water/L solution)
NaCl, 0.10 M (6 g/L solution)
Na_2CO_3, 0.050 M (5 g/L solution)
$NaHCO_3$, 0.10 M (8 g/L solution)
$NH_4C_2H_3O_2$, 0.10 M (8 g/L solution)
Each of the above solutions will be separately tested by dipping a stirring rod into each of the solutions and applying first to the wide-range pH paper and, if necessary, to the narrow-range paper. Remind students to clean and dry the stirring rod for each test. Procedure 2 requires the use of 5 mL of HCl, $HC_2H_3O_2$, and NaOH.

Titration of an Acid and a Base

EXPERIMENT

17

Experiments 17 and 18 should be completed during two consecutive laboratory days. The base that is standardized in 17 is used to determine the normality of the vinegar in experiment 18.

The technique of titration should be demonstrated before the students attempt the procedure. Emphasize the need for extremely well-rinsed burets. Discuss why putting distilled water in the flask does not affect the equivalence point.

The concentration of NaOH should be around 0.6 N. Reagent grade chemicals should be used in preparing the solutions. A fresh bottle of hydrochloric acid should be used, and preferably one that shows the actual assay of HCl rather than the average assay. At least 10 liters should be prepared in a large dispenser to ensure the same concentration for all lab groups. Five-gallon carboys with spigots make ideal dispensers for the acid and base solutions.

You may wish to have the students find the average deviation for the three trials. This will give a good indication of the student's titration skill.

MATERIALS NEEDED per student or pair

HCl, 0.5 N (43 mL conc./L solution)   NaOH, 0.6 N (24 g/L solution)   around 200 mL of each

phenolphthalein indicator (dissolve 10 g phenolphthalein in 500 mL   few drops (1 mL)
    denatured alcohol and add 500 mL water.)

EXPERIMENT 18

Percentage of Acetic Acid in Vinegar

This one-period experiment should be done on the day following the completion of experiment 17. The base that was standardized in experiment 17 is used as the standard for the titration of household vinegar. The percentage of acetic acid is then calculated.

Use distilled white vinegar. Vinegar that is not clear causes difficulty in determining the equivalence point. Instead of using vinegar, you can prepare a 4 or 5% solution of acetic acid.

MATERIALS NEEDED per student or pair

standardized solution of NaOH (see Expt. 17 notes)	around 200 mL
phenolphthalein indicator (see Expt. 17 notes)	few drops (1 mL)
white vinegar	around 200 mL

EXPERIMENT 19

Carbon

If part 1 of the procedure is performed as a demonstration, the experiment can be completed in a single period.

MATERIALS NEEDED per student or pair

HCl, 3.0 M (250 mL conc./L solution)	5 mL
NaOH, 1.0 M (40 g/L solution)	5 mL
HNO$_3$, 3.0 M (210 mL conc./L solution)	5 mL
dark-brown sugar solution (5 g dark-brown sugar/L solution)	50 mL
limewater (Add one liter of water to 5 g Ca(OH)$_2$. Shake well and allow the undissolved solids to settle. Decant the saturated solution to another bottle.)	2.5 mL
wooden splints	4
filter paper	1 piece
sugar (white)	2 g
activated charcoal, Norit A (for decoloring)	1 g
charcoal wood splinters	4

EXPERIMENT 20

Heat of Combustion

A small soup can (8 oz) is ideal for the calorimeter. Two holes for the stirring rod support are needed about 1 cm from the top of the can. For the chimney, use a large fruit juice can (48 oz). Use a beer can opener to punch out the air vents at the bottom. Then cut out the bottom. Bend the sharp ends back and forth until they snap off. Instead of punching holes, the chimney may be elevated on rubber stoppers. See Figure 20-1, page 214.

MATERIALS NEEDED per student or pair

1 candle   large supply of ice cubes   1 pack of matches

Heats of Reaction

This experiment requires a single period to complete. The experiment is simple to perform, and yet the results are very accurate. The concepts of heat of solution, heat of neutralization, and additivity of heats are all covered. Since students will need to know how to write net ionic equations, this experiment should not be performed until section 14.5 of the text is discussed.

Caution students about never handling NaOH directly. Also remind them how quickly NaOH absorbs water. You may wish to have the students weigh the pellets on a watch glass, instead of weighing paper.

MATERIALS NEEDED per student or pair

NaOH (pellets)	8 g
HCl, 2 M (172 mL conc./L solution)	50 mL
NaOH, 2 M (80 g/L solution)	50 mL
HCl, 1 M (86 mL conc./L solution)	100 mL

Rate of a Chemical Reaction

If all 3 parts of the experiment are to be performed by each student group, a full 50-minute period is required. You may wish to assign only one part to each group and collect class data. Since the results can vary by several seconds for any given trial, it would be wise to compile class data and then have the students record the averages of each set of trials.

This is an excellent experiment for investigating the effect of concentration, temperature, and a catalyst on the rate of a chemical reaction. The sudden change from a clear solution to deep blue is very spectacular. You might want to perform a "magic trick." Mix 20 mL of solutions A and B, stir for about 20 seconds, then cover the beaker with a cloth. Say a few magic words and then pull away the cloth. Presto, the clear liquid is now a deep-blue color!

Prepare solution A in the following manner. Add 50 g of KI to 1 g of Na_2SO_3 in a 1 liter volumetric flask. Add 10 mL of a 3% starch solution. Add enough distilled water to make 1 liter of solution. The solution must be prepared fresh, because the starch will begin to mildew within a week or so. You may wish to keep the starch separate and have the students add it each time a new trial is done. If so, have them add 4 drops of starch for each 20 mL of solution A. For solution B add 20 g of ammonium persulfate, $(NH_4)_2S_2O_8$, to enough distilled water to make 1 liter of solution. Have solutions A and B and the distilled water in 8 oz plastic squeeze bottles. Put the 0.01 M CuSO$_4$ in small dropper bottles.

MATERIALS NEEDED per student or pair

ice cubes	large supply
Solution A (see note above)	around 200 mL
Solution B (see note above)	around 200 mL
CuSO$_4$, 0.01 M (2.5 g CuSO$_4 \cdot$ 5H$_2$O/L solution)	5 drops (0.25 mL)
distilled water	15 mL

Equilibrium

This experiment can be completed during a 50-minute period. Each part can be performed separately, allowing the experiment to be completed in two different periods. The common-ion effect on equilibrium conditions is clearly demonstrated. The students are also given the opportunity to apply Le Chatelier's principle. The effect of concentration on equilibrium conditions is also investigated.

Methyl red indicator should be prepared by adding 0.5 g of dry methyl red to 100 mL of methanol. A 0.15% acetic acid solution can be prepared by adding 1.5 mL of glacial acetic acid to 1000 mL of solution.

methanol

The addition of Na_2HPO_4 to the $FeSCN^{++}$ complex in part III causes the formation of a colorless $FeHPO_4^+$ complex. As the Fe^{+++} ion is consumed, the $FeSCN^{++}$ ion breaks up to form more Fe^{+++} and SCN^- ions according to the principle of Le Chatelier.

MATERIALS NEEDED per student or pair

methyl red indicator (see note above)	few drops (1 mL)
acetic acid, 0.15% (see note above)	25 mL
CH_3COONa (crystals)	1 g
NH_4SCN (crystals)	0.5 g
K_2CrO_4, 0.1 M (20 g/L solution)	2 mL
NaOH, 1 M (40 g/L solution)	several drops (1 mL)
KSCN, 1 M (97 g/L solution)	1 mL
KCl (crystals)	0.5 g
$Fe(NO_3)_3$ (crystals)	0.5 g
Na_2HPO_4 (crystals)	0.5 g
$K_2Cr_2O_7$, 0.1 M (29 g/L solution)	2 mL
HCl, 1 M (86 mL conc./L solution)	several drops (1 mL)
$FeCl_3$, 1 M (Dissolve 270 g of $FeCl_3 \cdot 6H_2O$ in water to which 20 mL of conc. hydrochloric acid has been added. Dilute to one liter.)	1 mL

The Solubility Product Constant of Sodium Chloride

This experiment can be completed in a single period. Students are provided the opportunity to determine the solubility product constant of a salt. The experiment also gives the student practice in determining the concentrations of a solution and its corresponding ions.

Remind the students to place the evaporating dish 5–6 cm above the top of the flame to avoid overheating the solution. Also remind them to lower the flame when most of the water is driven off. You may wish to have the students place a watch glass over the evaporating dish to avoid losing any of the residue through spattering.

MATERIALS NEEDED per student or pair

NaOH (pellets)	2 pellets	NaOH, 2 M (80 g/L solution)	5 mL
NaCl	10 g		

Exercises and Experiments in Modern Chemistry, Teacher's Edition
Holt, Rinehart and Winston, Publishers

Oxidation-Reduction Reactions

This experiment can be completed in a single period. The relative strengths as oxidizing and reducing agents are determined for several metals.

Because of the high cost of silver and silver nitrate, you may wish to delete procedure 1. This part can be done as a demonstration or just simply discussed.

MATERIALS NEEDED per student or pair

copper strip, 1×5 cm	3
zinc strip, 1×5 cm	2
lead strip, 1×5 cm	1
silver strip, 1×5 cm	1
iron (II) sulfate (crystals)	3 crystals (0.5 g)
potassium permanganate (crystals)	2 crystals (0.5 g)
sulfuric acid, 6 M (add 333 mL conc. H_2SO_4 slowly with stirring rod to 667 mL of water)	5 drops
lead (II) nitrate, 0.1 M (33 g/L solution)	10 mL
silver nitrate, 0.1 M (17 g $AgNO_3$/L solution. Store in brown bottle.)	5 mL
tin (II) chloride, 0.1 M (Dissolve 23 g of $SnCl_2 \cdot 2H_2O$ in 35 mL conc. hydrochloric acid. Dilute to one liter with water. Add a few granules of tin. Should be freshly prepared.)	several drops (1 mL)
copper (II) nitrate, 0.1 M (30 g $Cu(NO_3)_2 \cdot 6H_2O$/L solution)	15 mL
zinc nitrate, 0.1 M (30 g $Zn(NO_3)_2 \cdot 6H_2O$/L solution)	10 mL
iron (III) chloride, 0.1 M (Dissolve 27 g $FeCl_3 \cdot 6H_2O$ in water to which 20 mL conc. HCl has been added. Dilute to 1 liter).	5 mL
sandpaper	1 piece

Relative Solubilities of the Group II Metals

This experiment can easily be completed in 30 minutes. The students are given the opportunity to analyze qualitatively an unknown solution. They will investigate the relative solubilities of the alkaline earth ions, and use this knowledge to devise a way in which to separate analytically two or more of these ions mixed in solution.

The ammonium carbonate solution should be prepared by adding 192 g of $(NH_4)_2CO_3$ to 80 mL of 15 M $NH_{3(aq)}$ per liter of solution. Place the reagents and alkaline earth ion solutions in dropper bottles. Acetate sheets used for overhead projection transparencies make excellent plastic sheets for the drops. Plastic wrap can also be used, but is not reusable.

The double unknown should be prepared by mixing 0.2 M solutions of the desired ions. The easiest combination to identify is magnesium and barium. Combinations used without magnesium are extremely difficult to identify.

The precipitate formed between Mg and $NH_{3(aq)}$ is very light. You may have to assist the students in identifying the precipitate.

MATERIALS NEEDED per student or pair

$(NH_4)_2C_2O_4$, 0.2 M (29 g ammonium oxalate/L solution)
$(NH_4)_2SO_4$, 1 M (132 g/L solution)
$Ca(NO_3)_2$, 0.1 M (17 g/L solution)
K_2CrO_4, 0.5 M (100 g/L solution)
$Ba(NO_3)_2$, 0.1 M (26 g/L solution)
$Sr(NO_3)_2$, 0.1 M (21 g/L solution)
$(NH_4)_2CO_3$ with $NH_{3(aq)}$ (see notes above)
$NH_{3(aq)}$, 6 M (Add 400 mL conc. ammonia-water solution to 600 mL water)

Students should dispense 2 or 3 drops of each of the above solutions from dropper bottles onto a clear acetate or plastic sheet.

Oxidation States of Transition Elements

This experiment can be completed in a single 50-minute period. The students investigate the different oxidation states of the transition metals chromium and iron. They also change the oxidation states of these metals and note the resultant color changes. This is a very colorful experiment.

Solutions should be placed in dropper bottles, where drop by drop addition is required.

MATERIALS NEEDED per student or pair

$FeSO_4$	0.5 g
H_2SO_4, 3 M (Add 166 mL conc. sulfuric acid slowly with stirring to 834 mL water)	2 mL
3% H_2O_2 (100 g of 30% H_2O_2 in 900 mL water)	2 mL
K_2CrO_4, 0.1 M (20 g/L solution)	5 mL
NaOH, 6 M (240 g/L solution)	6 mL
$Cr_2(SO_4)_3$, 0.16 M (115 g $Cr_2(SO_4)_3 \cdot 18H_2O$/L solution)	10 mL
$FeCl_3$, 0.1 M (Dissolve 27 g $FeCl_3 \cdot 6H_2O$ in water to which 20 mL conc. HCl has been added. Dilute to one liter.)	5 mL
$K_2Cr_2O_7$, 0.1 M (add 26 g/L solution)	5 mL
$SnCl_2$, 0.1 M (Dissolve 23 g $SnCl_2 \cdot 2H_2O$ in 35 mL conc. HCl. Dilute to one liter with water. Add a few granules of tin. Should be freshly prepared.)	2 mL
mossy zinc	2 pieces (1 g)

Aluminum and Its Compounds

This experiment can be easily completed in a single period. The students investigate some of the common properties of aluminum and also several of its compounds.

MATERIALS NEEDED per student or pair

aluminum chips or granules	3 chips (1g)
red and blue litmus papers	2 each color
$NH_{3(aq)}$, 4 M (267 mL conc. ammonia-water/L solution)	1 mL
H_2SO_4, 6 M (Add 333 mL conc. sulfuric acid slowly with stirring to 667 mL water.)	5 mL

Exercises and Experiments in Modern Chemistry, Teacher's Edition
Holt, Rinehart and Winston, Publishers

AlCl$_3$, 0.2 *M* (27 g AlCl$_3$/L solution)	10 mL
(NH$_4$)$_2$S, 0.3 *M* (47 mL of 20–24% ammonium sulfide solution/L solution. Store in brown bottle.)	5 mL
NaOH, 2.5 *M* (100 g/L solution)	6 mL
HCl, 6 *M* (516 mL conc. HCl/L solution)	6 mL
HNO$_3$, 6 *M* (375 mL conc. HNO$_3$/L solution)	5 mL
Al$_2$(SO$_4$)$_3$, 0.1 *M* (67 g/L solution)	15 mL
Na$_2$CO$_3$, 0.3 *M* (32 g/L solution)	1 mL

Halide Ions

This experiment can be completed in a single period. The students investigate the different properties of the halide ions and develop a scheme for identifying an unknown halide ion. Because of the high cost of silver nitrate, you may want to demonstrate or discuss procedure 2. If a mixture of halide ions is used for an unknown, double the concentration of each original solution.

MATERIALS NEEDED per student or pair

5% NaOCl (commercial bleach)	2 mL
3% starch solution (30 g boiled with 970 mL water)	20 mL
Ca(NO$_3$)$_2$, 0.5 *M* (82 g/L solution)	4 mL
KI, 0.2 *M* (33 g/L solution)	12 mL
NaF, 0.1 *M* (4 g/L solution)	12 mL
NH$_{3(aq)}$, 4 *M* (267 mL conc. ammonia water/L solution)	15 mL
Na$_2$S$_2$O$_3$, 0.2 *M* (50 g Na$_2$S$_2$O$_3$ · 5H$_2$O/L solution)	15 mL
KBr, 0.2 *M* (24 g/L solution)	12 mL
NaCl, 0.1 *M* (6 g/L solution)	12 mL
AgNO$_3$, 0.1 *M* (17 g/L solution)	4 mL

Radioactivity

This experiment requires approximately 35 minutes to complete. The range of beta particles is measured. The absorption of beta particles by paper and aluminum foil is also determined.

Thallium 204 is a safe and inexpensive beta source. A decade scaler is an ideal radioactive counter. Thorton has an excellent scaler that is one of the least expensive models available. Local Civil Defense offices usually will lend Geiger counters free of charge.

Have the instructions for the radioactive counter posted near the equipment. Although the source is safe, remind the students that they should never directly handle a radioactive source. Insist that they observe all the normal precautions, including washing their hands when finished.

MATERIALS NEEDED per student or pair

Thallium 204 (beta source). Have students work in groups and share beta sources.
index cards (several)
aluminum foil (several rectangular pieces the size of index cards)

Equilibrium Expression

The experiment requires approximately 25 minutes to complete. However, if only one color photometer is available, a few lab groups may have to obtain the absorbance values during the lab period. This experiment gives the student the opportunity to derive experimentally the equilibrium expression for a chemical reaction. In order to make this a real discovery, the experiment should be completed before sections 1–3 of Chapter 21 are read. The student also is given hands-on experience with a color photometer.

This experiment can also demonstrate the tremendous advantage of the use of a computer in performing a large number of tedious calculations. There are 45 separate calculations, many of which are repetitious. A great number of schools now have access to a computer. If your school is one of them, this experiment would be an ideal time to put it to use. There is often a student available who is a "computer freak." He or she could easily write a program. A sample program written in Basic language for a Radio Shack TRS-80 computer is included below. If you use a computer, simply have the students perform a sample calculation for test tube 3 in each step of the calculations section.

Place all solutions in plastic squeeze bottles. Prepare the 0.00200 M KSCN solution by adding 1.94 g in 100 mL of solution. Add 10 mL of this solution to 990 mL of distilled water. Prepare the 0.200 M $Fe(NO_3)_3$ by adding 80.8 g of $Fe(NO_3)_3 \cdot 9H_2O$ to 40.0 mL of concentrated HNO_3 to 1 liter of solution.

One color photometer can be sufficient for the entire class. It takes only 5 minutes or less to obtain the absorbance values. Have the instructions to the instrument posted nearby. Even better, record the instructions on a cassette tape and place the playback next to the photometer.

Fisher Educational Materials offers a color photometer for less than $200. The ideal instrument is a Spectronic 20, but it costs over three times as much. If the absorbance reading on your instrument can be adjusted, instruct the students to adjust the reading of test tube 1 so that its value is 1.0.

Since this is our first attempt at programming an experiment on a computer, we welcome any comments regarding the sample program written in Basic language for a Radio Shack TRS-80 computer and found on the following pages. Please write in and let us hear from you.

Permission to reproduce this programmed experiment is granted to users of Exercises and Experiments in Modern Chemistry, Teacher's Edition. We thank Dean M. Hurd, chemistry teacher at Carlsbad High School in Carlsbad, California, for submitting the experiment.

MATERIALS NEEDED per student or pair

HNO_3, 0.6 M (42 mL conc. HNO_3/L solution)	25 mL
$Fe(NO_3)_3$, 0.200 M (see notes above)	10 mL
KSCN, 0.00200 M (see notes above)	25 mL

```
10 CLEAR 200
20 CLS
30 T$="***EXPERIMENT SE-2***"
40 PRINTTAB(24)T$
50 PRINT
60 PRINTTAB(18)"REMEMBER YOUR SIGNIFICANT DIGITS!!!":PRINT
70 INPUT"ENTER YOUR FIRST NAME";N$
80 PRINT
90 FOR X=1 TO 6
100 IF X=2 THEN 130
110 PRINT"ENTER SPECTRONIC 20 VALUE FOR TUBE NUMBER ";X;:INPUT"";A(X)
120 PRINT
130 NEXT X
140 B(1)=0.1:B(3)=0.025:B(4)=0.0125:B(5)=0.00625:B(6)=0.00312
150 C(1)=0.001:C(3)=0.001:C(4)=0.001:C(5)=0.001:C(6)=0.001
160 FOR X=1 TO 6
170 IF X=2 THEN 190
180 E(X)=C(X)*A(X)
190 NEXT X
200 FOR X=1 TO 6
210 IF X=2 THEN 230
220 F(X)=B(X)-E(X)
230 NEXT X
240 FOR X=1 TO 6
250 IF X=2 THEN 270
260 G(X)=C(X)-E(X)
270 NEXT X
280 FOR X=1 TO 6
290 IF X=1 OR X=2 THEN 310
300 H(X)=E(X)/(F(X)+G(X))
310 NEXT X
320 FOR X=1 TO 6
330 IF X=1 OR X=2 THEN 350
340 I(X)=(F(X)*E(X))/G(X)
350 NEXT X
360 FOR X=1 TO 6
370 IF X=1 OR X=2 THEN390
380 J(X)=E(X)/(F(X)*G(X))
390 NEXT X
400 DEF FNMIN (A,B)=(A+B-ABS(A-B))/2
410 DEF FNMAX (A,B)=(A+B+ABS(A-B))/2
420 MN(1)=H(3):MX(1)=H(3)
430 FOR X=4 TO 6
440 MN(1)=FNMIN(MN(1),H(X))
450 MX(1)=FNMAX(MX(1),H(X))
460 NEXT X
490 MN(2)=I(3):MX(2)=I(3)
500 FOR X=4 TO 6
510 MN(2)=FNMIN(MN(2),I(X))
520 MX(2)=FNMAX(MX(2),I(X))
530 NEXT X
560 MN(3)=J(3):MX(3)=J(3)
570 FOR X=4 TO 6
580 MN(3)=FNMIN(MN(3),J(X))
590 MX(3)=FNMAX(MX(3),J(X))
600 NEXT X
```

```
630 FOR X=1 TO 3
640 RA(X)=MX(X)/MN(X)
650 NEXT X
660 MN(4)=RA(1)
670 FOR X=2 TO 3
680 MN(4)=FNMIN(MN(4),RA(X))
690 NEXT X
695 GOSUB5000
710 M$="###. #"
720 V$="###. ##"
721 A$="###. ###"
722 B$="###. ####"
724 C$="###. #####"
730 LPRINT CHR$(31)T$:LPRINT" "
740 LPRINT TAB(8) CHR$(15)"DATA"CHR$(14) CHR$(29):LPRINT" "
750 LPRINT TAB(19)CHR$(30)"SPECTRONIC 20 VALUE ":LPRINT" "
760 LPRINT CHR$(30)"TUBE"CHR$(31)" 1   3   4   5   6"CHR$(30)
770 LPRINT"NO. "CHR$(29):LPRINT TAB(10)USING M$;A(1);:LPRINT TAB(26)USING V$;A(3);:LPRINT TAB(42)USING V$;A(4);:LPRINT TAB(58)U
   V$;A(5);:LPRINT TAB(62)"              ";:LPRINT USING V$;A(6):LPRINT" "
780 LPRINT CHR$(31)"    "CHR$(15)"PROCESSED DATA"CHR$(14) CHR$(29):LPRINT" "
790 LPRINT CHR$(30)"TUBE"CHR$(31)" 1   3   4   5   6"CHR$(30):LPRINT"NO. "CHR$(29)
800 LPRINT CHR$(30)"INITIAL MOLARITY OF <FE3+> (COL A)"CHR$(29):LPRINT" "
810 LPRINT TAB(10)"0. 100        0. 0250        0. 0125        0. 00625        0. 00312"
820 LPRINT" ":LPRINT CHR$(30)"INITIAL MOLARITY OF <SCN-> (COL. B)"CHR$(29):LPRINT" "
830 LPRINT TAB(10)"0. 00100        0. 00100        0. 00100        0. 00100        0. 00100"
840 LPRINT" ":LPRINT CHR$(30)"ABSORBANCE VALUE  (COL. C)"CHR$(29):LPRINT" "
850 LPRINT TAB(9)USING M$;A(1);:LPRINTTAB(25)USING V$;A(3);:LPRINTTAB(42)USING V$;A(4);:LPRINTTAB(57)USING V$;A(5);:LPRINTTAB(63
        ";:LPRINTUSING V$;A(6)
860 LPRINT" ":LPRINT CHR$(30)"FINAL MOLARITY OF <FESCN2+>  (COL. D)"CHR$(29):LPRINT" "
870 LPRINT TAB(9)"0. 0010";:LPRINTTAB(25)USING C$;E(3);:LPRINTTAB(43)USING C$;E(4);:LPRINTTAB(58)USING C$;E(5);:LPRINTTAB(63)"
LPRINTUSING C$;E(6)
880 LPRINT" ":LPRINT CHR$(30)"FINAL MOLARITY OF <FE3+>  (COL. E)"CHR$(29):LPRINT" "
890 LPRINT TAB(9)"0. 099";:LPRINTTAB(25)USING A$;F(3);:LPRINTTAB(43)USING A$;F(4);:LPRINTTAB(58)USING B$;F(5);:LPRINTTAB(63)"
PRINTUSING B$;F(6)
900 LPRINT" ":LPRINT CHR$(30)"FINAL MOLARITY OF <SCN-> (COL. F)"CHR$(29):LPRINT" "
902 IF E(3)<=. 0009 THEN 908
904 D$="###. ######"
906 GOTO 910
908 D$=C$
910 LPRINT TAB(9)"0. 0";:LPRINTTAB(25)USING D$;G(3);:LPRINTTAB(43)USING C$;G(4);:LPRINTTAB(58)USING C$;G(5);:LPRINTTAB(63)"    ";
INTUSING C$;G(6)
920 LPRINT" ":LPRINT CHR$(30)"VALUE OF 'K' FOR    "CHR$(15)" <FESCN2+> "CHR$(14)
930 LPRINT"                       <FE3+>+<SCN-" CHR$(29)
932 FORN=3TO6:A(N)=H(N):NEXT N:GOSUB4000
940 LPRINT TAB(25)USING A$;H(3);:LPRINTTAB(43)USING A$;H(4);:LPRINTTAB(58)USING A$;H(5);:LPRINT"         ";:LPRINTUSIN
(6);H(6)
950 LPRINT" ":LPRINT CHR$(30)"VALUE OF 'K' FOR    "CHR$(15)"<FE3+><FESCN2+>" CHR$(14)
960 LPRINT"                       <SCN->" CHR$(29)
962 FOR N=3TO6:A(N)=I(N):NEXT N:GOSUB 4000
970 LPRINT TAB(25)USING A$;I(3);:LPRINTTAB(43)USING A$;I(4);:LPRINTTAB(58)USING A$;I(5);:LPRINT"         ";:LPRINTUSING
);I(6)
980 LPRINT" ":LPRINT CHR$(30)"VALUE OF 'K' FOR "CHR$(15)" <FESCN2+>  " CHR$(14)
990 LPRINT"                       <FE3+><SCN->" CHR$(29)
992 FOR N=3TO6:A(N)=J(N):NEXT:GOSUB4000
994 FOR N=3TO6:J(N)=A(N):NEXT
1000 LPRINT TAB(25)USING A$;J(3);:LPRINTTAB(43)USING A$;J(4);:LPRINTTAB(58)USING A$;J(5);:LPRINT"         ";:LPRINTUS
$(6);J(6)
1010 LPRINT" ":LPRINT CHR$(30)"RATIO OF LARGEST TO SMALLEST"
```

Exercises and Experiments in Modern Chemistry, Teacher's Edition
Holt, Rinehart and Winston, Publishers

```
1019 LPRINTCHR$(30)
1020 LPRINT CHR$(15)"  <FESCN2+>  " CHR$(14);:LPRINTTAB(33)USING R$(1);RA(1)
1025 LPRINT"<FE3+>+<SCN->":LPRINT" "
1030 LPRINT CHR$(15)"<FE3+><FESCN2+>" CHR$(14);:LPRINTTAB(33)USING R$(2);RA(2)
1035 LPRINT"    <SCN->":LPRINT" "
1040 LPRINT CHR$(15)"  <FESCN2+>  " CHR$(14);:LPRINTTAB(33)USING R$(3);RA(3)
1045 LPRINT"<FE3+><SCN->":LPRINT" "
1050 LPRINT" "
1055 LPRINT" ":LPRINT"RELATIONSHIP WITH LOWEST RATIO"
1058 IF RA(3)<=MN(4) THEN 1082
1070 IF RA(2)<=MN(4) THEN 1086
1080 IF RA(1)<=MN(4) THEN 1090
1082 LPRINT" ":LPRINT CHR$(30) TAB(16) CHR$(15)"  <FESCN2+>  " CHR$(14)
1084 LPRINTTAB(15)"<FE3+><SCN->":LR$="C":GOTO 1110
1086 LPRINT" ":LPRINT CHR$(30) TAB(15) CHR$(15)"<FE3+><FESCN2+>" CHR$(14)
1088 LPRINTTAB(17)" <SCN->":GOTO 1110
1090 LPRINT" ":LPRINT CHR$(30) TAB(16) CHR$(15)" <FESCN2+>  " CHR$(14)
1092 LPRINTTAB(15)"<FE3+>+<SCN->"
1110 LPRINT" ":LPRINT CHR$(31) N$
1120 LPRINT CHR$(29)"REMEMBER YOUR "CHR$(30)"SIGNIFICANT DIGITS!" CHR$(29)
1130 IF LR$="C" THEN 1180
1140 LPRINT CHR$(31) N$;" BLEW IT!" CHR$(29)
1150 FOR N=1 TO 4:LPRINT" ":NEXT
1160 LPRINT CHR$(7):FOR N=1 TO 1500:NEXT:LPRINT CHR$(7):FOR N=1 TO 1500:NEXT:LPRINT CHR$(7)
1170 GOTO 1190
1180 FOR N=1 TO 4:LPRINT" ":NEXT
1190 CLS
1200 FOR I=0 TO 4:READ A(I):NEXT I
1210 Y=-1
1220 Y=Y+1
1230 READ L
1240 IF L<0 GOTO 1220
1250 IF L>128 GOTO 1340
1260 L=L*2:READ R:R=R*2
1270 FOR X=L TO R STEP 2
1280 IF Y>47 GOTO 1320
1290 SET(X,Y):SET(X+1,Y)
1300 NEXT X
1310 GOTO 1230
1320 PRINT@425,"BYE NOW";
1330 FOR D=1 TO 10000:NEXT
1340 RESTORE
1350 DATA 2,21,14,25
1360 DATA 1,2,-1,0,2,45,50,-1,0,5,43,52,-1,0,7,41,52,-1
1370 DATA 1,9,37,50,-1,2,11,36,50,-1,3,13,34,49,-1,4,14,32,48,-1
1380 DATA 5,15,31,47,-1,6,16,30,45,-1,7,17,29,44,-1,8,19,28,43,-1
1390 DATA 9,20,27,41,-1,10,21,26,40,-1,11,22,25,38,-1,12,22,24,36,-1
1400 DATA 13,34,-1,14,33,-1,15,31,-1,17,29,-1,18,27,-1
1410 DATA 19,26,-1,16,28,-1,13,30,-1,11,31,-1,10,32,-1
1420 DATA 8,33,-1,7,34,-1,6,13,16,34,-1,5,12,16,35,-1
1430 DATA 4,12,16,35,-1,3,12,15,35,-1,2,35,-1,1,35,-1
1440 DATA 2,34,-1,3,34,-1,4,33,-1,6,33,-1,10,32,34,34,-1
1450 DATA 14,17,19,25,28,31,35,35,-1,15,19,23,30,36,36,-1
1460 DATA 14,18,21,21,24,30,37,37,-1,13,18,23,29,33,38,-1
1470 DATA 12,29,31,33,-1,11,13,17,17,19,19,22,22,24,31,-1
1480 DATA 10,11,17,18,22,22,24,24,29,29,-1
1490 DATA 22,23,26,29,-1,27,29,-1,28,29,-1,4096
1500 FOR E=1 TO 7
```

```
1510 PRINT@428,"HAPPY";
1520 PRINT@496,"EASTER";
1530 PRINT@565,"SWEETIE";
1540 RESET(28,29)
1550 FOR T=1 TO 300:NEXT
1560 PRINT@428,"        ";
1570 PRINT@496,"          ";
1580 PRINT@565,"            ";
1590 SET(28,29)
1600 FOR T=1 TO 300:NEXT
1610 NEXT E
1620 RUN
4000 FORN=3TO6
4002 IF A(N)>=1000 THEN 4120
4004 IF A(N)>=100 THEN 4130
4006 IF A(N)>=10 THEN 4140
4008 IF A(N)>=1 THEN 4150
4010 IF A(N)>=0.1 THEN 4100
4020 IF A(N)>= 0.01 THEN 4110
4030 A$(N)="##.####":NEXT:RETURN
4100 A$(N)="##.##":NEXT:RETURN
4110 A$(N)="##.###":NEXT:RETURN
4120 A(N)=A(N)+50:A(N) =INT(A(N)/100)*100:A$(N)="#####":NEXT:RETURN
4130 A(N)=A(N)+5:A(N)=INT(A(N)/10)*10:A$(N)="#####":NEXT:RETURN
4140 A$(N)="####":NEXT:RETURN
4150 A$(N)="###.#":NEXT:RETURN
5000 FOR N=1TO3
5010 IF RA(N)>=100 THEN 5090
5020 IF RA(N)>=10 THEN 5110
5030 R$(N)="##.#":NEXT: RETURN
5090 RA(N)=RA(N)+5
5100 RA(N)=INT(RA(N)/10)*10:R$(N)="#####":NEXT:RETURN
5110 R$(N)="####":NEXT:RETURN
```

Exercises and Experiments in Modern Chemistry, Teacher's Edition
Holt, Rinehart and Winston, Publishers

DATA

SPECTRONIC 20 VALUE

TUBE NO.	1	3	4	5	6
	1.0	0.94	0.89	0.80	0.72

PROCESSED DATA

TUBE NO.	1	3	4	5	6

INITIAL MOLARITY OF $\{Fe3+\}$ {COL. A}

	0.100	0.0250	0.0125	0.00625	0.00312

INITIAL MOLARITY OF $\{SCN-\}$ {COL. B}

	0.00100	0.00100	0.00100	0.00100	0.00100

ABSORBANCE VALUE {COL. C}

	1.0	0.94	0.89	0.80	0.72

FINAL MOLARITY OF $\{FeSCN2+\}$ {COL. D}

	0.0010	0.00094	0.00089	0.00080	0.00072

FINAL MOLARITY OF $\{Fe3+\}$ {COL. E}

	0.099	0.024	0.012	0.0055	0.0024

FINAL MOLARITY OF $\{SCN-\}$ {COL. F}

	0.0	0.000060	0.00011	0.00020	0.00028

VALUE OF 'K' FOR $\dfrac{\{FeSCN2+\}}{\{Fe3+\}+\{SCN-\}}$

	0.039	0.076	0.14	0.27

VALUE OF 'K' FOR $\dfrac{\{Fe3+\}\{FeSCN2+\}}{\{SCN-\}}$

	0.38	0.094	0.022	0.0062

VALUE OF 'K' FOR $\dfrac{\{FeSCN2+\}}{\{Fe3+\}\{SCN-\}}$

	650	700	730	1100

RATIO OF LARGEST TO SMALLEST

$\dfrac{\{FeSCN2+\}}{\{Fe3+\}+\{SCN-\}}$ 6.9

$\dfrac{\{Fe3+\}\{FeSCN2+\}}{\{SCN-\}}$ 61

$\dfrac{\{FeSCN2+\}}{\{Fe3+\}\{SCN-\}}$ 1.6

RELATIONSHIP WITH LOWEST RATIO

$$\dfrac{\{FeSCN2+\}}{\{Fe3+\}\{SCN-\}}$$

JOHN
REMEMBER YOUR SIGNIFICANT DIGITS!

Exercises and Experiments in Modern Chemistry, Teacher's Edition
Holt, Rinehart and Winston, Publishers

Chemicals and Apparatus Used

The following lists consist of materials, chemicals, and apparatus used during the school year. The lists indicate the amounts needed for a class of 30 students who are doing all the experiments. If you have five classes, you should multiply many of the quantities by a factor of "5" and get a figure for the total amount of material, chemical, or equipment that you will need to order for all classes for the entire school year. A modest surplus should be allowed for spillage, breakage, etc. It is advisable to check individual notes to experiments before making up a final purchase list, since some substitutions or deletions may be possible, using materials you already have on hand.

Chemicals

Chemical	Purchased As	Quantity	Used In
Acetamide	CH_3CONH_2	600 g	3, 14 See toxicity notes.
Acetic acid, glacial	$HC_2H_3O_2$	8 mL	16, 23
Alcohol, ethyl (denatured)		1000 mL	17, 18
Aluminum, chips		30 g	28
Aluminum, foil (household wrap)		1 roll	30
Aluminum, metal shot		600 g	2
Aluminum chloride	$AlCl_3$	27 g	28
Aluminum sulfate	$Al_2(SO_4)_3$	67 g	28
Ammonia, aqueous (conc. reagent)	NH_3	1021 mL	16, 26, 28, 29
Ammonium acetate	$NH_4C_2H_3O_2$	8 g	16
Ammonium carbonate	$(NH_4)_2CO_3$	192 g	26
Ammonium oxalate	$(NH_4)_2C_2O_4 \cdot H_2O$	29 g	26
Ammonium peroxydisulfate	$(NH_4)_2S_2O_8$	120 g	22
Ammonium sulfate	$(NH_4)_2SO_4$	132 g	26
Ammonium sulfide	$(NH_4)_2S$	47 mL	28
Ammonium thiocyanate	NH_4SCN	15 g	23
Barium chloride	$BaCl_2 \cdot 2H_2O$	174 g	7, 15
Barium nitrate	$Ba(NO_3)_2$	183 g	5, 15, 26
Calcium hydroxide (limewater)	$Ca(OH)_2$	5 g	19
Calcium nitrate	$Ca(NO_3)_2$	181 g	5, 26, 29
Carbon dioxide (see Expt.notes)	CO_2 (gas)	1 tank	10
Charcoal, activated (Norit A)		30 g	19
Charcoal wood splinters		120	19
Chromic sulfate	$Cr_2(SO_4)_3 \cdot 18H_2O$	115 g	27
Copper, metal shot		600 g	2
Copper, strip	foil	90	25
Copper, wire (18 gauge)		300 cm	1
Copper (II) nitrate	$Cu(NO_3)_2 \cdot 6H_2O$	30 g	25
Copper (II) sulfate	$CuSO_4 \cdot 5H_2O$	2.5 g	22

Exercises and Experiments in Modern Chemistry, Teacher's Edition
Holt, Rinehart and Winston, Publishers

Ferric chloride	$FeCl_3 \cdot 6H_2O$	351 g	6, 23, 25, 27
Ferric nitrate	$Fe(NO_3)_3 \cdot 9H_2O$	96 g	23, SE-2
Ferrous ammonium sulfate	$Fe(NH_4)_2(SO_4)_2 \cdot 6H_2O$	39 g	6
Ferrous sulfate	$FeSO_4 \cdot 7H_2O$	30 g	25, 27
Hydrochloric acid	HCl	3469 mL	5, 6, 8, 11, 16, 17, 19, 21, 23, 25, 27, 28
Hydrogen peroxide	$H_2O_2(30\%)$	100 mL	27
Lead, metal shot		600 g	2
Lead, strip	foil	30	25
Lead (II) nitrate	$Pb(NO_3)_2$	33 g	25
Lithium nitrate	$LiNO_3$	35 g	5
Magnesium, ribbon		3 g	11
Magnesium, chloride	$MgCl_2 \cdot 6H_2O$	150 g	7
Methanol	CH_3OH	100 mL	23
Methyl red		0.5 g	23
Nitric acid	HNO_3	667 mL	19, 28, SE-2
Oxygen (see Expt. notes)	O_2 (gas)	1 tank	10
Phenolphthalein		20 g	17, 18
Phosphoric acid	H_3PO_4	2 mL	16
Potassium bromide	KBr	24 g	29
Potassium chloride	KCl	165 g	7
Potassium chromate	K_2CrO_4	140 g	23, 26, 27
Potassium dichromate	$K_2Cr_2O_7$	58 g	23, 27
Potassium ferricyanide	$K_3Fe(CN)_6$	33 g	6
Potassium ferrocyanide	$K_4Fe(CN)_6 \cdot 3H_2O$	42 g	6
Potassium iodide	KI	335 g	22, 29
Potassium nitrate	KNO_3	202 g	7, 5
Potassium permanganate	$KMnO_4$	15 g	25
Potassium thiocyanate	KSCN	118 g	6, SE-2, 23
Sand, fine		90 g	1
Silver, strip (see Expt. notes)	foil	30	25
Silver nitrate (see Expt. notes)	$AgNO_3$	34 g	25, 29
Sodium acetate	CH_3COONa	30 g	23
Sodium aluminum sulfate	$AlNa(SO_4)_2 \cdot 12H_2O$	150 g	7
Sodium bicarbonate	$NaHCO_3$	98 g	8, 16
Sodium carbonate	Na_2CO_3	187 g	7, 16, 28
Sodium chloride	NaCl	1457 g	1, 5, 7, 15, 16, 24, 29
Sodium chromate	Na_2CrO_4	16 g	15
Sodium fluoride	NaF	4 g	29
Sodium hydroxide (pellets)	NaOH	1237 g	13, 16, 17, 18, 19, 21, 23, 24, 27, 28

Sodium hypochlorite (commercial bleach)	5% NaOCl	60 mL	29
Sodium nitrate	$NaNO_3$	52 g	5, 15
Sodium phosphate	Na_2HPO_4	15 g	23
Sodium sulfate	Na_2SO_4	165 g	7, 15
Sodium sulfite	Na_2SO_3	6 g	22
Sodium thiosulfate	$Na_2S_2O_3 \cdot 5H_2O$	680 g	12, 13, 29
Starch	soluble	60 g	22, 29
Strontium nitrate	$Sr(NO_3)_2$	127 g	5, 26
Sugar, sucrose (granulated, fine)		180 g	14, 19
Sugar, dark-brown		10 g	19
Sulfuric acid	H_2SO_4	832 mL	25, 27, 28
Thallium 204, beta source (see Expt. Notes)			30
Tin (II) chloride	$SnCl_2 \cdot 2H_2O$	46 g	25, 27
Vinegar, white		6000 mL	18
Zinc, mossy		30 g	27
Zinc, strip		60	25
Zinc, nitrate	$Zn(NO_3)_2 \cdot 6H_2O$	30 g	25

Miscellaneous Materials

Material	Quantity	Used In
Candle	30	29, SE-1
Ice cubes (see Expt. notes)	large supply	20, 22
Index cards	150	30
Litmus papers (red and blue)	60 each color	28
pH papers (wide and narrow range)	300 each range	16
Pack of matches	30	20, SE-1
Particle board (see Expt. notes)		4
Wooden splints	120	19
Thread (see Expt. notes)	750 cm	11
Thread, carpet (see Expt. notes)	360 cm	9

Apparatus

Item	Quantity	Used In
Aprons, safety	30	frequent use
Balance, centigram	30	1, 2, 3, 7, 8, 10, 12, 13, 14, 19, 21, 23, 24, 25, 27
Barometer	1	frequent use
Battery jar, 1 qt	30	11
Beaker, 50 mL	30	1, 11
100 mL	30	2, 21, 22
125 mL	30	17, 18
150 mL	60	17, 18, 24
250 mL	60	1, 11, 16, 19, 23

Exercises and Experiments in Modern Chemistry, Teacher's Edition
Holt, Rinehart and Winston, Publishers

400 mL	60	3, 12
600 mL	30	3, 14, 22
Beaker tongs	30	frequent use
Bottle, glass (2 liter)	30	10
Bottle, squeeze (8 oz)	90	22
Boyle's law apparatus	30	9
Buret	60	1, 17, 18
Buret clamp, single	30	1, 3, 11, 19
double	30	17, 18
Bunsen burner and tubing	30	frequent use
Calorimeter (2 plastic cups and lid. See Expt. 1, Fig. 1–15.)	30 sets	1
Clock, sweep-second hand	at least 2	3, 22
Cobalt glass plates	60	5
Color photometer (see Expt. notes)	1	SE-2
Crucible and cover	30	7, 19
Desiccator (see Expt. notes)		7
Dropper bottles	2 doz	15, 26, 27
Eudiometer, 50 mL	30	11
Evaporating dish	30	1, 8, 24
Eye dropper	30	8, 10, 25
Filter paper	60 pieces	1, 19
Flask Erlenmeyer, 125mL	30	19, 23
250 mL	30	13, 17, 18
Forceps	30	1, 5, 19, 25
Funnel	30	1, 19
Funnel rack	30	19
Glass plate	30	16
Gloves, safety	30	frequent use
Goggles, safety	30	frequent use
Graduated cylinder, 10 mL	30	6, 16, 24, 28, 29, SE-2
25 mL	60	2, 8, 22, 27
50 mL	30	16, 19, 24
100 mL	30	2, 12, 13, 20
125 mL	30	1, 23
Graph paper	90 pieces	30
Ice chest	1	20, 22
Labels, small, gummed	2 boxes	frequent use
Mat, heat resistant	30	frequent use
Metric ruler, plastic (15 cm)	30	2, 11, SE-1
Molecular model kit (Sargent)	30	19
Mortar and pestle	30	13
Paper, glazed, weighing	several boxes	frequent use
Pencil, glass marking	30	frequent use
Pinch clamp	30	10
Pipestem triangle	30	7, 19
Pipet with suction bulb	30	1

Plastic bag, 1 liter	30	10
Plastic sheet, acetate (see Expt. notes)	30	15, 26
Plastic teaspoon	30	13
Pneumatic trough	30	10
Radioactivity demonstrator (see Expt. notes)		30
Ring stand	30	1, 3, 7, 8, 11, 12, 14, 17, 18, 19, 20, 22, 24
Ring, iron	30	1, 3, 7, 8, 12, 14, 19, 20, 22, 24
Rubber band	30	10
Rubber stopper, # 00, 1 hole	30	11
# 2, solid	150	13, 19, 27, 28
# 4, solid	30	19
# 6, 1 hole	30	10
Rubber tubing	1500 cm	10
Sparker	30	frequent use
Spatula, plastic or porcelain	30	1, 7, 8, 13, 21
Stirring rod, glass	30	1, 16, 20, 21, 22, 23, 24, SE-2
Styrofoam cups 8 oz	30	12
12 oz	30	21
Thermometer	60	1, 2, 3, 11, 12, 13, 14, 20, 21, 22
Test tubes, hard glass, 18 × 150 mm	360	1, 5, 6, 16, 25, 27, 28, 29, SE-2
13 × 100 mm	240	23
Test tubes, Pyrex, 13 × 100 mm	30	19
25 × 100 mm	180	3, 12, 13, 14, 19, 24
18 × 150 mm	60	22, 27
Test tube brush	30	frequent use
Test tube clamp	30	12, 14, 27
Test tube holder	30	19
Test tube rack	30	frequent use
Tin can (see Expt. notes), 10 oz	30	20
46 oz	30	20
Tin can lid (see Expt. notes)	30	20
Tongs	30	7, 20, 24
Watch glass	30	21
Wash bottle, polyethylene	30	1, 17, 18
Weights, four 500-g (see Expt. notes)	120	9
Wire gauze (ceramic-centered)	30	frequent use
Wire, platinum or nichrome (see Expt. 5 apparatus list)	30	5

Exercises and Experiments in Modern Chemistry, Teacher's Edition
Holt, Rinehart and Winston, Publishers

Exercises and Experiments in
Modern Chemistry

H. Clark Metcalfe

John E. Williams

Joseph F. Castka

HOLT, RINEHART AND WINSTON, PUBLISHERS
New York ● London ● Toronto ● Sydney

H. Clark Metcalfe

P.O. Box V2, Wickenburg, Arizona, 85358; formerly teacher of chemistry at Winchester-Thursten School, Pittsburgh, Pennsylvania, and Head of the Science Department, Wilkinsburg Senior High School, Wilkinsburg, Pennsylvania

John E. Williams

Formerly teacher of chemistry and physics at Newport Harbor High School, Newport Beach, California, and Head of the Science Department, Broad Ripple High School, Indianapolis, Indiana

Joseph F. Castka

Formerly Assistant Principal for the Supervision of Physical Science, Martin Van Buren High School, New York City, and Adjunct Associate Professor of General Science and Chemistry, C. W. Post College, Long Island University, New York

Editorial Development   William N. Moore, Roland J. Cormier, Pamela Hirschfeld, Betsy Mastalski
Editorial Processing   Margaret M. Byrne, Regina Chilcoat, Anne Drouillard
Art, Production, and Photo Resources   Vivian Fenster, Fred C. Pusterla, Robin M. Swenson, Russell Dian, Annette Sessa-Galbo, Beverly Silver, Anita Dickhuth, Louise Hannibal
Product Manager   Laura Zuckerman
Advisory Board   Rhenida Bennett, John W. Griffiths, David J. Miller, Douglas A. Nash, William Paul, George Salinger, Jean Slankard, John Taggart
Consultant   John Matejowsky
Researchers   James R. George, Erica S. Felman
Safety Consultant   Franklin D. Kizer, Executive Secretary, Council of State Science Supervisors, Inc.

Exercises

The exercises supplement the work in the textbook. It is recommended that your assignment from the textbook be completed before the corresponding exercise is undertaken. For the most part, the exercises follow the section sequence in *Modern Chemistry,* 1982. This sequencing helps you to locate the answers to challenging problems and questions. The complete exercise serves as a good review before a scheduled test. Regular use of the exercise book will help you establish good work and study habits.

How the Experiments Are Organized

Title and Introduction. An opening paragraph sets the theme for the experiment and reviews major concepts included in the experiment. Each experiment is correlated to a chapter in *Modern Chemistry.* References are made to specific chapters and text sections. You can use these references to find additional information on the topic of the experiment. You are encouraged to read the entire experiment prior to performing it in the laboratory.

Objective. The objective at the beginning of each experiment states what is to be learned or accomplished by performing the experiment.

Apparatus and Materials lists. These lists enable you to organize all apparatus and materials needed to perform the experiment. Knowing the concentrations of solutions is vital information that you will need for calculations and for the questions at the end of the experiment.

Safety. The safety paragraph is placed at the beginning of the experiment to alert you to procedures for which special caution may be necessary. Before you begin you should review the safety rules and regulations needed to conduct the experiment.

Recording Your Results—Observations—Data. A simple directive tells you where to record your results, observations, or data.

Procedures. By following the procedures of an experiment, you are performing concrete laboratory operations that duplicate the fact-gathering techniques used by professional chemists. You are learning "chemist's skills" in the laboratory. The procedures clearly direct you as to how and where to record observations and data.

Data and Calculations Tables. The data that you should accumulate during the progress of an experiment are organized into separate, distinct tables. The entries you will make in the Calculations Table emphasize the mathematical, physical, and chemical relationships that exist among the accumulated data. Both tables should help you to think logically and to formulate a broad generalization as to what occurred during experimentation.

Calculations. Space is provided for all math work and computations based on the data you have gathered. All answers should be entered in the Calculations Table.

Questions. Based on the data and calculations, you should be able to develop a plausible explanation for the phenomena observed during experimentation. Questions are asked, and you must draw conclusions that are pertinent to the objective of the experiment.

Further Experimentation and Correlating Your Facts. These sections guide you in project activity or serve as a review of major concepts covered in the lab experiment and textbook.

Table of Contents

Measurements in Chemistry

EXERCISE **1**

DIRECTIONS: In the parentheses at the right of each word or expression in the second column, write the letter of the expression in the first column that is *most closely* related.

a. a chemical property	liter	(l) 1
b. resistance to change of position or motion	E = mc²	(g) 2
c. mass per unit volume	mass	(j) 3
d. definite shape and definite volume	$M \times 10^n$	(h) 4
e. capacity for doing work	energy	(e) 5
f. theory	density	(c) 6
g. conservation of mass and energy	inertia	(b) 7
h. scientific notation	solid	(d) 8
i. heat intensity within a system	inactivity	(a) 9
j. quantity of matter	50°C	(i) 10
k. dimensional analysis		
l. volume of a liquid or a gas		

DIRECTIONS: In the blank space at the right of each statement, write the word or expression that BEST completes the meaning when substituted for the corresponding number.

11. Chemistry is the science of materials, their composition and structure, and the (11).

changes they undergo _____ 11

12. Observing, generalizing, theorizing, and testing are four distinct phases of the (12).

scientific method _____ 12

13. A plausible explanation of observed natural phenomena in terms of a simple model with familiar properties is called a (13).

theory _____ 13

14. Matter is described as anything that (14).

has mass and occupies space _____ 14

15. The mass of a body is (15).

constant _____ 15

16–17. Liquids have definite (16) but not definite (17).

volume _____ 16

shape _____ 17

18. Properties that describe the behavior of a material in processes that alter its identity are (18) properties.

chemical _____ 18

19. The energy of motion is (19) energy.

kinetic _____ 19

20. In ordinary chemical reactions, the total mass of the reacting materials is (20) the total mass of the products.

equal to _____ 20

21. A special name for a cubic decimeter is (21).

a liter _____ 21

22–23. The magnitude of a physical quantity is described by a (22) and a (23).

number _____ 22

unit _____ 23

24. Length, mass, and time are (24) physical quantities.

fundamental _____ 24

25. The density of a gas is expressed in (25).

grams per liter _____ 25

26. The (26) of a system is a measure of its ability to transfer heat to or acquire heat from other systems.

temperature _____ 26

27. Systems in thermal (27) have the same temperature.

equilibrium _____ 27

28. (28) is measured as a quantity of energy.

Heat _____ 28

29. Celsius established his thermometer scale by defining (29) fixed points.

two _____ 29

30. The (30) is the quantity of heat required to raise the temperature of 1 kilogram of water through 1 Celsius degree.

kilocalorie _____ 30

31. One calorie is equivalent to (31) joules of heat energy.

4.19 _____ 31

32. The nearness of a measurement to its true, or accepted, value denotes its (32).

accuracy _____ 32

33. In laboratory experiments, relative errors are referred to as (33) errors.

percentage _____ 33

34. The agreement between the numerical values of a set of measurements that have been made in the same way denotes the (34) of the measurements.

precision _____ 34

35. Significant figures in a measurement are all the digits that are known with certainty plus the (35).

first digit that is uncertain _____ 35

36. In the measurement expression 0.04060, the number of significant figures is (36).

4 _____ 36

37. The scientific notation for the expression 10050 mL is (37) mL.

1.005×10^4 _____ 37

38. The scientific notation for the expression 0.0000015 cm is (38) cm.

1.5×10^{-6} _____ 38

39–41. The distance 402,2$\overline{0}$0 m is precise to (39) significant figures. Expressed in scientific notation it becomes (40) m. If rounded off to three significant figures it becomes (41).

5 _____ 39

4.0220×10^5 _____ 40

4.02×10^5 _____ 41

42. Before adding or subtracting measurements expressed in scientific notation, all terms must be adjusted to the same (42).

power of ten _____ 42

43. In multiplication with measurements expressed in scientific notation, the exponents are (added, subtracted) (43).

added _____ 43

44. For a mathematical equation to represent the correct solution to a problem, the sides of the equation must have the (44) dimensions.

same _____ 44

45. A length is measured to three significant figures as 1.30 m. The result, expressed in centimeters and precise to three significant figures, is (45).

13$\overline{0}$ _____ 45

46. When the numerical expression for the solution of a problem has been assembled, the units in the expression should be ''solved'' for the answer unit (46) the arithmetic is done.

before _____ 46

47–48. Measured quantities that vary with one another are directly proportional if their (47) is constant. A representative graph in which one variable is plotted as a function of the other is a (48).

quotient _____ 47

straight line _____ 48

49–50. Measured quantities that vary with one another are inversely proportional if their (49) is constant. A representative graph in which one variable is plotted as a function of the other is a (50).

product _____ 49

hyperbola _____ 50

Exercises and Experiments in Modern Chemistry
Holt, Rinehart and Winston, Publishers

Matter and Its Changes

EXERCISE

DIRECTIONS: Write the answers to the following in the space provided. Where appropriate, make complete statements.

1. What three general classes of matter do chemists recognize? **The three general classes of matter are (1) elements, (2) compounds, and (3) mixtures.**

1

2. What is a heterogeneous material? **A heterogeneous material is one made up of parts possessing different properties.**

2

3. What is a homogeneous material? **A homogeneous material is one that has identical properties throughout.**

3

4. How can you recognize that granite is a mixture of different materials? **Close examination of the surface of granite shows three distinctly different kinds of crystals.**

4

5. What kind of mixture is not heterogeneous? **A solution is an example of a mixture that is not heterogeneous.**

5

6. How can you tell that ordinary solutions are mixtures? **The amounts of materials that make up solutions can be varied, and the characteristics of each material may be recognized.**

6

7. What is the definition of a mixture? **A mixture is a material consisting of two or more kinds of matter, each retaining its own characteristic properties.**

7

8. Give an example of a homogeneous material that is not a pure substance. **A solution is homogeneous but consists of a mixture of two or more substances.**

8

9. Pure substances may be of what two kinds? **Pure substances may exist as compounds and elements.**

9

10. What distinction is made between these two kinds of pure substances? **Compounds are complex substances that can be decomposed by ordinary chemical means into two or more simpler substances. Elements are substances that cannot be further decomposed by ordinary chemical means.**

10

11. What are the two general classes of elements? **The two general classes of elements are metals and nonmetals. Elements called metalloids have certain properties characteristic of metals and others of nonmetals.**

11

12. What are the two general rules of capital letters that are used in writing the symbols of elements? **The first letter of a symbol is always capitalized. The second letter of a two-letter symbol is never capitalized.**

12

13. What does a chemical symbol represent quantitatively? **A chemical symbol stands for one atom of the element.**

13

14. What is an atom? **An atom is the smallest basic unit of an element that can enter into combination with other elements.**

14

15. Write the symbols for (a) the two elements that together account for almost 75% of the earth's crust, (b) the four elements whose compounds make up almost all of the earth's mantle, (c) the two metals that make up most of the earth's core. (a) __O, Si,_____

(b)__Mg, Fe, Si, O,__ , (c) ____Fe, Ni._____ 15

16. State the law of definite composition. __Each compound has a definite_____

__composition by mass._____ 16

17. In what type of changes do the identifying properties of substances remain unchanged?
__physical changes_____ 17

18. Changes in which different substances with new properties are formed are called _____
__chemical changes.__ 18

19. Chemical reactions involve either the absorption or the liberation of energy. Briefly state other types of evidence that may show that a chemical reaction has taken place. __The production__
__of a gas is usually evidence that a chemical reaction is taking place. The formation of an insoluble__

__solid, called a precipitate, may show that a chemical reaction has taken place as solutions are mixed.__ 19

20. List five agents by which chemists bring about chemical reactions or control those that have already started. __heat energy, light energy, electric energy, solution in water, catalysis_____ 20

21. The property that describes the disorder of a system is called __entropy._____ 21

22–23. Processes in nature are driven in two ways: toward __lowest energy,_____ 22

and toward __highest entropy._____ 23

24. In a nuclear change the new substance(s) is (are) formed by changes in the __identity_____
__of the atoms themselves.__ 24

25. Fill in the spaces below with *Yes* or *No* to indicate the general properties of metals and nonmetals.

	Metals	*Nonmetals*
a. usually have a luster	Yes	No
b. are often malleable	Yes	No
c. may be gaseous at room temperature	No	Yes
d. are generally poor conductors of heat	No	Yes
e. are usually good conductors of electricity	Yes	No

DIRECTIONS: Various changes in matter are listed below. Indicate by letter which are characteristically physical, P, which are chemical, C, and which are nuclear, N.

26. iron rusts	C 26	**31.** coal burns	C 31
27. ice melts	P 27	**32.** alcohol evaporates	P 32
28. radium decays to lead	N 28	**33.** gunpowder explodes	C 33
29. sugar dissolves in water	P 29	**34.** steam condenses	P 34
30. milk sours	C 30	**35.** limestone is crushed	P 35

Exercises and Experiments in Modern Chemistry
Holt, Rinehart and Winston, Publishers

Atomic Structure

EXERCISE **3**

DIRECTIONS: Complete the following statements, forming accurate and complete sentences.

1. Dalton's atomic theory satisfactorily explained several quantitative laws of (a) __chemical__
__combination__, such as Proust's law of (b) __definite composition.__ _____ 1

2. All matter is made up of __very small particles__ called __atoms.__ _____ 2

3. Atoms of the same element are chemically __alike__; atoms of different elements are
chemically __different.__ _____ 3

4. While individual atoms of an element may not all have the same mass, the atoms of an element,
as it occurs naturally, have, for practical purposes, a definite _____
__average mass characteristic of the element.__ _____ 4

5. While individual atoms of different elements may have nearly identical masses, the atoms of
different naturally occurring elements have __different average masses.__ _____ 5

6. Atoms are not subdivided during __chemical reactions.__ _____ 6

7. The central part of an atom is called (a) __the nucleus__, is (b) __positively__ charged, is very
dense, and has a diameter that is about (c) __10^{-4}__ _____ Å. 7

8. In Rutherford's gold-foil experiment, the slight deflection of a few and the great deflection of a
very few high-speed positively charged particles were explained by assuming that the particles were
__turned from their path by the nucleus.__ _____ 8

9. Electrons moving about the nucleus and having similar energies comprise a(n) (a) __shell__
_____ and are said to be in the same (b) __energy level.__ _____ 9

10. Each atom is electrically neutral since the __total positive charge of the nucleus__
__is equal to the total negative charge of the electron cloud.__ _____ 10

DIRECTIONS: Fill in the spaces below with information about each of the following:

	Mass in grams	_Mass number_	_Charge_	_Position in the atom_	
11. electron	9.110×10^{-28} g	0	−1	in the shells	11
12. proton	1.673×10^{-24} g	1	+1	in the nucleus	12
13. neutron	1.675×10^{-24} g	1	0	in the nucleus	13

DIRECTIONS: Write the answers to the following in the spaces provided. Where appropriate, make
complete statements.

14. The three known forms of hydrogen atoms are (a) __protium__, (b) __deuterium__, and
(c) __tritium.__ _____ 14

15. The atomic number of an atom is the number of __protons in the nucleus.__ ____ 15

16. Isotopes are atoms of the same element that have different __masses.__ _____ 16

17. Isotopes are nuclides having the same **atomic number, or number of protons.** _____ 17

18. The mass number of an atom is the sum of the number of **protons and neutrons** _____

in its nucleus. _____ 18

19. A certain atom consists of 16 protons, 18 neutrons, and 16 electrons. What is its (a) atomic number? __**16**___ (b) mass number? __**34**___ (c) electron configuration?

two K-shell electrons, eight L-shell electrons, six M-shell electrons _____ 19

20. What is the atomic mass of an atom? **The atomic mass of an atom is the mass of an** _____

atom expressed in atomic mass units, _u_. One amu, 1 _u_, is exactly ¹⁄₁₂ the mass of a _____

carbon-12 atom, or 1.6605655 × 10⁻²⁴ g. _____ 20

21. What is the relationship between mass number and atomic mass of an atom? _____
The mass number is the whole number closest to the atomic mass. _____ 21

22. Why is the Avogadro number said to be a constant? **The Avogadro number is a constant because**

the number of atoms in the gram-atomic mass of any nuclide is the same, 6.022045 × 10²³ atoms. __ 22

23. To three significant figures, state the value of the Avogadro number. **6.02 × 10²³** _____ 23

24. What is a mole of a substance? **A mole of a substance is the amount of the substance** ____

containing the Avogadro number of any kind of chemical unit. _____ 24

25. What is the gram-atomic weight of an element? **The gram-atomic weight of an** _____

element is the mass in grams of one mole of naturally occurring atoms of the element. ___ 25

26. How is the atomic weight of an element related to its gram-atomic weight? **The** _____
numerical portion of the gram-atomic weight of an element is its atomic weight. _____ 26

27. The atomic weight of fluorine is 18.9984. (a) How many atoms are there in 4.7496 g of this element? **1.5055 × 10²³ atoms** (b) How many moles of atoms? **0.25000 mole** _____ 27

28. The mass of 3.01101 × 10²³ atoms of nitrogen-14 is 7.00154 g. What is the atomic mass of this nuclide? **14.0031** _____ 28

29. What is the mass in grams of 2.50 moles of gallium atoms? **174 g** _____ 29

30. How many moles of atoms are there in 8.994 g of aluminum? **0.3333 mole** _____ 30

31. Complete the following table:

Name of nuclide	Atomic number	Mass number	Composition of nucleus		Electron configuration		
			Protons	Neutrons	K	L	M
hydrogen-2 (deuterium)	1	2	1	1	1		
lithium-7	3	7	3	4	2	1	
nitrogen-14	7	14	7	7	2	5	
fluorine-19	9	19	9	10	2	7	
magnesium-24	12	24	12	12	2	8	2
silicon-28	14	28	14	14	2	8	4
sulfur-32	16	32	16	16	2	8	6
argon-40	18	40	18	22	2	8	8

Exercises and Experiments in Modern Chemistry
Holt, Rinehart and Winston, Publishers

Arrangement of Electrons in Atoms

EXERCISE **4**

DIRECTIONS: Complete the following statements, forming accurate and complete sentences.

1. The nucleus has a positive charge because of its protons. A neutral atom contains an equal number of protons and negatively charged electrons. Therefore, we might expect electrons to be held in an atom by the **attraction between oppositely charged particles.** _____ 1

2. The observed behavior of oppositely charged particles is not satisfactory for explaining the motion of electrons about the nucleus of an atom because we know that electrons **do not fall into the nucleus and atoms do not collapse.** _____ 2

3. The speed of any wave motion equals the product of its **frequency and wavelength.** _____ 3

4. The energy of a photon, E, may be represented by the expression $E =$ **hf.** _____ 4

5. When excited atoms radiate energy, the radiation is given off in units called **photons.** _____ 5

6. When excited atoms return to their normal states, they emit light. If this light is passed through a spectroscope, we may observe a(n) **bright-line spectrum.** _____ 6

7. Energy changes within an atom do not provide a continuous flow of energy, but are **fixed,** _____ **definite amounts of energy.** _____ 7

8. The kinds of spectra that are explained satisfactorily by the Bohr model of the atom are **the spectra of one-electron particles.** _____ 8

9. A space orbital is **a highly probable location in which an electron may be found.** _____ 9

10. Occupation of the same space by two free atoms is prevented by **their electron clouds.** _____

_____ 10

11. The quantum number that indicates the most probable distance of the electron from the nucleus of the atom is the **principal quantum number.** _____ 11

12. The number of orbital shapes possible in the 2nd energy level is **two.** _____ 12

DIRECTIONS: **13–16.** Furnish the required information for each sublevel.

Sublevel	Number of space orbitals	Maximum number of electrons	Lowest energy level having this sublevel	
s	1	2	1st	13
p	3	6	2nd	14
d	5	10	3rd	15
f	7	14	4th	16

DIRECTIONS: Write answers to the following in the space provided. Make complete statements where appropriate.

17. What is the most stable state of an atom called? **The most stable state of an atom is the** _____

ground state. _____ 17

18. Under what conditions may two electrons occupy the same space orbital? __Two electrons__
__may occupy the same space orbital if they have opposite spins.__ ____ 18

19. What is an electron pair? __An electron pair consists of two electrons of opposite__
__spin in the same space orbital.__ ____ 19

20. What name is given to an outer shell containing eight electrons? __An outer shell__
__containing eight electrons is called an octet.__ ____ 20

21. Which sublevels of the 3rd energy level are filled (a) in the element argon (Ar-atomic number 18)? __The 3s and 3p are filled in the element argon.__

(b) in the element krypton (Kr-atomic number 36)? __The 3s, 3p, and 3d are filled in the__
__element krypton.__ ____ 21

22. When do successive electrons entering the 2p orbitals start to pair up? __Electrons do not__
__pair up in the 2p orbitals until each of the three 2p space orbitals is occupied by a single electron.__ ____ 22

23. What is the electron-dot symbol for potassium (atomic number 19)? __K·__ ____ 23

24. In what order do successive electrons usually occupy the sublevels of the atoms of the fourth series? __Successive electrons usually occupy the orbitals of the fourth-series elements__
__in the order 1s, 2s, 2p, 3s, 3p, 4s, 3d, 4p.__ ____ 24

25. Which atoms in the fourth series have structures that appear to be irregular because of the stability of (a) a half-filled 3d sublevel? __chromium__

(b) a completely filled 3d sublevel? __copper__ ____ 25

26. Write the electron-dot symbol for an atom having an atomic number of 13 and a mass number of 27. __Al:__ ____ 26

27. In which series of elements do electrons occupy the 4f sublevel? __Electrons occupy the__
__4f sublevel in the sixth series.__ ____ 27

28. Complete the following table:

Symbol- Atomic number	Electron configuration notation	Electron-dot notation	Orbital notation						
			1s	2s	2p	3s	3p	3d	4s
Li-3	1s² 2s¹	Li ·	↑↓	↑	_ _ _				
B-5	1s² 2s² 2p¹	Ḃ:	↑↓	↑↓	↑ _ _				
N-7	1s² 2s² 2p³	·Ṅ:	↑↓	↑↓	↑ ↑ ↑				
F-9	1s² 2s² 2p⁵	:F̈:	↑↓	↑↓	↑↓ ↑↓ ↑				
Mg-12	1s² 2s² 2p⁶ 3s²	Mg:	↑↓	↑↓	↑↓ ↑↓ ↑↓	↑↓			
Si-14	1s² 2s² 2p⁶ 3s² 3p²	·Si:	↑↓	↑↓	↑↓ ↑↓ ↑↓	↑↓	↑↓ ↑ ↑ _		
S-16	1s² 2s² 2p⁶ 3s² 3p⁴	·S̈:	↑↓	↑↓	↑↓ ↑↓ ↑↓	↑↓	↑↓ ↑↓ ↑ ↑		
Ar-18	1s² 2s² 2p⁶ 3s² 3p⁶	:Är:	↑↓	↑↓	↑↓ ↑↓ ↑↓	↑↓	↑↓ ↑↓ ↑↓ ↑↓		
Ca-20	1s² 2s² 2p⁶ 3s² 3p⁶ 4s²	Ca:	↑↓	↑↓	↑↓ ↑↓ ↑↓	↑↓	↑↓ ↑↓ ↑↓ ↑↓		↑↓
Sc-21	1s² 2s² 2p⁶ 3s² 3p⁶ 3d¹ 4s²	✕	↑↓	↑↓	↑↓ ↑↓ ↑↓	↑↓	↑↓ ↑↓ ↑↓ ↑↓	↑ _ _ _ _	↑↓

Exercises and Experiments in Modern Chemistry
Holt, Rinehart and Winston, Publishers

The Periodic Law

DIRECTIONS: Write the answers to the following in the space provided. Where appropriate, make complete statements.

1. Who did the pioneer work on the periodic table we use today? **Mendeleev** _____   1

2. On what did he base his table of the elements, and what two predictions did he make? _____
Mendeleev's table was based on the properties of the elements and the order of their atomic
weights. He predicted that new elements would be discovered to fill gaps, and
the properties of these new elements.   2

3. In what order are the elements listed in the present periodic table? **They are listed in** _____
order of increasing atomic numbers.   3

4. How did Moseley account for the fact that the X-ray wavelengths obtained from two apparently successive elements sometimes had twice the expected variation? **An undiscovered** _____
element belonged between them in the periodic table.   4

5. State the periodic law. **The physical and chemical properties of elements are periodic** _____
functions of their atomic numbers.   5

6. What name is given to the elements in a vertical column of the periodic table? _____
group or family   6

7. What name is given to the elements in a horizontal row of the periodic table? _____
period or series   7

8. What name is given to elements whose atoms usually differ in electron configuration by the entrance of successive electrons in a d sublevel? **transition elements** _____   8

9. What name is given to elements whose atoms usually differ in electron configuration by the entrance of successive electrons in an f sublevel? **rare-earth elements** _____   9

10. Fill in the blocks with the symbols, atomic numbers, electron-configuration notation, and brief statements of properties of the elements of the second and third periods, as has been done for beryllium and magnesium below.

Li 3, Soft, silvery, active metal	$1s^2$ $2s^1$	Be 4 Silvery metal	$1s^2$ $2s^2$	B 5, Black solid, few me-tallic proper-ties	$1s^2$ $2s^2$ $2p^1$	C 6, Solid, proper-ties be-tween metals and non-metals	$1s^2$ $2s^2$ $2p^2$	N 7, Color-less gas, non-metallic proper-ties	$1s^2$ $2s^2$ $2p^3$	O 8, Color-less gas, strong non-metallic proper-ties	$1s^2$ $2s^2$ $2p^4$	F 9, Pale-yellow gas, very strong non-metallic proper-ties	$1s^2$ $2s^2$ $2p^5$	Ne 10, Color-less, in-ert gas	$1s^2$ $2s^2$ $2p^6$
Na 11, Soft, silvery, active metal	$1s^2$ $2s^2$ $2p^6$ $3s^1$	Mg 12 Silvery metal	$1s^2$ $2s^2$ $2p^6$ $3s^2$	Al 13, Silvery metal, some non-metallic proper-ties	$1s^2$ $2s^2$ $2p^6$ $3s^2$ $3p^1$	Si 14, Dark non-metallic element	$1s^2$ $2s^2$ $2p^6$ $3s^2$ $3p^2$	P 15, Solid non-metallic element	$1s^2$ $2s^2$ $2p^6$ $3s^2$ $3p^3$	S 16, Solid, yellow, non-metallic	$1s^2$ $2s^2$ $2p^6$ $3s^2$ $3p^4$	Cl 17, Yellow-green gas, strong non-metallic proper-ties	$1s^2$ $2s^2$ $2p^6$ $3s^2$ $3p^5$	Ar 18 Color-less, in-ert gas	$1s^2$ $2s^2$ $2p^6$ $3s^2$ $3p^6$

11. Fill in the blocks with the names, symbols, atomic numbers, electron configurations, and other designated information.

Group VIII

		helium He 2	2

Group I			Group II			Group V			Group VII				
lithium Li 3	2 1		beryllium Be 4	2 2		nitrogen N 7	2 5		fluorine F 9	2 7		neon Ne 10	2 8
sodium Na 11	2 8 1		magne- sium Mg 12	2 8 2		phospho- rus P 15	2 8 5		chlorine Cl 17	2 8 7		argon Ar 18	2 8 8
potassium K 19	2 8 8 1		calcium Ca 20	2 8 8 2		arsenic As 33	2 8 18 5		bromine Br 35	2 8 18 7		krypton Kr 36	2 8 18 8
rubidium Rb 37	2 8 18 8 1		strontium Sr 38	2 8 18 8 2		antimony Sb 51	2 8 18 18 5		iodine I 53	2 8 18 18 7		xenon Xe 54	2 8 18 18 8
cesium Cs 55	2 8 18 18 8 1		barium Ba 56	2 8 18 18 8 2		bismuth Bi 83	2 8 18 32 18 5		astatine At 85	2 8 18 32 18 7		radon Rn 86	2 8 18 32 18 8
francium Fr 87	2 8 18 32 18 8 1		radium Ra 88	2 8 18 32 18 8 2									

	Sodium Family	Calcium Family		Nitrogen Family		Halogen Family	Noble Gas Family
Name of family	Sodium Family	Calcium Family		Nitrogen Family		Halogen Family	Noble Gas Family
Nature of properties	**Very active metallic**	**Active metallic**		**Nonmetallic to metallic**		Very active nonmetallic	**Top 3 inert bottom 3 reactive**
Direction of increasing activity	**Generally from top to bottom of table**	From top to bottom of table				**From bottom to top of table**	

12. What arrangement of outer-shell electrons identifies elements with generally similar properties?

Similar arrangement of outer-shell electrons identifies elements with generally similar

properties.
12

13. Excluding the noble gases, state the location in the periodic table of (a) the most active metal and (b) the most active nonmetal. (a) **Lower left-hand corner** (b) **Upper right-hand corner**
13

Exercises and Experiments in Modern Chemistry
Holt, Rinehart and Winston, Publishers

14. Which of the noble gases have no known compounds? **No compounds of helium, neon, and argon are known.**

14

15. What does the electron population of the outermost shell of the atoms of the transition elements reveal about their properties? **The transition elements are metals.**

15

16. Why do elements of the lanthanide series have almost identical chemical properties? **The two outer shells of the atoms of these elements are almost the same.**

16

17. What is the significance of the zigzag line running diagonally down and to the right near the right end of the periodic table? **This zigzag line separates the metals from the nonmetals.**

17

18. What properties do metalloids show? **Metalloids show both metallic and nonmetallic properties under different conditions.**

18

19. Why isn't the volume of an atom a completely definite quantity? **The volume of an atom is not a completely definite quantity because the boundary of an atom's electron cloud is not a distinct surface but is somewhat fuzzy and indefinite.**

19

20. Compose two statements describing the periodicity of atomic radii.

(a) **In a family of elements, the atomic radius increases with atomic number.**

(b) **In a period of elements, the atomic radius generally decreases from Group I to Group VIII.**

20

21. In the reaction $A + energy \rightarrow A^+ + e^-$, (a) what kind of a particle is A^+? **A singly charged positive ion.**

(b) What name describes the energy involved? **ionization energy**

21

22. In Question 21, what kind of element is A generally if the quantity of energy (a) is low? **a metal** (b) is high? **a nonmetal** (c) is of intermediate value? **a metalloid**

22

23. What two properties of the noble gases furnish strong evidence for the unusual stability of the outer-shell octet? **The chemical inertness and the unusually high ionization energies.**

23

24. (a) How does the ionization energy vary with atomic number within a group? (b) Why?

(a) **Ionization energy generally decreases with increasing atomic number.**

(b) **The outer-shell electrons of the elements of higher atomic number are farther from the nucleus, causing increasing atomic radius and decreasing strength of attraction between the outer-shell electrons and the nucleus.**

24

25. Explain the decrease in first ionization energy between Groups II and III in Periods 2 and 3. **The s sublevel is filled and the p sublevel is started. Less energy is required to remove an unpaired electron than to remove one electron of a pair.**

25

26. Between which two other groups in Periods 2 and 3 is there another decrease in first ionization energy? **There is a decrease between Group V and Group VI as the p sublevel becomes half-filled.**

26

27. Explain the sharp decrease in ionization energy between the last transition element and the Group III element in Period 4. **The d sublevel is filled and the p sublevel is started.**

27

28. What apparently causes the observed irregularities in the general increase in ionization energy in each series? The irregularities are apparently related to the extra stability of completed and half-completed sublevels. _____ 28

29. Why is the ionization energy required to remove the second electron from Na atoms so very much greater than that needed to remove the first electron? Each successive electron must be removed from a particle with increasingly greater net positive charge. The second electron is a 2p electron. _____ 29

30. Why is the ionization energy needed to remove the first two electrons from Mg atoms relatively low? Both electrons are 3s electrons. _____ 30

31. Why is it easier to remove the first electron from Al atoms than it is to remove the first electron from Mg atoms? The first aluminum electron is a 3p electron, which is in a slightly higher energy sublevel than the first magnesium electron, which is a 3s electron. _____ 31

32. What is electron affinity? Electron affinity is a measure of the tendency of a neutral atom to acquire additional electrons. It is measured as the energy released when a neutral atom gains an electron. _____ 32

33. Write the equation representing (a) the energy change for the electron affinity for most atoms, (b) the energy change for the relatively few other atoms. (a) $A + e^- \rightarrow A^- + energy$ _____, (b) $A + e^- \rightarrow A^- - energy$ _____ 33

34. What type of energy change occurs for (a) and (b) in Question 33? (a) exothermic _____, (b) endothermic _____ 34

35. What are the magnitude and sign of an atom's electron affinity if (a) the electron acquired is strongly bound, (b) the electron acquired is weakly bound? (a) high and positive _____, (b) low and positive _____ 35

36. Which elements have zero or negative electron affinities? _____ Group II, zinc subfamily (Zn, Cd, Hg), noble gases _____ 36

37. Why is there usually a decrease in the experimental values of the electron affinities in the numbered families from the third through the sixth periods? The added electron takes a position in the atom farther from the nucleus. Not as much energy is released; the electron is not so strongly held. _____ 37

38. There is an increase in electron affinity between Groups III and IV. Explain why the addition of an electron to the atoms of these groups produces this result. The addition of an electron to a Group III atom results in an ion with 2 electrons in the outer p sublevel. The addition of an electron to a Group IV atom results in an ion with 3 electrons in the outer p sublevel, a half-filled p sublevel. The half-filled p sublevel has greater stability than the one having 2 electrons. _____ 38

39. Of which group do the elements in each period have the highest electron affinities? Group VII 39

40. What are the present uses of the periodic table? It is a useful, systematic classification of elements according to their properties, which helps make the study of chemistry easier. _____ 40

Chemical Bonds

EXERCISE **6**

DIRECTIONS: In the blank space at the right of each statement, write the word or expression that BEST completes the meaning when substituted for the corresponding number.

1–2. The electrons in an incomplete outer shell of an atom are called the __(1)__ electrons. The balance of the atom is called the __(2)__ .

3. The transfer or sharing of valence electrons between atoms produces chemical __(3)__ between the atoms.

4. Electron transfer results in __(4)__ bonding.

5. Electron sharing produces __(5)__ bonding.

6–7. When one atom combines with another atom, both atoms usually attain an outer shell having a(n) __(6)__ producing a structure that has __(7)__ .

8–9. The process of electron transfer always involves the __(8)__ of energy. If energy is absorbed during electron sharing, the process is said to be __(9)__ .

10. A shorthand method of using chemical symbols to represent the composition of a compound is known as a(n) __(10)__ .

11–12. A sodium ion has a single excess __(11)__ charge and a chloride ion has a single excess __(12)__ charge.

13. The electron-dot symbol for the sodium atom is __(13)__ .

14. The electron-dot symbol for the chlorine atom is __(14)__ .

15. In the electron-dot formula for sodium chloride, the chloride ion is represented as __(15)__ .

16. The amount of energy required to remove one mole of electrons from one mole of sodium atoms is the __(16)__ .

17. The amount of energy released when one mole of chloride ions is produced from one mole of chlorine atoms is the __(17)__ .

18. The energy change in the formation of all ionic compounds from their elements is __(18)__ .

19. The preferred equation showing the formation of a sodium ion from a sodium atom is __(19)__ .

20. The oxidation number of elemental sodium is __(20)__ .

21. A chemical reaction in which an element attains a more positive oxidation state is called __(21)__ .

22. The algebraic sum of the oxidation numbers of all the atoms in the formula of a compound is __(22)__ .

valence	1
kernel	2
bonds	3
ionic	4
covalent	5
noble-gas configuration	6
chemical stability	7
release	8
endothermic	9
chemical formula	10
positive	11
negative	12
Na·	13
·C̈l̤:	14
:C̈l̤:⁻	15
ionization energy	16
electron affinity	17
exothermic	18
Na → Na⁺ + e⁻	19
zero	20
oxidation	21
zero	22

23–25. In the formation of magnesium bromide, the electron(s) transferred from the magnesium atom has (have) the electron-configuration notation ___(23)___ . The number of bromine atoms needed to react with one magnesium atom is ___(24)___ . The ionic formula for magnesium bromide is ___(25)___ .

26. All formulas for ionic compounds are ___(26)___ formulas.

27–28. Some ___(27)___ elements can transfer the electrons in the outermost level and sometimes with very little additional energy can transfer one or two electrons from the ___(28)___ level.

29. The electron-dot formula for the ionic compound potassium bromide is ___(29)___ .

30–31. Metallic ions are (larger, smaller) ___(30)___ than the corresponding metallic atoms; nonmetallic ions are (larger, smaller) ___(31)___ than the corresponding nonmetallic atoms.

32–33. Positive ions are called ___(32)___ , while negative ions are called ___(33)___ .

34–35. Within a group of elements the ion size (increases, decreases) ___(34)___ with atomic number because of ___(35)___ addition.

36. Within a period of elements, the Group I, II, and III cations show a sharp ___(36)___ in ionic radius.

37–39. The electron-dot formula for the diatomic hydrogen molecule is ___(37)___ . Its structural formula is ___(38)___ . Its shape is ___(39)___ .

40. The energy required to break chemical bonds to form neutral atoms is called the ___(40)___ .

41–42. Both atoms of chlorine in a chlorine molecule have the stable electron arrangement of the noble gas ___(41)___ with an octet in the ___(42)___ energy level.

43–44. The structure of a nitrogen molecule indicates the sharing of ___(43)___ pair(s) of electrons. Its structural formula is ___(44)___ .

45. Each atom in the molecules of elements forming diatomic molecules is assigned an oxidation number of ___(45)___ .

46. The reaction for the formation of one mole of hydrogen chloride molecules from one-half mole of hydrogen molecules and one-half mole of chlorine molecules is a(n) ___(46)___ reaction.

47–48. The two possible shapes of a molecule composed of three atoms are described as being either ___(47)___ or ___(48)___ .

49. Water molecules decompose according to the following equation: 1 mole H_2O + 222 kcal → 2 moles H + 1 mole O. The H—O bond energy is ___(49)___ kcal/mole.

$3s^2$	23
two	24
$Mg^{++}Br^-_2$	25
empirical	26
transition	27
next-to-outermost	28
$K^+ : \ddot{B}r :^-$	29
smaller	30
larger	31
cations	32
anions	33
increases	34
shell	35
decrease	36
H ː H	37
H − H	38
linear (straight-line)	39
bond energy	40
argon	41
third	42
three	43
N ≡ N	44
zero	45
exothermic	46
linear	47
bent	48
111	49

Exercises and Experiments in Modern Chemistry
Holt, Rinehart and Winston, Publishers

50. In compounds, the oxidation number of oxygen is usually (50) .

51. An ammonia molecule has the shape of a(n) (51) .

52. Methane molecules have a(n) (52) shape.

53. The neutral particle that results from the covalent bonding of atoms is a(n) (53) .

54. The combining of two or more orbitals of nearly the same energy into new orbitals of equal energy is called (54) .

55. The four equivalent orbitals of carbon in the methane molecule are called the (55) orbitals.

56. The angles between the N—H bonds in ammonia are known to be 108°, which agrees quite well with the (56) angle value of 109.5°.

57. The bond angle in the water molecule is only 105°. The unshared electron pairs on the oxygen atom tend to repel each other (more than, less than) (57) the shared electrons repel each other.

58. A covalent bond in which there is an unequal attraction for the shared electrons and a resulting unbalanced distribution of charge is called a(n) (58) covalent bond.

59. Metals are characterized by (high, low) (59) electronegativity.

60. Within each numbered group, electronegativity generally (decreases, increases) (60) with increasing atomic number.

61. The lower the electronegativity, the (more, less) (61) active is the metal.

62. In combinations involving nonmetals, the oxidation number of the less electronegative element is (62) .

63. If all the bonds in a molecule are nonpolar, the molecule is (63) .

64. If the polar bonds in a molecule are all alike, the polarity of the molecule as a whole depends only on the (64) of the bonds.

65–66. Carbon dioxide and water have triatomic molecules in which the bonds are (65) . The carbon dioxide molecule is nonpolar, since its shape is (66) .

67. The concept of (67) is an attempt to make up for the deficiencies of the electron-dot structures of certain molecules written in accord with the electron-pair and electron-octet rules.

68. Charged groups of covalently bonded atoms are called (68) .

69–70. A molecule of oxygen is represented by the formula (69) , while two separate, unbonded oxygen atoms are written as (70) .

−2 _____ 50

pyramid _____ 51

tetrahedral _____ 52

molecule _____ 53

hybridization _____ 54

sp^3 _____ 55

tetrahedral _____ 56

more than _____ 57

polar _____ 58

low _____ 59

decreases _____ 60

more _____ 61

positive _____ 62

nonpolar _____ 63

spatial arrangement _____ 64

polar _____ 65

linear _____ 66

resonance _____ 67

polyatomic ions _____ 68

O_2 _____ 69

2O _____ 70

71. The number that appears, or is understood to appear, in front of a symbol or formula and that gives the number of particles whose composition is given by the symbol or formula is known as a(n) (71) .

72. For the following expressions, write the oxidation number of the element whose symbol is underlined:

(a) $\underline{Fe}_2O_3$ _____ **+3** _____

(b) $K^+\underline{Mn}O_4^-$ _____ **+7** _____

(c) $\underline{P}O_4{}^{---}$ _____ **+5** _____

(d) $\underline{O}_2$ _____ **0** _____

(e) $HC\underline{l}O_3$ _____ **+5** _____

(f) $\underline{N}H_4{}^+$ _____ **−3** _____

73. Draw the orbital notations for (a) F_2; (b) KCl

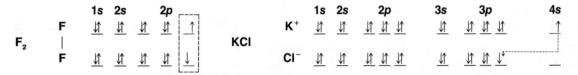

74. Draw electron-dot formulas for the following:

(a) H_2O

H : Ö :
    ..
    H

(c) CH_4

    H
    ..
H : C : H
    ..
    H

(e) CS_2

:S : : C : : S:

(g) HBr

        ..
H : Br :
        ..

(b) NH_3

H : N : H
    ..
    H

(d) $Mg^{++}Br^-{}_2$

:Br :⁻ Mg⁺⁺ : Br :⁻

(f) H_2O_2

H :Ö:
   •x
   xÖx H
   xx

(h) $NH_4{}^+$

    H
    ..
H : N : H⁺
    ..
    H

Exercises and Experiments in Modern Chemistry
Holt, Rinehart and Winston, Publishers

Chemical Composition

EXERCISE **7**

DIRECTIONS: In the blank space at the right of each statement, write the word or expression that BEST completes the meaning when substituted for the corresponding number.

1–2. The ions of Group I and Group II metals have the electron configurations of the   (1) . Where metals have more than one oxidation number, the name includes the number in   (2)   in parentheses.

preceding noble gases _____ 1

Roman numerals _____ 2

3–5. According to the ion-charge method for writing formulas, the total charge of the first (positive) part of the compound must be   (3)   and opposite to the total charge of the second (negative) part of the compound. The total charge of an ion is found by multiplying the charge of the ion by the number of   (4) . This method yields a(n)   (5)   formula.

equal _____ 3

that ion taken _____ 4

empirical _____ 5

6–7. When a polyatomic ion is to be taken more than once in a formula, the polyatomic ion must be enclosed in   (6)   and the number of times the polyatomic ion is taken represented by a(n)   (7)   placed outside.

parentheses _____ 6

subscript _____ 7

8. Compounds consisting of two elements only are called   (8)   compounds.

binary _____ 8

9. The correct name for As_2S_5 is   (9) .

diarsenic pentasulfide _____ 9

10. When it is known that a substance exists as simple molecules, its formula is known as a(n)   (10)   formula.

molecular _____ 10

11. The formula representing the simplest whole-number ratio of atoms of the elements in a compound is the   (11)   formula.

empirical _____ 11

12. The formula weight of any compound is the   (12)   of the atomic weights of all the atoms present in the formula.

sum _____ 12

13. The formula weight of NaCl is   (13) .

58.5 _____ 13

14. The term   (14)   is a more general term than molecular weight and therefore is preferred by chemists.

formula weight _____ 14

15. Atomic weights and formula weights are useful because they tell us the   (15)   weights of elements or compounds that combine or react.

relative _____ 15

16. The law of   (16)   states that the percentage composition of a chemical compound is always the same regardless of the source.

definite composition _____ 16

17. John Dalton recognized the possibility that two kinds of atoms could combine in more than one way and in more than one   (17) .

proportion _____ 17

18. The number of carbon-12 atoms in exactly 12 grams of this nuclide is approximately   (18) .

6.02×10^{23} _____ 18

19. The numerical portion of the gram-atomic weight of an element is the   (19)   of the element.

atomic weight _____ 19

20. The mass in grams of one mole of naturally occurring atoms of an element is the __(20)__ of the element.

gram-atomic weight _____ 20

21. The number of grams of sulfur containing the same number of atoms as 5.00 moles of oxygen atoms is __(21)__ .

16$\bar{0}$ g _____ 21

22. The gram-molecular weight of a diatomic element is the mass of __(22)__ of molecules of the element.

one mole _____ 22

23. Since 1.00 mole of Cl atoms has a mass of 35.5 g, 1.00 mole of Cl_2 molecules has a mass of __(23)__ grams.

71.0 _____ 23

24. The mass of 2.00 moles of sodium chloride is __(24)__ grams.

117 _____ 24

25. The formula for a compound may represent the composition of the compound and the mass of __(25)__ of that compound.

one mole _____ 25

DIRECTIONS: In the space at the right, give the formulas for the following compounds.

26. calcium fluoride _____ CaF_2 _____

27. mercury(II) chloride _____ $HgCl_2$ _____

28. potassium nitrite _____ KNO_2 _____

29. antimony trichloride _____ $SbCl_3$ _____

30. barium carbonate _____ $BaCO_3$ _____

31. aluminum hydroxide _____ $Al(OH)_3$ _____

32. carbon monoxide _____ CO _____

33. silver chromate _____ Ag_2CrO_4 _____

34. iron(II) carbonate _____ $FeCO_3$ _____

35. copper(I) sulfide _____ Cu_2S _____

36. diarsenic pentasulfide _____ As_2S_5 _____

37. lead(II) phosphate _____ $Pb_3(PO_4)_2$ _____

38. ammonium nitrate _____ NH_4NO_3 _____

39. calcium hydroxide _____ $Ca(OH)_2$ _____

40. chromium(III) sulfite _____ $Cr_2(SO_3)_3$ _____

41. iron(II) oxide _____ FeO _____

42. magnesium acetate _____ $Mg(C_2H_3O_2)_2$ _____

43. sodium peroxide _____ Na_2O_2 _____

44. potassium chlorate _____ $KClO_3$ _____

45. zinc iodide _____ ZnI_2 _____

DIRECTIONS: Using approximate atomic weights of the elements, write the formula weight of each compound in the space provided at right.

46. KNO_3 _____ 101.1 _____

47. NaOH _____ 40.0 _____

48. $CaCO_3$ _____ 100.1 _____

49. $PbSO_4$ _____ 303.3 _____

50. $CaSO_4$ _____ 136.2 _____

51. $(NH_4)_3PO_4$ _____ 149.0 _____

52. $AgC_2H_3O_2$ _____ 166.9 _____

53. $Cu(NO_3)_2$ _____ 187.5 _____

54. $Fe_3(PO_4)_2$ _____ 357.4 _____

55. $Na_2CO_3 \cdot 10H_2O$ _____ 286.0 _____

56–58. State the steps used to determine the percentage composition of a constituent element in a compound of known formula.

Step 1: **Determine the formula weight by adding the atomic weights of all the atoms present.**

_____ 56

Step 2: **Express the total atomic weight contributed by the element of interest**

(the at. wt. × no. atoms) as a fractional part of the formula weight.

_____ 57

Step 3: **Multiply this fractional part of the formula weight by 100% to give the**

percentage of the element present in the compound.

_____ 58

Exercises and Experiments in Modern Chemistry
Holt, Rinehart and Winston, Publishers

59–68. What is the percentage composition of each element present in each of the following compounds? Show each step in smooth form in the appropriate column.

Compound	Step 1	Steps 2 and 3	Percentage composition	
NaCl	58.5			
59. % Na	23.0	23.0 ÷ 58.5 × 100%	39.3%	59
60. % Cl	35.5	35.5 ÷ 58.5 × 100%	60.7%	60
K_2CO_3	138.2			
61. % K	78.2	78.2 ÷ 138.2 × 100%	56.6%	61
62. % C	12.0	12.0 ÷ 138.2 × 100%	8.7%	62
63. % O	48.0	48.0 ÷ 138.2 × 100%	34.7%	63
Fe_3O_4	231.4			
64. % Fe	167.4	167.4 ÷ 231.4 × 100%	72.3%	64
65. % O	64.0	64.0 ÷ 231.4 × 100%	27.7%	65
$C_3H_5(OH)_3$	92.0			
66. % C	36.0	36.0 ÷ 92.0 × 100%	39.1%	66
67. % H	8.0	8.0 ÷ 92.0 × 100%	8.7%	67
68. % O	48.0	48.0 ÷ 92.0 × 100%	52.2%	68

69–71. By what three steps can you determine the empirical formula of a compound if either the mass or mass percentage of each constituent element is known?

Step 1: **Determine the relative number of moles of atoms of each element by**

dividing the mass of each element by the mass per mole of that element. (Percentage

composition data are converted to relative mass data on the basis of a 100-gram sample.)

_____ 69

Step 2: **Find the smallest ratio of atoms by dividing the relative number of**

moles of atoms of each element by the smallest relative number of moles of atoms.

_____ 70

Step 3: **Find the simplest whole-number ratio (if not found in Step 2) by expressing**

as fractions and clearing.

_____ 71

72–80. What is the empirical formula of each compound for which the analysis is given below?

72. Analysis: H = 1.24%, Br = 98.76%.   **HBr** _____ 72

73. Analysis: K = 44.9%, S = 18.4%, O = 36.7%.   **K₂SO₄** _____ 73

74. Analysis: Iron = 17.21 g, chlorine = 32.79 g.   **FeCl₃** _____ 74

75. Analysis: K = 28.71%, H = 0.73%, S = 23.57%, O = 46.99%.   **KHSO₄** _____ 75

76. Analysis: Ba = 80.2%, O = 18.7%, H = 1.2%   **Ba(OH)₂** _____ 76

77. Analysis: Mg = 27.73%, P = 23.58%, O = 48.69%.

78. Analysis: Cu = 39.79%, S = 20.11%, O = 40.10%.

79. Analysis: Mg = 20.18%, S = 26.66%, O = 53.16%.

80. A certain hydrocarbon was found to be 80.0% carbon and 20.0% hydrogen. The molecular weight was determined to be $3\overline{0}$. What is the molecular formula?

$Mg_3(PO_4)_2$ _____ 77

$CuSO_4$ _____ 78

$MgSO_4$ _____ 79

C_2H_6 _____ 80

Exercises and Experiments in Modern Chemistry
Holt, Rinehart and Winston, Publishers

Equations and Mass Relationships

EXERCISE **8**

DIRECTIONS: Write the answers to the following in the space provided. Where appropriate, make complete statements.

1. Why may a balanced formula equation be said to have quantitative significance? **It represents**
facts concerning reactions that have been established experimentally. It also

indicates the identities and relative quantities of reactants and products

in a chemical reaction system. 1

2. What important fact concerning a reaction is not revealed by the balanced equation?
The equation reveals nothing of the mechanism by which reactants are converted into products.

2

3. What three factors must be considered in writing a balanced chemical equation? _____
The three factors in equation writing are (1) The equation must represent the facts.

(2) The equation must include the correct symbols and formulas for all elements and compounds

involved as reactants and products. (3) The equation must satisfy the law of conservation

of atoms. 3

4. What are the three steps in an orderly procedure used to write equations? _____
The three steps in equation writing are (1) Represent the facts. (2) Write correct

formulas for compounds balanced as to oxidation number or ion charge.

(Formulas for elemental substances with diatomic molecules must also be correctly written.) (3) Balance

the equation according to the law of conservation of atoms. 4

5. What are the four general types of chemical reactions? Write the general form equation representing each reaction type.

Type of Reaction	*General Form Equations*
Composition reaction:	**A + X → AX**
Decomposition reaction:	**AX → A + X**
Replacement reaction:	**A + BX → AX + B; Y + BX → BY + X**
Ionic reaction:	**A^+(aq) + B^-(aq) → AB; AX + BY → AY + BX** 5

6. What are the six generally recognized types of decomposition reactions? _____
(1) Metallic carbonates, when heated, form metallic oxides and carbon dioxide.

(2) Many metallic hydroxides, when heated, decompose into metallic oxides and water.

(3) Metallic chlorates, when heated, decompose into metallic chlorides and oxygen.

(4) Some acids, when heated, decompose into nonmetallic oxides and water.

(5) Some oxides, when heated, decompose.

(6) Some decomposition reactions are produced by an electric current.

6

7. What are the four classes of replacement reactions? _____

(1) Replacement of a metal in a compound by a more active metal.

(2) Replacement of hydrogen in water by metals.

(3) Replacement of hydrogen in acids by metals.

(4) Replacement of halogens. _____ 7

8. What are reversible reactions? **Reactions in which the products of a chemical**

reaction can react to produce the original reactants. _____ 8

9. What are two rules related to the activity series of the elements that help predict the course
of replacement reactions? _____

Atoms of a more active metal lose electrons to positively charged ions of a less active

metal. Atoms of more active nonmetals acquire electrons from negatively charged ions

of less active nonmetals. _____ 9

10. What are the four steps used in *setting up* a mass problem for solution by the mole method?

(1) Write the balanced equation. (2) Show the problem specifications: what is given

and what is required. (3) Show the mole proportions, writing the number of moles

indicated by the equation under each substance involved in the problem. (4) Determine

the mass of one mole of each substance involved in the problem.

_____ 10

11. What are the four main operations that follow the problem setup in *solving* a mass-mass
problem by the mole method? _____

(1) Determine the number of moles of the substance whose mass is given in the problem.

(2) Determine the number of moles of the substance whose mass is required.

(3) Determine the mass of the substance required. (4) Check the units assigned to make

sure they yield the proper units for the answer and estimate the answer.

_____ 11

12. How do you convert the given mass of the substance to moles? _____

The given mass is converted to moles by multiplying the mass by the fraction mole/mass

of one mole of the substance. _____ 12

13. How do you determine the number of moles of substance whose mass is required?

Multiply the number of moles of the substance whose mass was given by the ratio of

the number of moles of substance whose mass is required and the number of moles

of substance whose mass is given as indicated by the balanced equation.

_____ 13

14. How do you determine the mass of the substance required? _____

Multiply the number of moles of the substance whose mass is required by the number

of grams per mole of that substance. _____ 14

Exercises and Experiments in Modern Chemistry
Holt, Rinehart and Winston, Publishers

DIRECTIONS: Write the balanced chemical equation in the space provided under each word equation. Identify the type of reaction.

15. sulfur + oxygen → sulfur dioxide (g)
$S + O_2 → SO_2$ (g)   composition reaction _____ 15

16. zinc + sulfuric acid(H_2SO_4) → zinc sulfate (aq) + hydrogen (g)
$Zn + H_2SO_4 → ZnSO_4$ (aq) + H_2 (g)   replacement reaction _____ 16

17. hydrogen + nitrogen → ammonia (g)
$3 H_2 + N_2 → 2 NH_3$ (g)   composition reaction _____ 17

18. hydrogen + chlorine → hydrogen chloride (g)
$H_2 + Cl_2 → 2 HCl$ (g)   composition reaction _____ 18

19. carbon + water(steam) → carbon monoxide (g) + hydrogen (g)
$C + H_2O → CO$ (g) + H_2 (g)   replacement reaction _____ 19

20. calcium oxide + water → calcium hydroxide (aq)
$CaO + H_2O → Ca(OH)_2$ (aq)   composition reaction _____ 20

21. phosphorus + oxygen → diphosphorus pentoxide (molecular formula, P_4O_{10}) (s)
$4 P + 5 O_2 → P_4O_{10}$ (s)   composition reaction _____ 21

22. hydrochloric acid(HCl) + sodium hydroxide → sodium chloride (aq) + water
$HCl + NaOH → NaCl$ (aq) + H_2O ionic reaction _____ 22

23. barium chloride + sulfuric acid → barium sulfate (s) + hydrochloric acid
$BaCl_2 + H_2SO_4 → BaSO_4$ (s) + $2 HCl$ ionic reaction _____ 23

24. aluminum sulfate + calcium hydroxide → aluminum hydroxide (s) + calcium sulfate (s)
$Al_2(SO_4)_3 + 3 Ca(OH)_2 → 2 Al(OH)_3$ (s) + $3 CaSO_4$ (s)   ionic reaction _____ 24

25. copper + chlorine → copper(I) chloride (s)
$2 Cu + Cl_2 → 2 CuCl$ (s)   composition reaction _____ 25

26. aluminum oxide → aluminum (l) + oxygen (g)
$2 Al_2O_3 → 4 Al$(l) + $3 O_2$ (g)   decomposition reaction _____ 26

DIRECTIONS: Complete the word equation and write the balanced formula equation. Identify the type of reaction and give a reason for the product(s). Consult the Activity Series (Section 8.8) and Appendix Table 12, Solubility Chart, as necessary.

27. calcium + oxygen → **calcium oxide.** _____
$2 Ca + O_2 → 2 CaO$ composition; the product is more stable than the reactants. _____ 27

28. copper(II) carbonate → **copper(II) oxide + carbon dioxide (g).** _____
$CuCO_3 → CuO + CO_2$ (g)   decomposition of a metallic carbonate _____ 28

29. aluminum + hydrochloric acid → **aluminum chloride + hydrogen (g).** _____
$2 Al + 6HCl → 2AlCl_3 + 3H_2$ (g)   replacement; aluminum is more active than hydrogen. _____ 29

30. potassium iodide + chlorine → ___potassium chloride + iodine.___

$2KI + Cl_2 \rightarrow 2KCl + I_2$ **replacement of halogens; chlorine is a more active nonmetal than iodine.**

_30

31. barium chloride + sodium sulfate → ___sodium chloride + barium sulfate(s).___

$BaCl_2 + Na_2SO_4 \rightarrow 2NaCl + BaSO_4 \text{ (s)}$ **ionic; barium sulfate precipitates.**

_31

32. copper + silver nitrate → copper(II) nitrate + ___silver(s).___

$Cu + 2AgNO_3 \rightarrow Cu(NO_3)_2 + 2Ag \text{ (s)}$ **replacement; copper is more active than silver.**

_32

33. barium hydroxide + sulfuric acid → ___water + barium sulfate(s).___

$Ba(OH)_2 + H_2SO_4 \rightarrow 2H_2O + BaSO_4 \text{ (s)}$ **ionic; water is formed, barium sulfate precipitates.**

_33

34. zinc sulfate + ammonium sulfide → ___ammonium sulfate + zinc sulfide(s).___

$ZnSO_4 + (NH_4)_2 S \rightarrow (NH_4)_2 SO_4 + ZnS(s)$ **ionic; zinc sulfide precipitates.**

_34

35. sodium + water → ___sodium hydroxide + hydrogen (g).___

$2Na + 2H_2O \rightarrow 2NaOH + H_2 \text{ (g)}$ **replacement; sodium is more active than hydrogen.**

_35

36. magnesium + sulfuric acid → ___magnesium sulfate + hydrogen (g).___

$Mg + H_2SO_4 \rightarrow MgSO_4 + H_2 \text{ (g)}$ **replacement; magnesium is more active than hydrogen.**

_36

37. mercury(II) oxide → ___mercury + oxygen (g).___

$2HgO \rightarrow 2Hg + O_2 \text{ (g)}$ **decomposition; some metallic oxides decompose on heating.**

_37

DIRECTIONS: Solve the following problems using the method outlined in Chapter 8 of MODERN CHEMISTRY. Place the labeled answers in the spaces provided at the right. Have the solutions to all problems worked out in smooth form on separate paper (or in your problem notebook) to be turned in to your instructor if requested.

38. How many grams of oxygen can be produced by completely decomposing $1\overline{0}$ g of mercury(II) oxide?

0.74 g O_2 _38

39. How many grams of mercury are produced in Problem 38?

9.3 g Hg _39

40. An excess of sulfuric acid reacts with 8.10 g of magnesium. (a) How many moles of hydrogen are produced? (b) How many grams of hydrogen are produced? (c) How many grams of magnesium sulfate are produced?

(a) 0.333 mole H_2 _40a

(b) 0.671 g H_2 _40b

(c) 40.1 g $MgSO_4$ _40c

41. In a reaction between carbon and oxygen, 11.0 g of carbon dioxide is formed. How many grams of carbon were burned?

3.00 g C _41

42. What mass in grams of copper is precipitated when 13.5 g of aluminum reacts with copper(II) sulfate in solution?

47.6 g Cu _42

43. How many grams of calcium nitrate are produced in the reaction between 12.6 g of nitric acid(HNO_3) and an excess of calcium hydroxide?

16.4 g $Ca(NO_3)_2$ _43

44. Suppose that 10.0 g of calcium reacts completely with water. (a) How many moles of hydrogen gas could be collected? (b) How many grams of calcium hydroxide are produced?

(a) 0.249 mole H_2 _44a

(b) 18.5 g $Ca(OH)_2$ _44b

Exercises and Experiments in Modern Chemistry
Holt, Rinehart and Winston, Publishers

Two Important Gases: Oxygen and Hydrogen

DIRECTIONS: In the blank space at the right of each statement, write the word or expression that BEST completes the meaning when substituted for the corresponding number.

1. Oxygen ranks __(1)__ in abundance in the earth's crust.

2. Oxygen atoms rank __(2)__ in abundance in the known universe.

3. By volume, the fraction of the earth's atmosphere that is oxygen is __(3)__ .

4. Water contains almost __(4)__ percent oxygen by mass in combination with hydrogen.

5. Priestley prepared oxygen by strongly heating __(5)__ .

6–8. The experimental observations or conclusions that Lavoisier made, which led to rejection of the phlogiston theory, were as follows: oxygen is a(an) __(6)__ ; it is a component of the __(7)__ ; when some substances burn in air or oxygen they __(8)__ mass.

9. One catalyst used in the decomposition of hydrogen peroxide is __(9)__ .

10. Gases that are not very soluble in water may be collected by the method known as __(10)__ .

11. The products of the reaction between sodium peroxide and water are oxygen and __(11)__ .

12. The products of the thermal decomposition of potassium chlorate are oxygen and __(12)__ .

13. In the electrolysis of water, oxygen collects at the __(13)__ terminal.

14. When liquid air is permitted to stand, the element that boils away first is __(14)__ .

15. Oxygen is __(15)__ soluble in water.

16. The slight attraction of liquid oxygen by a magnet leads chemists to believe that there are __(16)__ electrons in an oxygen molecule.

17. In oxides, the oxidation number of oxygen is __(17)__ .

18. When oxides are formed by direct combination of the elements, the reaction is usually (endothermic, exothermic) __(18)__ .

19. The oxygen compounds of the metals of Groups I and II are __(19)__ .

20. The combustion of potassium, rubidium, and cesium in oxygen yields compounds called __(20)__ .

first	1
third	2
one-fifth	3
89	4
mercury(II) oxide	5
element	6
atmosphere	7
gain	8
manganese dioxide	9
water displacement	10
sodium hydroxide	11
potassium chloride	12
positive	13
nitrogen	14
slightly	15
unpaired	16
−2	17
exothermic	18
ionic	19
peroxides	20

21–22. The oxides of nonmetals contain __(21)__ bonds and exist as __(22)__ .

covalent _____ 21

molecules _____ 22

23. The oxide of iron formed when steel wool burns in pure oxygen has the formula __(23)__ .

Fe_3O_4 _____ 23

24. The most important industrial use of oxygen is in the __(24)__ industry.

iron and steel _____ 24

25. The gas mixture that can be used to make synthetic gasoline, methanol, or ammonia consists of the two gases __(25)__ .

hydrogen and carbon monoxide _____ 25

26. In sewage disposal plants, waste water is exposed to the air in order to increase the amount of __(26)__ oxygen.

dissolved _____ 26

27–28. The __(27)__ rays from the sun change some of the oxygen in the upper atmosphere into ozone. The maximum concentration of ozone occurs at an altitude of __(28)__ km.

ultraviolet _____ 27

25 _____ 28

29–30. The preparation of ozone from oxygen is an (endothermic, exothermic) __(29)__ reaction; ozone, therefore, has a (higher, lower) __(30)__ energy content than oxygen.

endothermic _____ 29

higher _____ 30

31–32. Two or more forms of the same element in the same physical phase are known as __(31)__ . These different forms of the same element are explained in terms of differences in __(32)__ structure.

allotropes _____ 31

molecular _____ 32

33. The concept of __(33)__ helps us to describe ozone's molecular structure.

resonance _____ 33

34. The oxygen-oxygen bonds in the ozone molecule are (weaker, stronger) __(34)__ than the oxygen-oxygen bonds in the oxygen molecule.

weaker _____ 34

35. The uses of ozone are applications of its __(35)__ properties.

oxidizing _____ 35

36–37. Hydrogen ranks __(36)__ in abundance by mass in the earth's surface environment. In the known universe, the number of hydrogen atoms causes it to be ranked __(37)__ .

ninth _____ 36

first _____ 37

38. Free hydrogen is not common on earth because of its __(38)__ .

flammability _____ 38

39–40. Cavendish called hydrogen __(39)__ and proved that the only product formed when hydrogen burns in air is __(40)__ .

inflammable air _____ 39

water _____ 40

41–45. The rate at which hydrogen is given off from acids by replacement with metals depends on the __(41)__ of metal surface exposed, the __(42)__ of metal used, the __(43)__ of the metal, and the __(44)__ and __(45)__ of acid used.

amount _____ 41

kind _____ 42

purity _____ 43

strength _____ 44

kind _____ 45

46. Another factor upon which the rate depends is the __(46)__ .

temperature _____ 46

47. One metal that reacts so vigorously with water that the heat of the reaction ignites the hydrogen is __(47)__ .

potassium _____ 47

Exercises and Experiments in Modern Chemistry
Holt, Rinehart and Winston, Publishers

48. Since calcium is more reactive than magnesium, it will replace hydrogen from cold (48) .

water _____ 48

49. Hydrogen is prepared commercially by replacement from water using the (49) reaction.

iron-steam _____ 49

50–51. When methane reacts with steam in the presence of a catalyst at a high temperature, the gases produced are hydrogen and (50) . When this mixture is cooled and compressed, the (51) liquefies.

carbon monoxide _____ 50

carbon monoxide _____ 51

52–56. When steam is passed over red-hot coke or coal, the mixture of gases formed is called (52) . It consists mainly of (53) and (54) . When this mixture is passed with steam over the catalyst iron oxide at a temperature below 500 °C, additional (55) is produced and the (56) produced is separated by dissolving it in water under moderate pressure.

water gas _____ 52

hydrogen _____ 53

carbon monoxide _____ 54

hydrogen _____ 55

carbon dioxide _____ 56

57. The density of hydrogen is only one (57) that of air.

fourteenth _____ 57

58. When a substance adheres to the surface of another, the process is called (58) .

adsorption _____ 58

59. Scientists believe that it is possible, under very high pressure, to convert hydrogen into a solid having (59) properties.

metallic _____ 59

60–63. Hydrogen combines with nonmetals to form (60) compounds. The polarity of the bonds in these compounds depends on the (61) of the nonmetal. The H—C bond is almost (62) , while the H—F bond is highly (63) .

molecular _____ 60

electronegativity _____ 61

nonpolar _____ 62

polar _____ 63

64–65. Thrusting a burning splint slowly into a bottle of hydrogen held mouth downward indicates that hydrogen does (64) but does not (65) .

burn _____ 64

support combustion _____ 65

66. Hydrogen and chlorine combine explosively in the presence of (66) .

direct sunlight _____ 66

67. Hydrogen has an oxidation number of -1 in the (67) ion.

hydride _____ 67

68–69. Ninety percent of elemental hydrogen produced today is used for preparing the two hydrogen compounds (68) and (69) .

ammonia _____ 68

methanol _____ 69

70. Millions of pounds of cottonseed oil are changed each year from liquid to solid or semisolid fat by the process of (70) .

hydrogenation _____ 70

71–72. Hydrogen is sometimes used as a(an) (71) agent to recover certain metals from their oxide ores. However, the element (72) is usually used because it is less expensive.

reducing _____ 71

carbon _____ 72

73. Hydrogen compounds are used as fuels. The hydrogen compound that is the main constituent of natural gas has the formula (73) .

CH_4 _____ 73

74–75. The mass of deuterium atoms compared to that of protium atoms is almost __(74)__ . Because of this significant mass difference, the rates of reaction of deuterium and deuterium compounds are generally much (slower, faster) __(75)__ than those of protium and protium compounds.

double _____ 74

slower _____ 75

The Gas Laws

EXERCISE **10**

DIRECTIONS: In the blank space at the right of each statement, write the word or expression that BEST completes the meaning when substituted for the corresponding number.

1–3. The three basic assumptions of the kinetic theory are that matter is composed of __(1)__ ; the particles of matter are in __(2)__ ; and the total kinetic energy of colliding particles __(3)__ .

4. The process of spreading out spontaneously to occupy a space uniformly is known as __(4)__ .

5. Matter in the gaseous phase occupies a volume about __(5)__ times that which it does in the liquid or solid phase.

6–7. If the temperature of a sample of gas within a container is raised, the molecules on an average have more __(6)__ , which is related to the speed of the molecules by the equation __(7)__ .

8. The lowest temperature at which a substance can exist as a gas at atmospheric pressure is called the __(8)__ .

9–12. Substances that consist of low-molecular-weight nonpolar covalent molecules can exist as gases at very __(9)__ temperatures. Similar substances that have higher molecular weights have condensation temperatures somewhat __(10)__ room temperature. The condensation temperature of ammonia is much higher than that of methane (a molecule of similar weight and complexity) because the molecule of ammonia is __(11)__ . Ionic compounds, covalent network substances, and metals have condensation temperatures that are all __(12)__ .

13–14. Generally, the higher the molecular weight of a nonpolar molecule, the __(13)__ its condensation temperature will be. The strength of dispersion interaction forces depends on the number of __(14)__ in a molecule.

15. If the volume that one mole of gas molecules occupies remains constant, the pressure exerted by the gas will __(15)__ if the temperature is lowered.

16. At a constant temperature, the pressure exerted by one mole of gas molecules will __(16)__ if the volume available to the gas is increased.

17–18. Standard temperature is exactly __(17)__ degrees Celsius. Standard pressure is the pressure exerted by a column of mercury exactly __(18)__ high.

19. Standard pressure is the average atmospheric pressure at __(19)__ .

20–22. The volume of a definite quantity of dry gas is __(20)__ proportional to the pressure, provided the __(21)__ remains constant. This statement is known as __(22)__ law.

very tiny particles _____	1
continual motion _____	2
remains constant _____	3
diffusion _____	4
1000 _____	5
kinetic energy _____	6
$E_k = \dfrac{1}{2}\,mv^2$ _____	7
condensation temperature _____	8
low _____	9
above _____	10
polar _____	11
very high _____	12
higher _____	13
electrons _____	14
decrease _____	15
decrease _____	16
zero _____	17
760 mm _____	18
sea level _____	19
inversely _____	20
temperature _____	21
Boyle's _____	22

Exercises and Experiments in Modern Chemistry
Holt, Rinehart and Winston, Publishers

23–25. The experiments of Jacques Charles revealed that (a) all gases expand or contract at the (23) rate with changes in temperature, providing the pressure is (24) ; and (b) the change in volume amounts to (25) of the original volume at 0 °C for each Celsius degree the temperature is changed.

26. The temperature of the triple point of water is defined as (26) °K.

27. Kelvin temperatures are (27) degrees higher than Celsius temperatures.

28–29. Charles' law states that the volume of a definite quantity of dry gas varies (28) with the (29) temperature, provided the pressure remains constant.

30. Charles' law holds for real gases with considerable accuracy except at (30) .

same _____ 23

constant (unchanged) _____ 24

$\dfrac{1}{273}$ _____ 25

273.16 _____ 26

273 _____ 27

directly _____ 28

Kelvin _____ 29

low temperatures _____ 30

DIRECTIONS: Place the properly labeled answers to the following problems in the spaces provided at the right. Use cancellation wherever possible. Observe the rules for significant figures. Show all calculations in your notebook or on a separate sheet of paper. Use the methods outlined in Chapter 10 of MODERN CHEMISTRY.

31. A gas occupies a volume of 75.0 mL when the pressure is $38\overline{0}$ mm. What volume does the gas occupy at $114\overline{0}$ mm?

25.0 mL _____ 31

32. The hydrogen in a eudiometer has a volume of 80.0 mL when the pressure is $74\overline{0}$ mm. What is its volume at standard pressure?

77.9 mL _____ 32

33. If $60\overline{0}$ mL of hydrogen is collected when the temperature is 27 °C, what volume will the gas occupy at 23 °C?

592 mL _____ 33

34. The volume of a gas is 1164 mL at 18 °C. What is its volume at standard temperature?

1.09×10^3 mL _____ 34

35. To what Celsius temperature must $58\overline{0}$ mL of oxygen at 17 °C be raised to increase its volume to $70\overline{0}$ mL?

77 °C _____ 35

36. Given $70\overline{0}$ mL of oxygen at 7 °C and 80.0 cm pressure, what volume does it have at 27 °C and 50.0 cm pressure?

1.20×10^3 mL _____ 36

37. A gas has a volume of $114\overline{0}$ mL at 37 °C and $62\overline{0}$ mm pressure. Calculate its volume at STP.

819 mL _____ 37

38. A volume of 50.0 mL of gas is collected by displacement of mercury at 17 °C and $76\overline{0}$ mm pressure. The mercury level inside the eudiometer is 30.0 mm higher than that outside. What volume will the gas occupy at STP?

45.2 mL _____ 38

39. A gas occupies a volume of 40.0 mL at 734.8 mm and 22 °C. The gas was collected by displacement of water, and the water level inside the eudiometer is the same as that outside. What is the volume of dry gas at STP?

34.8 mL _____ 39

40. A eudiometer contains 45.0 mL of oxygen when the barometer reading is 731.7 mm and the temperature is 27 °C. The water level inside the tube is 68 mm higher than that outside. What volume does the dry oxygen occupy at STP?

37.7 mL _____ 40

Exercises and Experiments in Modern Chemistry
Holt, Rinehart and Winston, Publishers

Molecular Composition of Gases

EXERCISE

DIRECTIONS: In the blank space at the right of each statement, write the word or expression that BEST completes the meaning when substituted for the corresponding number.

1–2. The law of combining volumes is attributed to (1) . It states that under similar conditions of temperature and pressure, the volumes of reacting gases and of their gaseous products are expressed in the ratios of (2) .

Gay-Lussac	1
small whole numbers	2

3–4. The law of combining volumes was explained by (3) . This explanation states that under the same conditions of temperature and pressure, equal volumes of all gases contain the same number of (4) .

Avogadro	3
molecules	4

5–11. The reaction between 1 volume of hydrogen and 1 volume of chlorine produces 2 volumes of hydrogen chloride. All molecules of hydrogen chloride have the same composition according to the law of (5) . The molecular proportions for the reaction are (6) molecule(s) of hydrogen to (7) molecule(s) of chlorine to (8) molecule(s) of hydrogen chloride. Therefore, the smallest number of atoms of hydrogen that can be present in each molecule of hydrogen chloride is (9) , and the smallest number of atoms of chlorine that can be present in each molecule of hydrogen chloride is (10) . The smallest number of atoms per molecule of hydrogen and/or chlorine that satisfies the requirements of the reaction is (11) .

definite composition	5
1	6
1	7
2	8
1 atom	9
1 atom	10
2 atoms	11

12. The word that describes the number of atoms in each molecule of an active gaseous element is (12) .

diatomic	12

13. The word that describes the number of atoms in each molecule of a noble gas is (13) .

monatomic	13

14. At high temperatures, molecules of mercury are (14) .

monatomic	14

15–16. The volume occupied by 1 mole of a gas at STP is called the (15) and is (16) liters.

molar volume	15
22.4	16

17. One mole of O_2 contains (17) molecules.

6.02×10^{23}	17

18. The gram-molecular weight of a gaseous substance is the mass in grams of (18) liters of the gas measured at STP.

22.4	18

DIRECTIONS: Solve the following problems using the methods outlined in Chapter 11 of MODERN CHEMISTRY. Place the labeled answers in the spaces provided. Have the solutions worked out in smooth form on separate paper or in your notebook.

19. Calculate the mass of 1.00 liter of carbon monoxide, CO, at STP.

1.25 g	19

20. A gaseous compound of uranium has the formula UF_6. What is the molecular weight of this gas?

352	20

21. Find the density of the gas in Problem 20.

15.7 g/L	21

22. The density of bromine vapor is 7.15 g/L. What is the molecular weight of bromine vapor?

$16\overline{0}$ _____ 22

23. At standard conditions, $50\overline{0}$ mL of a gas has a mass of 0.995 g. What is the molecular weight of the gas?

44.6 _____ 23

24. The mass of $20\overline{0}$ mL of acetylene is 0.234 g. What is its molecular weight?

26.2 _____ 24

25. A compound contains the following: carbon, 92.3%; hydrogen, 7.7%. One liter of its vapor has a mass of 3.48 g. What is the empirical formula?

CH _____ 25

26. What is the molecular weight of the compound in Problem 25?

78.0 _____ 26

27. What is the molecular formula for the compound in Problem 25?

C_6H_6 _____ 27

28. What is the mass of 1.00 liter of oxygen at STP?

1.43 g _____ 28

29. What is the mass in grams of 250 mL of CO_2 at STP?

0.49 g _____ 29

30. What is the value of the gas constant R calculated from $pV = nRT$?

0.082057 liter atm/mole °K _____ 30

NOTE: Assume STP conditions for Problems 31–47.

31. Carbon combines with oxygen to form carbon dioxide gas. How many milliliters of carbon dioxide are produced when 16.5 mL of oxygen is used?

16.5 mL CO_2 _____ 31

32. How many milliliters of oxygen are necessary to form 64.5 mL of sulfur dioxide gas (SO_2) by the combustion of sulfur?

64.5 mL O_2 _____ 32

33. If 16 liters of carbon monoxide is burned forming carbon dioxide, how many liters of oxygen are required?

8.0 liters O_2 _____ 33

34. How many liters of carbon dioxide are produced in Problem 33?

16 liters CO_2 _____ 34

35. How many liters of hydrogen chloride are produced when 37 liters of hydrogen is united with chlorine?

74 liters HCl _____ 35

36. If 12 liters of acetylene (C_2H_2) is used, how many liters of oxygen are required for its complete combustion to carbon dioxide and water vapor?

$3\overline{0}$ liters O_2 _____ 36

37. How many liters of carbon dioxide are produced in Problem 36?

24 liters CO_2 _____ 37

38. Heptane, C_7H_{16}, is one of the compounds present in gasoline that forms a vapor in the automobile engine. This vapor unites with oxygen when combustion occurs, forming carbon dioxide and water vapor. How many liters of oxygen are necessary to completely burn $9\overline{0}$ liters of heptane vapor?

990 liters O_2 _____ 38

39. If air is 21% oxygen, how many liters of air are needed to furnish the necessary oxygen for Problem 38?

4700 liters air _____ 39

40. How many liters of carbon dioxide are formed in Problem 38?

630 liters CO_2 _____ 40

41. How many liters of hydrogen are set free when 6.08 grams of magnesium reacts with hydrochloric acid?

5.60 liters H_2 _____ 41

Exercises and Experiments in Modern Chemistry
Holt, Rinehart and Winston, Publishers

42. How many grams of iron are needed to set free 112 liters of hydrogen from sulfuric acid? Iron(II) sulfate is the other product.

43. How many liters of hydrogen must be used to reduce 119 grams of hot copper(II) oxide?

44. If 1.00 kilogram of water was produced by the reaction of hydrogen and oxygen, how many liters of oxygen were used?

45. It is determined that 5.6 liters of hydrogen sulfide gas are needed for a particular purpose. How many grams of iron(II) sulfide reacting with hydrochloric acid to form hydrogen sulfide and iron(II) chloride must be used in the reaction?

46. Sulfur (12.0 g) is burned in oxygen. How many liters of sulfur dioxide gas are produced?

47. Oxygen (56.0 liters) is combined with phosphorus to form diphosphorus pentoxide. How many grams of phosphorus are used?

48. A sample of a vapor having a mass of 0.519 g occupies 123 mL at $10\overline{0}$ °C and 745 mm. What is its molecular weight?

49. How many grams of zinc must react with hydrochloric acid in order to produce 250 mL of hydrogen at $2\overline{0}$ °C and $77\overline{0}$ mm?

50. How many liters of oxygen, collected by displacement of water at 22 °C and 760 mm, are produced by the decomposition of 5.92 g of potassium chlorate?

279 g Fe	42
33.6 liters H$_2$	43
623 liters O$_2$	44
22 g FeS	45
8.37 liters SO$_2$	46
62.0 g P$_4$	47
131	48
0.689 g Zn	49
1.80 liters O$_2$	50

Liquids-Solids-Water

EXERCISE **12**

DIRECTIONS: Write the answers to the following in the space provided. Where appropriate, make complete statements.

1. What are the five readily observed properties of liquids? (a) __definite volume__
(b) __fluidity__ (c) __noncompressibility__ (d) __diffusion__ (e) __evaporation.__ 1

2. Why is a liquid practically noncompressible? __The particles of a liquid are almost__
__as close together as it is possible for them to be.__ 2

3. What kind of forces exist between nonpolar molecules? _____
__The relatively weak dispersion interaction forces exist between nonpolar molecules.__ 3

4. Why are substances composed of polar molecules usually liquids at room temperature?
__The attractive forces between these molecules are the combined dispersion interaction__
__and dipole-dipole forces.__ 4

5. Why is the diffusion of liquids slower than that of gases? __The liquid molecules__
__move more slowly and are closer together; thus their movement is hindered.__ 5

6. What is meant by a physical equilibrium? __A dynamic state in which two opposing__
__physical changes occur at equal rates in the same system.__ 6

7. How does raising the temperature of the liquid in a liquid-vapor equilibrium system affect
the system? __The equilibrium is disturbed and the concentration of vapor molecules__
__above the liquid surface is increased. The increased chance of collision with escaping__
__vapor molecules causes an increase in the rate of condensation. Soon the equilibrium is__
__reestablished at a higher equilibrium vapor pressure.__ 7

8. On what two factors does the amount of the equilibrium vapor pressure of a liquid depend?
__It depends on the nature of the liquid and its temperature.__ 8

9. To what kinds of dynamic equilibria does Le Chatelier's principle apply? _____
__This principle applies to all kinds of dynamic equilibria.__ 9

10. What will be the effect of lowering the temperature of an equilibrium system represented
by liquid + energy $\rightleftarrows$ vapor? __The reverse reaction is favored, and equilibrium will be reestablished__
__at a lower temperature with a reduced vapor concentration.__ 10

11. The temperature of the equilibrium system liquid + energy $\rightleftarrows$ vapor is kept constant, but the
volume of the system is increased. When equilibrium is restored, how do the following characteristics
of the system at the new equilibrium compare in magnitude with the same characteristics in
the original equilibrium? (a) vapor pressure __the same__ (b) vapor molecule concentration
__the same__ (c) volume of vapor __larger__ (d) number of liquid molecules
__smaller__ 11

12. What is the relationship between the boiling point of a liquid and its vapor pressure?
__The boiling point of a liquid is the temperature at which the equilibrium vapor pressure of the__
__liquid is equal to the prevailing atmospheric pressure.__ 12

13. During the boiling of a liquid, how do the kinetic energies of the liquid and vapor compare? _The kinetic energies of linear motion of the liquid and vapor molecules must be the same._ 13

14. What are the two operations involved in liquefying a gas? _The gas must be compressed and the heat of compression removed. The cooled compressed gas is permitted to expand without absorbing external energy._ 14

15. Why does compressing a gas always raise its temperature? _Energy is acquired by the gas molecules when work is done on them to push them closer together._ 15

16. What is meant by the critical temperature of a gas? _The critical temperature is the highest temperature at which it is possible to liquefy the gas with any amount of pressure._ 16

17. The magnitude of the critical temperature is a measure of what characteristic of molecules? _It is a measure of the attractive forces between molecules._ 17

18. What must be done (a) to the temperature of a gas and, (b) simultaneously, to its pressure in order to liquefy the gas? _(a) The temperature must be lowered to or below the critical temperature. (b) The pressure must be raised to or above the vapor pressure of the liquefied gas at this temperature._ 18

19. The critical temperature of sulfur dioxide is 157.5 °C, while that of water is 374.2 °C. What does this indicate about the polarity of the sulfur dioxide molecules compared to that of the water molecules? _The sulfur dioxide molecules are less polar than the water molecules._ 19

20. What effect does increase in molecular weight have on the critical temperatures of a series of gases whose molecules are nonpolar? _The higher the molecular weight of a gas, the higher its critical temperature will be._ 20

DIRECTIONS: In the blank space at the right of each statement, write the word or expression that BEST completes the meaning when substituted for the corresponding number.

21–23. The observed properties of solids include (21) shape, (22) volume, and (23) diffusion.

definite	21
definite	22
very slow	23

24–27. Solids that have a regular arrangement of particles are (24) , while those having a random particle arrangement are (25) . The particles of a solid are in (26) motion about their fixed positions. At low temperatures, the kinetic energy of the particles is (27) .

crystalline	24
amorphous	25
weak vibratory	26
small	27

28–31. The freezing of a liquid involves a (28) of energy by the liquid. The reverse physical change, melting, involves a (29) of (30) energy by the particles of the solid. The heat energy required to melt one mole of solid at its melting point is its (31) .

loss	28
gain	29
potential	30
molar heat of fusion	31

32–34. A solid in contact with its vapor can reach the equilibrium solid + energy $\rightleftarrows$ vapor and exhibit a characteristic equilibrium (32) , which, like that of a liquid, depends only on the (33) . The change of phase from a solid to a vapor is known as (34) .

vapor pressure	32
temperature	33
sublimation	34

Exercises and Experiments in Modern Chemistry
Holt, Rinehart and Winston, Publishers

35. Recently prepared amorphous forms of metal alloys are called __(35a)__ . They are made by __(35b)__ cooling of a thin film of melted metal.

metallic glass	35a
very rapid	35b

36. The pattern of points that describes the arrangement of particles in a crystal structure is known as the __(36a)__ , the smallest portion of which determines the pattern of the structure and is called the __(36b)__ .

crystal lattice	36a
unit cell	36b

37–39. Crystals of common salt, NaCl, belong to the __(37)__ system. They may form from solution by the process of __(38)__ . Crystals that form __(39)__ will be more nearly perfect.

cubic	37
evaporation	38
slowly	39

40–42. Generally, ionic crystals result from Group I or Group II __(40)__ combining with Group VI or Group VII __(41)__ , or the __(42)__ polyatomic ions.

metals	40
nonmetals	41
nonmetallic	42

43–45. The oceans, rivers, and lakes cover about __(43)__ % of the surface of the earth. Significant quantities of water are frozen in glaciers that cover almost __(44)__ % of the land surface. Water vapor is always present in the air, and there are large quantities of __(45)__ water.

75	43
10	44
underground	45

46–49. From 70% to __(46)__ % of the weight of living things is water. The Viking mission has produced evidence that leads scientists to believe that the planet __(47)__ has an underground layer of ice. Studies have shown that water vapor is present in the planet __(48)__ atmosphere. Voyager spacecraft photographs show the presence of large amounts of __(49)__ on the surfaces of two of Jupiter's moons.

90	46
Mars	47
Jupiter's	48
water ice	49

50–52. As water solidifies, it __(50)__ heat and __(51)__ one ninth in volume. Consequently, ice has a density of about __(52)__ g/cm^3.

releases	50
increases (expands)	51
0.9	52

53–54. Liquid water has its maximum density at the temperature __(53)__ . The boiling temperature of water is raised above 100 °C by __(54)__ the pressure above the boiling water.

4 °C	53
increasing	54

55–61. The structural formula for water may be represented as __(55)__ . The angle between the two hydrogen-oxygen bonds is about __(56)__ degrees. The H—O bond is a(n) __(57)__ bond. The bonds in the water molecule do not lie on __(58)__ , and the molecule as a whole is __(59)__ . Water molecules associate into groups of molecules because of their __(60)__ and the formation of __(61)__ bonds.

O ⁄＼ H H	55
105	56
polar covalent	57
the same straight line	58
polar	59
polarity	60
hydrogen	61

62–63. When water is warmed from 0 °C, two opposing effects occur. Hydrogen bonds __(62)__ , enabling water molecules to crowd more closely together. The water molecules tend to spread apart as a result of their __(63)__ .

break	62
increased energy	63

64–72. Water is a very (stable, unstable) (64) compound. Active metals such as sodium react with cold water to set free hydrogen and form a(n) (65) solution. Red-hot iron reacts with steam to form hydrogen and (66) . Ionic oxides of the very active metals react with water to form (67) . Such oxides are (68) anhydrides. The oxides of nonmetals such as carbon and sulfur are (69) compounds that contain (70) bonds. They unite with water to form a solution containing a(n) (71) . Such oxides are known as (72) anhydrides.

stable	64
metallic hydroxide	65
iron oxide	66
soluble hydroxides	67
basic	68
molecular	69
polar covalent	70
acid	71
acid	72

73–75. The name given to crystals such as $CuSO_4 \cdot 5H_2O$ that contain water is (73) . Since there is always a definite mass of water combined with a definite mass of copper(II) sulfate, these crystals illustrate the law of (74) . The loss of water by crystals such as $Na_2CO_3 \cdot 10H_2O$, on exposure to air, is called (75) .

hydrates	73
definite composition	74
efflorescence	75

76–77. The property of certain substances, such as calcium chloride, to take up water from the air to form a solution is called (76) . Insoluble materials, such as wool and hair, that take up water from the air are classed as (77) .

deliquescence	76
hygroscopic	77

78–81. The possible combinations of the various isotopes of hydrogen and oxygen result in the existence of (78) types of water molecules. Water containing atoms of hydrogen-2 has the formula (79) . It is possible to separate this water from H_2O by (80) . The most important use of deuterium oxide is in (81) .

9	78
D_2O	79
electrolysis	80
nuclear reactors	81

82–85. Complete the following table for the type of crystal lattice listed.

Type	Particles composing lattice	Properties	Examples	
82. ionic	positive and negative ions	hard, brittle, rather high melting points, good insulators	NaCl, MgF_2	82
83. covalent network	atoms sharing electrons with neighboring atoms	giant molecules, very hard, brittle, high melting point	diamond C_x, $(SiO_2)_x$, S, C	83
84. metallic	lattice of positive ions and electron gas (valence electrons)	hardness and melting point vary over wide range, high electric conductivity	Fe, Cu, Na, Ag	84
85. covalent molecular	molecules (weak dispersion interaction forces for nonpolar molecules; both types of van der Waals attractions for polar molecules)	low melting points, relatively soft, volatile, good insulators	H_2, O_2, CH_4, I_2, CCl_4, C_6H_6, CO_2, NH_3, H_2O	85

Exercises and Experiments in Modern Chemistry
Holt, Rinehart and Winston, Publishers

Solutions

EXERCISE **13**

DIRECTIONS: In the blank space at the right of each statement, write the word or expression that BEST completes the meaning when substituted for the corresponding number.

1. A homogeneous mixture of two or more substances, the composition of which may vary within characteristic limits, is known as a(n) (1) .

solution _____ 1

2. A two-phase system having dispersed particles suspended in a dispersing medium is called a(n) (2) suspension.

colloidal _____ 2

3. Substances that form water solutions that conduct electricity are called (3) .

electrolytes _____ 3

4. Nonelectrolytes do not conduct an electric current. They are usually composed of (4) substances that form molecular solutions with water.

covalent _____ 4

5. A solution in which the dissolved and undissolved solutes are in equilibrium is said to be (5) .

saturated _____ 5

6. The solubility of a solute is defined as the (6) amount of that solute that can dissolve in a given amount of a certain solvent, under specified conditions.

maximum _____ 6

7. The rapid escape of a gas from a liquid in which it is dissolved is called (7) .

effervescence _____ 7

8–9. The attractive forces between gas molecules are (8) , and the motions of the molecules are relatively (9) .

negligible _____ 8

free _____ 9

10. The solubility of a gas in a liquid is limited to its (10) concentration under existing conditions.

equilibrium _____ 10

11. The solubility of a gas in a liquid is (11) proportional to the pressure of the gas above the liquid.

directly _____ 11

12. The statement of Question 11 is known as (12) law.

Henry's _____ 12

13. Gases that react chemically with their liquid solvents are generally (more, less) (13) soluble than those gases that do not.

more _____ 13

14. In a given mixture of gases, the partial pressure of each gas is proportional to the number of (14) of that gas.

molecules _____ 14

15. The solubility of a gas (increases, decreases) (15) as the temperature of the solvent is increased.

decreases _____ 15

DIRECTIONS: In the space at the right, place the letter or letters indicating each choice that forms a correct statement.

16. The solubility of a solid depends on (a) the pressure on the solvent, (b) the solvent used, (c) the temperature, (d) the nature of the solid.

b, c, d _____ 16

17. When a solid is dissolved in a liquid, we would normally expect (a) the temperature of the solution to be lowered, (b) heat to be given up, (c) the temperature of the solution to rise, (d) heat to be absorbed.

a, d _____ 17

18. In the case of liquids dissolved in liquids, we would normally expect small changes in temperature because (a) only a small amount of solute can dissolve, (b) all liquids are completely miscible, (c) no change in phase occurs, (d) hydration prevents chemical activity.

c _____ 18

19. A solution process that occurs endothermically may take place spontaneously because (a) the attraction of solute particles for solvent particles gives up energy, (b) the entropy change is favorable even though the energy change is unfavorable, (c) both the entropy change and the energy change are favorable, (d) the mixture of solute and solvent represents a more disordered state than that of the unmixed solid and liquid.

b, d _____ 19

20. When the dissolving process is exothermic (a) the heat of solution is said to be negative, (b) the solution usually cools as dissolving proceeds, (c) the heat content of the solution is less than that of its separate components, (d) heating results in increased solubility.

a, c _____ 20

21. The equilibrium system $KCl(s) + H_2O(l) + heat \rightleftarrows$ solution is initially at equilibrium. The addition of heat to the system results in (a) an increase in the rate of the endothermic reaction, (b) faster dissolving than crystallizing until the stress is relieved, (c) an increase in the concentration of KCl in solution, (d) a decrease in the solubility of the solute.

a, b, c _____ 21

22. The equilibrium system $solid + H_2O \rightleftarrows heat +$ solution is initially at equilibrium. The addition of heat to the system results in (a) an increase in the rate of the endothermic reaction, (b) faster dissolving than crystallizing until the stress is relieved, (c) an increase in the concentration of solid in solution, (d) a decrease in the solubility of the solute.

a, d _____ 22

23. The rate at which a solid dissolves in a liquid may be increased by (a) agitating the mixture, (b) using a cooling bath to maintain a constant temperature, (c) powdering the solid, (d) heating the solvent.

a, c, d _____ 23

24. The molality of a solution is defined as an expression of (a) the number of moles of solute per liter of solution, (b) the number of moles of solute per kilogram of solvent, (c) the number of moles of solute per kilogram of solution, (d) the volume of solute per liter of solvent.

b _____ 24

25. The water molecule is frequently referred to as the water dipole because it contains (a) nonpolar covalent bonds unsymmetrically distributed, (b) polar covalent bonds unsymmetrically distributed, (c) polar covalent bonds symmetrically distributed, (d) nonpolar covalent bonds symmetrically distributed.

b _____ 25

26. Hydrogen bonds explain in part the (a) abnormally high boiling point of water, (b) abnormally low freezing point of water, (c) complete miscibility of water and ethyl alcohol, (d) abnormally high vapor pressure of water.

a, c _____ 26

27. The properties of a solvent that are quantitatively decreased by the addition of a solid solute are (a) boiling point, (b) freezing point, (c) vapor pressure, (d) volume.

b, c _____ 27

Exercises and Experiments in Modern Chemistry
Holt, Rinehart and Winston, Publishers

28. It was found that 85.5 g of a certain nonelectrolyte dissolved in 1 kg of water lowered the freezing point of water 0.465 °C. The molecular weight of the solute is (a) 171, (b) 342, (c) 855, (d) 85.5.

29–35. The following questions refer to the diagram below, which shows vapor pressure of solvent as a function of temperature plotted for a pure solvent and dilute solutions of molalities X and 2X.

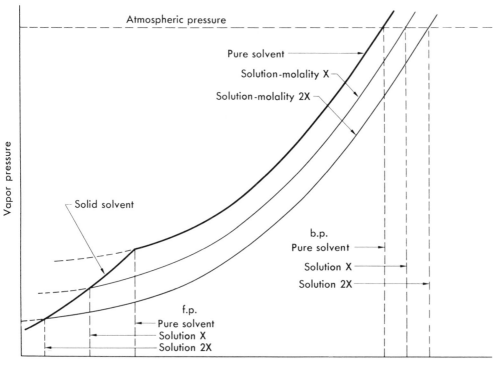

29. At any temperature, the vapor pressure is highest for (a) pure solvent; (b) solution X; (c) solution 2X.

30. The presence of solute particles in solution (a) has no effect on the escaping tendency of solvent molecules; (b) lowers the escaping tendency of the solvent molecules; (c) raises the escaping tendency of the solvent molecules.

31. Increasing the concentration of the solution (a) extends the liquid range of the solution; (b) shortens the liquid range of the solution; (c) has no effect on the liquid range of the solution.

32. The freezing point is lowest for (a) the pure solvent; (b) solution X; (c) solution 2X.

33. When a dilute solution is cooled enough for freezing to occur, the crystals produced are those of the (a) solution; (b) pure solute; (c) pure solvent.

34. The boiling point is lowest for (a) the pure solvent; (b) solution X; (c) solution 2X.

35. For solutions of equal molality, the effect on the freezing point would be greatest for (a) alcohol; (b) ethylene glycol; (c) common salt.

DIRECTIONS: The following questions refer to the solubility curves shown in the graph below. Write the answers to the questions in the space provided.

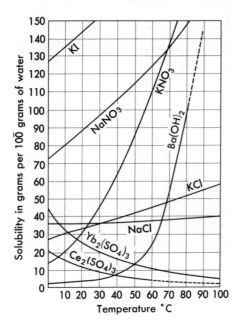

36. What is the solubility of KNO_3 at 30 °C?

45 g/10̄0 g H₂O
_____ 36

37. What is the solubility of KNO_3 at 70 °C?

14̄0 g/10̄0 g H₂O
_____ 37

38. Which compound varies the least in solubility over the temperature range of the graph?

NaCl
_____ 38

39. What change occurs in the solubility of $Ce_2(SO_4)_3$ as the temperature of the solution increases from 20 °C to 100 °C?

The solubility decreases.
_____ 39

40. What is the difference between the solubilities of KNO_3 and NaCl at 24 °C?

(zero) They are identical.
_____ 40

41. What is the difference between the solubilities of KCl and NaCl at 75 °C?

12 g/10̄0 g H₂O
_____ 41

42. What is the average rate of change of solubility of $NaNO_3$ in grams per 10̄0 g of water per Celsius degree in the range from 10 °C to 30 °C?

0.9 g/10̄0 g H₂O/C°
_____ 42

DIRECTIONS: The following questions refer to the solubility curves shown in the graph below. Write the answers to the questions in the space provided.

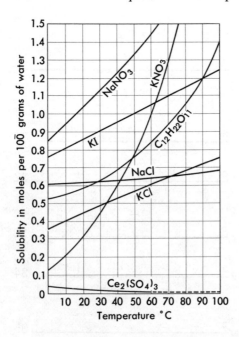

43. At what temperature does NaCl have the same solubility in moles per 10̄0 grams of water as sugar $(C_{12}H_{22}O_{11})$?

28 °C
_____ 43

44. In terms of solubility in grams per 10̄0 grams of water, how does the solubility of sugar compare with that of NaCl at the temperature given as the correct answer to Question 43?

It is much greater
_____ 44

45. Which pair of compounds has the positions of their *general* solubilities reversed when such positions in the graphs for items 36–42 and 43–45 are compared? (a) KI and $NaNO_3$; (b) $NaNO_3$ and KNO_3; (c) KNO_3 and KCl; (d) KCl and $Ce_2(SO_4)_3$.

a
_____ 45

Exercises and Experiments in Modern Chemistry
Holt, Rinehart and Winston, Publishers

Ionization

EXERCISE **14**

DIRECTIONS: Write brief answers to the following questions in the space provided.

1. What term best describes the ability of pure water to conduct an electric current?

2. What do we call solutes whose water solutions do not conduct electricity?

3. What two kinds of substances conduct an electric current when they dissolve in water?

4. Do electrolytes have a greater or lesser effect on the freezing point of water than nonelectrolytes of equal molal concentration?

5. What did Faraday call the particles that carried electricity in water solution?

6. How did Arrhenius explain production of ions?

7. How does the total negative ionic charge compare with the total positive ionic charge in the water solution of an electrolyte?

8. What determines the oxidation number of a monatomic ion?

9. How do electrovalent compounds usually exist?

10. Which end of water dipoles exerts an attractive force on the positive ions of solid sodium chloride?

11. What process occurs when ions separate from the crystals of ionic compounds during the solution process?

12. What name is given to the process by which water molecules attach themselves to the ions of the solute?

13. For the equilibrium system represented by the equation $Na^+Cl^-(s) \rightleftarrows Na^+(aq) + Cl^-(aq)$, how does the tendency toward minimum energy compare with the tendency toward maximum entropy?

14. What concentrations of aqueous ions are present in water solutions of ionic compounds of very slight solubility?

15. What is the net ionic equation for the reaction that occurs when fairly concentrated solutions of KCl and $AgNO_3$ are mixed?

16. Which are the spectator ions in the reaction occurring in Question 15?

17. What effect does melting an ionic compound have upon its ions?

18. What name is given to the process by which polar solute molecules react with water to form ions?

19. Does hydrogen chloride, as a pure liquid, conduct electricity?

a nonconductor (for all practical purposes) _____ 1

nonelectrolytes _____ 2

ionic substances, polar covalent compounds _____ 3

greater (2 to 3 times) _____ 4

ions _____ 5

ionization of molecules of electrolytes in water solution _____ 6

they are equal _____ 7

the charge on the monatomic ion _____ 8

as crystals _____ 9

the negative oxygen end _____ 10

dissociation _____ 11

hydration _____ 12

they are equal _____ 13

very low concentrations _____ 14

$Ag^+(aq) + Cl^-(aq) \rightarrow Ag^+Cl^-(s)$ _____ 15

$K^+(aq)$ and $NO_3^-(aq)$ _____ 16

ions become mobile and conduct an electric current _____ 17

ionization _____ 18

no _____ 19

20. What name is given to hydrated protons?

hydronium ions _____ 20

21. Why does a solution of hydrogen chloride in water have properties that are decidedly different from those of hydrogen chloride gas?

because hydrogen chloride ionizes in water solution _____ 21

22. What is the nature of the bonds in the aluminum halides?

covalent with partial ionic character 22

23. Which of the hydrogen halides (HF, HCl, HBr, HI) is a weak electrolyte?

HF _____ 23

24. What kind of a conductor is a water solution of acetic acid?

poor conductor _____ 24

25. To what extent does water ionize?

very slightly, about two molecules in a billion _____ 25

26. How does the ionization of water probably begin?

with the formation of hydrogen bonds between two water molecules 26

27. How is the abnormal lowering of the freezing point of water by hydrogen chloride explained?

each molecule of hydrogen chloride that ionizes separates into two particles _____ 27

28. To what extent, compared to the effect of a solution of a nonelectrolyte of the same molality, should a dilute solution of sulfuric acid lower the freezing point of the solvent?

3 times _____ 28

29. What can be determined about the ionization of a solute by measuring the lowering of the freezing point by an ionized solute in a measured amount of solvent?

the apparent degree of ionization 29

30. The more dilute a sodium chloride solution is, the more nearly the freezing point depression approaches twice the value for a molecular solute. What theory accounts for this?

the Debye-Hückel theory of attraction between ions _____ 30

DIRECTIONS: In the space provided, indicate which of the following are considered to be electrolytes, E, and which are considered to be nonelectrolytes, N.

31. pure water _____ **N** _____   34. glycerol (glycerin) _____ **N** _____   37. nitric acid _____ **E** _____

32. ethanol (alcohol) _____ **N** _____   35. sodium hydroxide _____ **E** _____   38. copper(II) sulfate _____ **E** _____

33. potassium nitrate _____ **E** _____   36. zinc chloride _____ **E** _____   39. carbon tetrachloride _____ **N** _____

DIRECTIONS: In the space provided, write ionic equations for the dissociation of the electrovalent substances in water solution according to the example: $Na^+Cl^-(s) \rightarrow Na^+(aq) + Cl^-(aq)$. Write the equations for ionization of the polar covalent substances in water showing the part played by the water dipoles according to the example: $HCl(g) + H_2O(l) \rightarrow H_3O^+(aq) + Cl^-(aq)$

40. $HBr(g)$ **$HBr(g) + H_2O(l) \rightarrow H_3O^+(aq) + Br^-(aq)$** _____ 40

41. $(NH_4^+)_3PO_4^{---}(s)$ **$(NH_4^+)_3PO_4^{---}(s) \rightarrow 3NH_4^+(aq) + PO_4^{---}(aq)$** _____ 41

42. $K^+OH^-(s)$ **$K^+OH^-(s) \rightarrow K^+(aq) + OH^-(aq)$** _____ 42

43. $H_2O(l)$ **$H_2O(l) + H_2O(l) \rightleftarrows H_3O^+(aq) + OH^-(aq)$** _____ 43

44. $Al_2Cl_6(s)$ **$Al_2Cl_6(s) + 12H_2O(l) \rightarrow 2Al(H_2O)_6^{+++} + 6Cl^-$** _____ 44

45. $H_2SO_4(l)$ (complete ionization)   **$H_2SO_4(l) + 2H_2O(l) \rightarrow 2H_3O^+(aq) + SO_4^{--}(aq)$** _____ 45

46. $NH_3(g)$ **$NH_3(g) + H_2O(l) \rightleftarrows NH_4^+(aq) + OH^-(aq)$** _____ 46

Exercises and Experiments in Modern Chemistry
Holt, Rinehart and Winston, Publishers

Acids, Bases, and Salts

EXERCISE **13**

DIRECTIONS: In the blank space at the right of each statement, write the word or expression that BEST completes the meaning when substituted for the corresponding number.

1. The organic acid in lemons is __(1)__ acid.

2. Inorganic acids are more commonly known as __(2)__ acids.

3. The water solutions of the traditional acids are called __(3)__ acids.

4. The consumption of __(4)__ acid is an index to the state of industrialization and prosperity of a country.

5. A chemist whose company makes fertilizers and explosives would consider __(5)__ acid to be important.

6. The industrial acid that is a weak acid is __(6)__ acid.

7–8. In diluting sulfuric acid, the __(7)__ must be added slowly to the __(8)__ while stirring.

9. The acid whose pure solution is colorless but which may turn brown on standing is __(9)__ acid.

10. Concentrated hydrochloric acid is a water solution containing about __(10)__ % hydrogen chloride.

11–12. Acids are essentially __(11)__ bonded structures and have one element in common, __(12)__ .

13. Acids ionize in water solution because of the __(13)__ action of the water dipoles.

14. The acidic properties of the water solutions of acids are due to the presence of __(14)__ ions.

15–16. High concentrations of the ion that is usually represented by the expression __(15)__ are characteristic of (weak, strong) __(16)__ acids.

17. When hydrogen chloride is dissolved in a nonpolar solvent, such as toluene, the solution is a (conductor, nonconductor) __(17)__ .

18–19. Hydrogen chloride dissolved in ammonia transfers __(18)__ to the solvent much as it does in __(19)__ .

20. According to the Brønsted theory, hydrogen chloride is an acid because it is a(n) __(20)__ donor.

21. Water is a(n) __(21)__ when gaseous ammonia is dissolved in it.

22–23. The strength of an acid depends upon the __(22)__ in water solution and not upon the amount of __(23)__ in the molecule.

citric	1
mineral	2
aqueous	3
sulfuric	4
nitric	5
phosphoric	6
sulfuric acid	7
water	8
nitric	9
36	10
covalently	11
hydrogen	12
hydrating	13
hydronium	14
H_3O^+	15
strong	16
nonconductor	17
protons	18
water	19
proton	20
acid	21
degree of ionization	22
hydrogen	23

24. As is the case with diprotic acids, ion concentration in the first stage of ionization of phosphoric acid is much __(24)__ than in the second stage.

greater _____ 24

25–28. Aqueous acids have a __(25)__ taste, change the color of litmus to __(26)__ , neutralize __(27)__ , and if nonoxidizing, react with metals such as zinc to release __(28)__ .

sour _____ 25

red _____ 26

hydroxides _____ 27

hydrogen _____ 28

29–30. The formula for chloric acid is __(29)__ , and the formula for chlorous acid is __(30)__ .

$HClO_3$ _____ 29

$HClO_2$ _____ 30

31–33. The oxides formed with nonmetals on the right side of the periodic table are, in general, __(31)__ structures which react with water to form __(32)__ containing one or more __(33)__ groups.

covalent molecular _____ 31

oxyacids _____ 32

O—H _____ 33

34. The formula for the acid anhydride of carbonic acid is __(34)__ .

CO_2 _____ 34

35. The acid used in the production of other acids because it is relatively inexpensive and has a high boiling point is __(35)__ .

sulfuric acid _____ 35

36. Lye is a commercial grade of __(36)__ .

sodium hydroxide _____ 36

37–38. Brønsted bases are broadly defined as substances that acquire __(37)__ from another substance. Water solutions of soluble metallic hydroxides are referred to as __(38)__ .

protons _____ 37

aqueous bases _____ 38

39. When HCl is dissolved in liquid ammonia, the __(39)__ acts as the base.

ammonia _____ 39

40–41. Hydroxides of active metals furnish __(40)__ ions in solution, which change the color of phenolphthalein to __(41)__ .

hydroxide _____ 40

red _____ 41

42–46. When hydroxide ions are added to a solution of an aluminum salt, insoluble __(42)__ precipitates. An excess of strongly basic OH⁻ ions causes the precipitate to redissolve, and the precipitate acts as a(n) __(43)__ . It also dissolves in an excess of hydronium ions yielding __(44)__ ions and __(45)__ . Metallic hydroxides that behave in this way are said to be __(46)__ .

hydrated aluminum hydroxide _____ 42

acid _____ 43

hydrated aluminum _____ 44

water _____ 45

amphoteric _____ 46

47. The slight ionization of water shows that it is __(47)__ .

amphoteric _____ 47

48. The basic ion produced in the slight ionization of liquid ammonia is the __(48)__ ion.

amide(NH_2^-) _____ 48

49. The oxides of active metals are __(49)__ anhydrides.

basic _____ 49

50–51. As the oxidation state of the atom combined with the O—H group increases, the bond between this atom and the O—H group becomes more __(50)__ in character and the removal of an OH⁻ ion becomes more __(51)__ .

covalent _____ 50

difficult _____ 51

52. Hydroxides of atoms of high electronegativity and high oxidation states are __(52)__ .

acidic _____ 52

53. From structural considerations, the molecular formula for sulfuric acid could be written as __(53)__ .

$SO_2(OH)_2$ _____ 53

Exercises and Experiments in Modern Chemistry
Holt, Rinehart and Winston, Publishers

54–55. The species that remains after an acid has given up a proton is called the __(54)__ . When a base takes on a proton, a(n) __(55)__ is formed.

56–58. The HSO_4^- ion is __(56)__ , since it is *both* the __(57)__ of SO_4^{--} and the __(58)__ of H_2SO_4.

59–60. The stronger an acid is, the weaker is its __(59)__ ; the stronger a base, the weaker its __(60)__ .

61–62. According to the Brønsted theory, protolysis reactions favor the production of the (weaker, stronger) __(61)__ acid and the (weaker, stronger) __(62)__ base.

63. The solid that remains after the solution resulting from the reaction between zinc and hydrochloric acid is evaporated to dryness is classified as a(n) __(63)__ .

64. The reaction between CaO and CO_2 produces a compound classified as a(n) __(64)__ .

65–67. A salt is a compound composed of the __(65)__ of an aqueous base and the __(66)__ of an aqueous acid. All true salts are __(67)__ substances.

68–70. The names of anions (negative ions) of oxyacids take the same root and __(68)__ as the acid in which they occur. However, the acid ending *-ic* is changed to __(69)__ , and the ending *-ous* is changed to __(70)__ .

71. Salts of binary acids take the ending __(71)__ .

conjugate base	54
conjugate acid	55
amphoteric	56
conjugate acid	57
conjugate base	58
conjugate base	59
conjugate acid	60
weaker	61
weaker	62
salt	63
salt	64
positive ions	65
negative ions	66
ionic	67
prefix	68
- ate	69
- ite	70
- ide	71

DIRECTIONS: Write the required information in the space provided.

72. Name the following:

a. NaBr _____ sodium bromide _____

b. $Fe_2(SO_4)_3$ _____ iron(III) sulfate _____

c. $HClO_4$ _____ perchloric acid _____

d. $Ca(HCO_3)_2$ _____ calcium hydrogen carbonate _____

e. $NaClO_3$ _____ sodium chlorate _____

f. Na_2SO_3 _____ sodium sulfite _____

73. State the formulas of the following:

a. chlorous acid _____ $HClO_2$ _____

b. magnesium phosphate _____ $Mg_3(PO_4)_2$ _____

c. ammonium nitrite _____ NH_4NO_2 _____

d. sodium hydrogen carbonate _____ $NaHCO_3$ _____

e. hypochlorous acid _____ $HClO$ _____

f. manganese(IV) chloride _____ $MnCl_4$ _____

74. Write the expression for the conjugate:

a. base of H_2SO_4 _____ HSO_4^- _____

b. base of HCO_3^- ion _____ CO_3^{--} _____

c. base of H_3O^+ ion _____ H_2O _____

d. base of NH_4^+ ion _____ NH_3 _____

e. acid of OH^- ion _____ H_2O _____

f. acid of SO_4^{--} ion _____ HSO_4^- _____

g. acid of $C_2H_3O_2^-$ ion _____ $HC_2H_3O_2$ _____

h. acid of NH_2^- ion _____ NH_3 _____

75. Write balanced ionic equations for the following reactions:

zinc and an acid (net) $\underline{Zn + 2H_3O^+ \rightarrow Zn^{++} + 2H_2O + H_2(g)}$

nitric acid and water $\underline{HNO_3 + H_2O \rightleftarrows H_3O^+ + NO_3^-}$

hydrogen chloride and ammonia $\underline{HCl + NH_3 \rightarrow NH_4^+ \, Cl^-}$

ionization of phosphoric acid (first stage) $\underline{H_3PO_4 + H_2O \rightarrow H_3O^+ + H_2PO_4^-}$

sodium hydroxide and hydrochloric acid (net) $\underline{OH^- + H_3O^+ \rightarrow 2H_2O}$

copper(II) oxide and sulfuric acid (net) $\underline{CuO + 2H_3O^+ \rightarrow Cu^{++} + 3H_2O}$

carbon dioxide and water $\underline{CO_2 + 2H_2O \rightleftarrows H_3O^+ + HCO_3^-}$

ammonia and water $\underline{NH_3 + H_2O \rightleftarrows NH_4^+ + OH^-}$

self-ionization of ammonia $\underline{NH_3 + NH_3 \rightleftarrows NH_4^+ + NH_2^-}$

solutions of barium chloride and sodium sulfate

$\underline{Ba^{++} + 2Cl^- + 2Na^+ + SO_4^{--} \rightarrow 2Na^+ + 2Cl^- + BaSO_4(s)}$

76. Write electron-dot formulas for the following substances or reactions.

(a) chlorous acid H⨯ Ö ⦂ C̈l ⦂ Ö ⦂

(b) sulfuric acid H⨯ Ö ⦂ S̈ ⦂ Ö ⨯H with :Ö: above and :Ö: below S

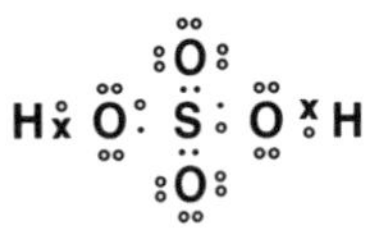

(c) hydrogen chloride reacting with ammonia H⨯ C̈l⦂ + H⨯ N̈⨯H → H⨯ N̈⨯H (with H⁺ above, H below) + ⨯C̈l⦂⁻

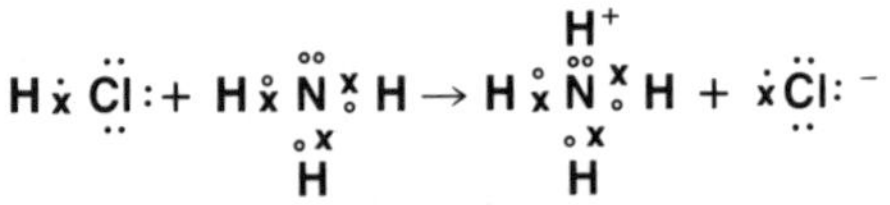

(d) ammonia reacting with water H⦂N⨯H + H⨯Ö⦂ ⇌ H⦂N⨯H + ⨯Ö⦂⁻ (with H⁺ above)

Exercises and Experiments in Modern Chemistry
Holt, Rinehart and Winston, Publishers

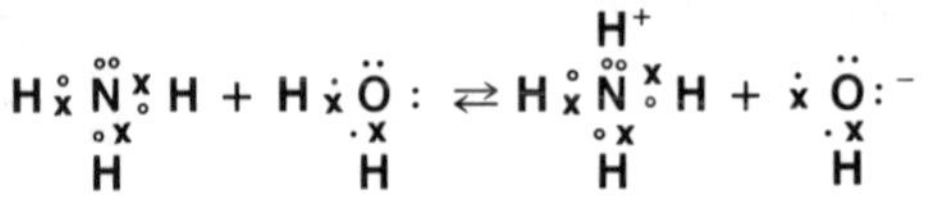

Acid-Base Titration and pH

EXERCISE **16**

DIRECTIONS: In the blank space at the right of each statement, write the word or expression that BEST completes the meaning when substituted for the corresponding number.

1–4. The molality of a solution is an expression of the number of (1) of solute per (2) of solvent. For a given solvent, two solutions of equal molality have the same (3) of solute to solvent (4) .

5–8. The molarity of a solution is an expression of the number of (5) of solute per (6) of solution. Equal (7) of molecular solutions of equal molarity have the same number of (8) .

9–10. The molecular weight of H_2SO_4 is 98. To make 100 mL of a 1-M solution, we would use (9) g of H_2SO_4 as the solute. To make one liter of a 0.5-M solution, we would use (10) g of H_2SO_4 as the solute.

11. Equivalents are the quantities of substances that have the same (11) in chemical reactions.

12. KOH has the formula weight 56. In the reaction H_2SO_4 + 2KOH → K_2SO_4 + $2H_2O$, 49 g of H_2SO_4 is chemically equivalent to (12) g of KOH.

13–15. For complete neutralizations, one equivalent of a monoprotic acid is the same as (13) mole of the acid; of a diprotic acid is the same as (14) mole of acid; of a triprotic acid is the same as (15) mole of acid.

16. For H_2SO_4 + NaOH → $NaHSO_4$ + H_2O, one equivalent of H_2SO_4 is the same as (16) of the acid.

17. The chemical equivalent of a reactant in an electron-transfer reaction is that quantity in grams that supplies or acquires 1 mole of (17) in a chemical reaction.

18. One equivalent of an element can be determined by dividing 1 g-at wt of the element by the change in (18) taking place during the chemical reaction.

19. The mass of one mole of Na_2SO_4 is 142 g. One equivalent of this salt has a mass of (19) g.

20–21. The normality of a solution is an expression of the number of (20) of solute per (21) of solution.

22–23. One mole of hydrogen chloride has a mass of 36.5 g. One liter of its 0.100-N solution contains (22) g of anhydrous HCl and furnishes (23) mole of H_3O^+ ions per liter.

24–25. A 1-M solution of $CuSO_4$ is also a(n) (24) -N solution. A 1-N solution of $CuSO_4$ is also (25) -M.

moles	1
kilogram	2
ratio	3
molecules	4
moles	5
liter	6
volumes	7
solute molecules	8
9.8	9
49	10
combining capacity	11
56	12
one	13
1/2	14
1/3	15
one mole	16
electrons	17
oxidation state	18
71	19
equivalents	20
liter	21
3.65	22
0.100	23
2	24
0.5	25

26–32. The self-ionization of water is sometimes referred to as __(26)__ and probably starts with __(27)__ bond formation. In water at 25 °C, the concentration of H_3O^+ ions is __(28)__ mole of H_3O^+ ions per liter of H_2O. Water is (neutral, acidic, basic) __(29)__ . The product of the ion concentrations in water is therefore __(30)__ mole^2/liter^2. The principle of __(31)__ tells us that an increase in $[H_3O^+]$ in an aqueous mixture at equilibrium will cause a(n) __(32)__ in $[OH^-]$.

autoprotolysis	26
hydrogen	27
10^{-7}	28
neutral	29
10^{-14}	30
Le Chatelier	31
decrease	32

33–34. In an acid solution, $[H_3O^+]$ is (larger, smaller) __(33)__ than 10^{-7} mole/liter. In an alkaline solution, $[H_3O^+]$ is (larger, smaller) __(34)__ than 10^{-7} mole/liter.

larger	33
smaller	34

35–36. Numerically, the pH of a solution is the __(35)__ of the number of liters of solution that contains __(36)__ of H_3O^+ ions.

common logarithm	35
one mole	36

37. The generally useful form of equation for solving for pH is pH = __(37)__ .

$-\log[H_3O^+]$ or $\log \dfrac{1}{[H_3O^+]}$	37

38–41. The pH of pure water is __(38)__ . The pH of a solution that contains 0.00001 mole of H_3O^+ ions per liter is __(39)__ . The $[H_3O^+]$ for a solution whose pH is 9 is __(40)__ , and the solution is (neutral, acidic, alkaline) __(41)__ .

7	38
5	39
1×10^{-9}	40
alkaline	41

42–43. Consult Figure 16-4 of the student text. The pH of a solution whose $[H_3O^+]$ is 1.6×10^{-3} is __(42)__ . The $[H_3O^+]$ of a solution whose pH is 1.3 is __(43)__ .

2.8	42
0.05-M	43

44–45. The pH of a 0.01-M solution of KOH is __(44)__ . The pH of a 0.1-M solution of $HC_2H_3O_2$ is 2.9. Its $[H_3O^+]$ is (1.3×10^{-3}, 7.7×10^{-12}) __(45)__ .

12	44
1.3×10^{-3}	45

46–48. The process in which chemically equivalent quantities of H_3O^+ and OH^- ions combine is called __(46)__ . The process by which the capacity of a solution of unknown concentration to combine with one of known concentration is quantitatively measured is called __(47)__ . In this process, a dye may serve as an indicator if a color transition takes place within the pH range in which a(n) __(48)__ point occurs.

neutralization	46
titration	47
end (equivalence)	48

49. In the reaction HCl + NaOH → NaCl + H_2O, 20.0 mL of the NaOH solution reacts with 10.0 mL of 0.01-M HCl solution. The molarity of the NaOH solution is __(49)__ .

0.005-M	49

50. In the reaction H_2SO_4 + 2NaOH → Na_2SO_4 + $2H_2O$, 20.0 mL of the NaOH solution reacts completely with 10.0 mL of the 0.01-M H_2SO_4 solution. The molarity of the NaOH solution is __(50)__ .

0.01-M	50

51. In problems involving molarity, the ratio of the moles of unknown solute to the moles of known solute is gotten from a __(51)__ .

balanced equation	51

52. The equation form that expresses the relationship between volumes and normalities in titration is __(52)__ .

$V_1N_1 = V_2N_2$; $V_aN_a = V_bN_b$	52

Exercises and Experiments in Modern Chemistry
Holt, Rinehart and Winston, Publishers

53–55. In the reaction $HC_2H_3O_2 + NaOH \rightarrow NaC_2H_3O_2 + H_2O$, 25.0 mL of 0.100-$N$ solution of NaOH reacted with 10.0 mL of the acid. The normality of the acid solution is __(53)__. In the reaction $H_2SO_4 + 2NaOH \rightarrow Na_2SO_4 + 2H_2O$, 25.0 mL of 0.100-$N$ solution of NaOH reacted completely with 10.0 mL of the acid. The normality of the acid solution is __(54)__. The molarity of this sulfuric acid solution is __(55)__.

0.250 *N*	53
0.250 *N*	54
0.125 *M*	55

56–59. In the acid-base titration curves, the pH end (equivalence) point for weak acid-strong base is (lower, higher) __(56)__ than the end (equivalence) point for strong acid-strong base; a suitable indicator for the weak acid-strong base reaction is (litmus, methyl orange, phenolphthalein) __(57)__. The indicator that performs most satisfactorily for a strong acid-weak base titration is (litmus, methyl orange, phenolphthalein) __(58)__. For the strong acid-strong base titration, the pH end (equivalence) point has a value of about __(59)__.

higher	56
phenolphthalein	57
methyl orange	58
7	59

60. If an indicator added to different solutions assumes the same transition color, the solutions may be considered to have the same __(60)__.

pH	60

61. How many milliliters of concentrated HCl are needed to make up 1.00 liter of a 0.200-N solution if the concentrated HCl assays 37.4% HCl and has a density of 1.189 g/mL?

16.4 mL	61

62. An approximately 0.02-N solution of NaOH when standardized was found to contain 0.0189 mole of OH^- per liter of solution. What was the precise normality of this standard solution?

0.0189 *N*	62

63. How many grams of OH^- ion were contained in each $10\overline{0}$ mL of the solution in Question 62?

0.0321 g	63

64. What was the molarity of the solution in Question 63?

0.0189 *M*	64

65. The end (equivalence) point was reached when 30.0 mL of the standard solution in Question 62 was titrated against 20.0 mL of a sulfuric acid solution. What is the normality of the acid solution?

0.0284 *N*	65

66. What is the molarity of the acid solution in Question 65?

0.0142 *M*	66

67. Complete the following table.

Substance	Mass of one mole	Mass of 1 equiv
K	39.1 g	39.1 g
Zn	65.4 g	32.7 g
Al	27.0 g	9.0 g
NaBr	102.9 g	102.9 g
$MgCl_2$	95.3 g	47.6 g
H_3PO_4	98.0 g	32.7 g
$Ca(OH)_2$	74.1 g	37.0 g
$Ca_3(PO_4)_2$	310.3 g	51.7 g

Carbon and Its Oxides

EXERCISE **17**

DIRECTIONS: In the blank space at the right of each statement, write the word or expression that BEST completes the meaning when substituted for the corresponding number.

1. The study of carbon compounds is a branch of chemistry called (1) chemistry.

2–14. Carbon has the atomic number (2) . Its two (3) electrons are tightly bound to the nucleus. Its valence electrons are the two (4) electrons and the two (5) electrons. Carbon atoms show a very strong tendency to form (6) bonds. The (7) valence electrons make it possible to form (8) covalent bonds. In (9) hybridization, these bonds are directed in space toward the (10) vertices of a regular (11) ; the (12) of the atom is at the (13) of this (14) .

15. There are several times as many carbon compounds as noncarbon compounds because carbon atoms can (15) .

16–17. The two solid allotropic forms of carbon are (16) and (17) .

18–21. In diamond, each carbon atom is (18) oriented to its four nearest neighbors. Diamond has a covalent network structure, which accounts for its extremely high (19) . A diamond is a nonconductor of electricity because its valence electrons (20) . Diamond is the best conductor of heat. In diamond, heat is conducted by the (21) from one carbon atom to another.

22–29. The carbon atoms in graphite are arranged in layers of thin (22) plates. Each carbon atom in a layer is bonded to only (23) other carbon atoms in that layer. The layers of graphite have a(n) (24) structure in which the carbon-carbon bonds are intermediate in character between (25) bonds. The layers of carbon atoms are held together by weak (26) forces, which account for the (27) of graphite and its (28) feel. The mobile electrons in each carbon-atom layer make graphite a fairly good (29) .

organic	1
6	2
1s	3
2s	4
2p	5
covalent	6
four	7
four	8
sp³	9
four	10
tetrahedron	11
nucleus	12
center	13
tetrahedron	14
link together in different ways	15
diamond	16
graphite	17
tetrahedrally	18
melting point	19
cannot migrate	20
transfer of energy of vibration	21
hexagonal	22
three	23
resonance	24
single and double	25
dispersion interaction	26
softness	27
greasy	28
conductor of electricity	29

30. The most important use of synthetic graphite is in (30) for electric-arc steelmaking furnaces.

electrodes _____ 30

31. The five successive stages in coal formation are (31) .

peat, lignite, subbituminous, bituminous, anthracite _____ 31

DIRECTIONS: Write answers to the following in the space provided. Where appropriate, make complete statements.

32. What is *destructive distillation?* **The heating of a complex carbon-containing material in a closed container without access to air or oxygen to decompose it is destructive distillation.** _____ 32

33. What forms of carbon are produced by destructive distillation? **Destructive distillation produces coke, charcoal, and boneblack.** _____ 33

34. What are the volatile products of the destructive distillation of bituminous coal? _____
The volatile products are coal gas, coal tar, and ammonia. _____ 34

35. Why is coke used in obtaining the metals from the ores of iron, tin, copper, and zinc? _____
Coke is an excellent reducing agent of great structural strength and freedom from volatile impurities. 35

36. How is activated carbon produced? **Destructive distillation of carbon-containing materials is followed by treatment with steam or carbon dioxide at about 100 °C.** _____ 36

37. What is adsorption? **Adsorption is the concentration of a gas, liquid, or solid on the surface of a liquid or solid with which it is in contact.** _____ 37

38. How does the porosity of activated carbon account for its ability to adsorb gases? _____
Porosity accounts for a very large internal surface area. _____ 38

39. What are the best sources of gas-adsorbent activated carbon? _____
Coconut and other nut shells are the best sources. _____ 39

40. What form of carbon was first used for liquid-phase adsorption? _____
Boneblack was first used. _____ 40

41. What are the uses of liquid-adsorbent activated carbon? **The uses are refining cane sugar, beet sugar, and corn syrup, and in water treatment to adsorb harmful materials as well as impurities responsible for objectionable odor and taste.** _____ 41

42. What type of burning produces soot? **Burning liquid or gaseous fuels composed of carbon and hydrogen in an insufficient supply of air.** _____ 42

43. What are the three materials introduced into the furnace when making carbon black?
A spray of liquid fuel or the gaseous fuel vapor; an additional fuel such as petroleum refinery gas; air as a source of oxygen. _____ 43

44. Why are the fuels only partially burned in the furnace process for making carbon black?
The fuels are partially burned because the supply of oxygen is insufficient for complete combustion. _____ 44

45. Why is carbon black used in tires? **Carbon black preserves the rubber and makes the tire wear longer.** _____ 45

Exercises and Experiments in Modern Chemistry
Holt, Rinehart and Winston, Publishers

46. How is petroleum coke produced? __Petroleum coke is produced by destructive__
__distillation of oil residues from the refining of crude petroleum.__ _____ 46

47. To what substance are rods of petroleum coke converted so that they can be used as electrodes?
__The rods are converted to synthetic graphite.__ _____ 47

DIRECTIONS: In the blank space at the right of each statement, write the word or expression that BEST completes the meaning when substituted for the corresponding number.

48–50. The amount of carbon dioxide in the atmosphere is about (48) by volume. Much more carbon dioxide occurs (49) in the earth's (50) .

0.03% _____ 48

dissolved _____ 49

surface waters (rivers, lakes, oceans) _____ 50

51–55. The common methods of preparing carbon dioxide include the following: by burning (51) ; by reacting steam and (52) ; by fermentation of (53) ; and by the action of a(n) (54) on a(n) (55) .

materials containing carbon _____ 51

natural gas _____ 52

molasses _____ 53

acid _____ 54

carbonate _____ 55

56–59. There are (56) reactions involved in the usual laboratory method for preparing carbon dioxide. The unstable product of the first reaction is (57) . Carbon dioxide may be collected either by (58) or (59) .

two _____ 56

H_2CO_3 _____ 57

water displacement _____ 58

upward displacement of air _____ 59

60–61. Carbon dioxide molecules are believed to be resonance hybrids of (60) electron structures that contribute about (61) to the actual structure.

4 _____ 60

equally _____ 61

62–64. Carbon dioxide is a gas at room temperature because of its simple (62) molecular structure. It is about (63) dense as air. Because its molecules are heavier than those of oxygen and nitrogen, it diffuses more (64) .

nonpolar _____ 62

1.5 times as _____ 63

slowly _____ 64

65–66. Solid carbon dioxide is called (65) . Since its vapor pressure equals atmospheric pressure at − 78.5 °C, solid carbon dioxide (66) at this temperature.

Dry Ice _____ 65

sublimes _____ 66

67. A piece of burning magnesium continues to burn in a bottle of carbon dioxide because the burning magnesium is hot enough to (67) the carbon dioxide.

decompose _____ 67

68–69. Carbon dioxide forms a(n) (stable, unstable) (68) compound with water known as (69) .

unstable _____ 68

carbonic acid _____ 69

70–71. When carbon dioxide is bubbled through limewater, a white precipitate of (70) is produced. This serves as a test for (71) .

calcium carbonate _____ 70

carbon dioxide _____ 71

72–73. In the process of (72) , green plants use carbon dioxide from the air and water from the soil in the presence of sunlight and the catalyst (73) to produce glucose and oxygen.

photosynthesis _____ 72

chlorophyll _____ 73

74–76. The soda-acid type of fire extinguisher contains separate solutions of (74) and (75) . The function of the carbon dioxide produced by their reaction is to (76) .

sodium hydrogen carbonate _____ 74

sulfuric acid _____ 75

force liquid out of the extinguisher 76

77–78. Carbonated beverages are made by dissolving _(77)_ in flavored water under _(78)_ .

carbon dioxide	77
pressure	78

79–81. Yeast produces _(79)_ that act on dough to change the _(80)_ present to ethanol and _(81)_ .

enzymes	79
starches and sugars	80
carbon dioxide	81

82–84. Baking powders contain _(82)_ as a source of carbon dioxide, a substance that produces a(n) _(83)_ when water is added, and _(84)_ to keep the powder dry.

sodium hydrogen carbonate	82
acid	83
cornstarch	84

85. A refrigerant that leaves no liquid residue is _(85)_ .

Dry Ice	85

DIRECTIONS: Write answers to the following in the space provided. Where appropriate, make complete statements. Questions 86–90 refer to the diagram, which shows a laboratory method of preparing carbon monoxide.

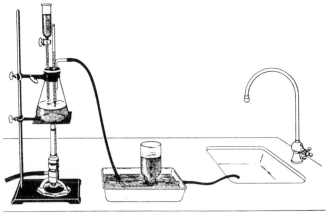

86. What is the liquid in the flask?
concentrated sulfuric acid _____ 86

87. What is its function in this preparation?
dehydrating agent _____ 87

88. What is the liquid in the dropping funnel?
formic acid _____ 88

89. The equation for the reaction occurring in the flask is

$$HCOOH(l) \xrightarrow{H_2SO_4} H_2O(l) + CO_2 (g)$$
89

90. What physical property of carbon monoxide is demonstrated by the method of collecting the gas? Its low solubility in water. _____ 90

91. What properties of carbon monoxide make it particularly hazardous? It is poisonous, colorless, odorless, and tasteless. It induces drowsiness and is not readily adsorbed by charcoal. _____ 91

92. What use is made of the fact that carbon monoxide reacts readily with oxides at high temperatures? Carbon monoxide is used to reduce oxide ores. _____ 92

93–97. Write the equation for the following reactions:

Combustion of CO $2CO(g) + O_2(g) \rightarrow 2CO_2(g)$ _____ 93

Fermentation of sugar $C_6H_{12}O_6(aq) \rightarrow 2C_2H_5OH(aq) + 2CO_2(g)$ _____ 94

Heating $CaCO_3$ $CaCO_3(s) \rightarrow CaO(s) + CO_2(g)$ _____ 95

Carbonate and acid (ionic) $CO_3^{--} + 2H_3O^+ \rightarrow 3H_2O + CO_2(g)$ _____ 96

Calcium hydroxide and CO_2 (ionic) $Ca^{++} + 2OH^- + CO_2 \rightarrow Ca^{++}CO_3^{--}(s) + H_2O$ _____ 97

Hydrocarbons

DIRECTIONS: In the parentheses at the right of each word or expression in the second column, write the letter of the expression in the first column that is *most closely* related.

a. butyl group	C_4H_6	(**k**)	1
b. phenyl group	C_4H_{10}	(**f**)	2
c. naphthalene	C_4H_9	(**a**)	3
d. methanol	C_2H_4	(**j**)	4
e. vinyl group	C_6H_5—	(**b**)	5
f. 2-methyl propane	C_5H_8	(**i**)	6
g. anthracene	$CH_2{=}CH$—	(**e**)	7
h. ethyne	$C_{10}H_8$	(**c**)	8
i. isoprene	C_7H_8	(**l**)	9
j. olefin	C_2H_2	(**h**)	10
k. butadiene			
l. toluene			

a. containers and transparent wrappings	sulfur	(**g**)	11
b. dimerization	2,2,4-trimethyl pentane	(**c**)	12
c. octane rating determination	petroleum	(**j**)	13
d. styrofoam	naphthalene	(**e**)	14
e. ring hydrocarbon	vinyl acetylene	(**b**)	15
f. coagulation of latex	polystyrene	(**d**)	16
g. vulcanization	*SBR* rubber	(**i**)	17
h. natural gas	polyethylene	(**a**)	18
i. tire treads	neoprene	(**l**)	19
j. fractional distillation	methane	(**h**)	20
k. *n*-pentane			
l. gasoline delivery hoses			

DIRECTIONS: In the blank space at the right of each statement, write the word or expression that BEST completes the meaning when substituted for the corresponding number.

21–22. The very large number of carbon compounds that exist is possible because carbon atoms link together by means of (21) , and the same number of carbon atoms can be arranged in (22) .

covalent bonds _____ 21

different ways _____ 22

23. Compounds that have the same molecular formula with different structures are called (23) .

isomers _____ 23

24. Two compounds have the molecular formula C_2H_6O for which only two structural formulas may be written. One compound reacts with sodium liberating one sixth of its hydrogen. It also reacts with PCl_3 to form the compound C_2H_5Cl. The indicated structure of this compound is (24) .

```
      H  H
      |  |
  H—C—C—O—H
      |  |
      H  H
```
_____ 24

25–26. In a structural formula, a dash (—) represents a shared (25) forming a(n) (26) bond.

electron pair _____ 25

covalent _____ 26

27–30. Some of the differences between organic and in-organic compounds include the following: a smaller pro-portion of organic compounds are soluble in __(27)__ ; organic compounds are usually decomposed by heat __(28)__ easily; organic reactions proceed at much __(29)__ rates; and the units of organic compounds are __(30)__ consisting of atoms joined by covalent bonds.

31. Petroleum is a complex mixture of __(31)__ .

32. Petroleum and __(32)__ are the most common sources of energy.

33. "Bottled gas" fuel consists of hydrocarbons having __(33)__ carbon atoms per molecule.

34. Petroleum refining is a continuous process using a pipe still and a(n) __(34)__ .

35–36. The straight- or branched-chain hydrocarbons with two double bonds between carbon atoms are the __(35)__ . The aromatic hydrocarbons such as benzene have carbon-carbon bonds in which each such bond in the benzene part of the compound is a(n) __(36)__ bond.

37–38. The members of the alkane series constitute a(n) __(37)__ series with the general formula __(38)__ .

39. The compound n-heptane has a higher melting point and boiling point than n-hexane because n-heptane has a higher __(39)__ .

40. The molecular formula for 2-methylbutane is __(40)__ .

41. The alkanes react with halogens such as bromine to form __(41)__ .

42. The process of breaking up complex organic molecules into simpler molecules by the action of heat or heat and a catalyst is called __(42)__ .

43. The reaction of alkenes with Br_2, H_2, or HBr is called __(43)__ .

44. Molecules of ethene join together at 15 °C and 200 atmospheres pressure by the process of __(44)__ .

45. The electron-dot structure for calcium carbide is __(45)__ .

46. Two molecules of ethyne may combine to form the dimer whose structural formula is __(46)__ .

47. Butadiene is prepared by cracking petroleum fractions containing __(47)__ .

48. The benzene ring is sometimes abbreviated and rep-resented by __(48)__ .

49. The C_6H_5— group derived from benzene is called the __(49)__ group.

water	27
more	28
slower	29
molecules	30
hydrocarbons	31
natural gas	32
3–4	33
fractionating tower	34
alkadienes	35
resonance hybrid	36
homologous	37
C_nH_{2n+2}	38
molecular weight	39
C_5H_{12}	40
substitution products	41
cracking	42
addition	43
polymerization	44

$$\overset{Ca^{++}}{^-\!\!\overset{x}{\underset{x}{\cdot}}C\!::\!C\overset{o}{\underset{x}{\cdot}}^-} \qquad 45$$

$$\underset{H}{\overset{H}{\diagup}}C\!\!=\!\!\underset{}{\overset{H}{\underset{}{C}}}\!-\!C\!\equiv\!C\!-\!H \qquad 46$$

butane	47

	48
phenyl	49

50. Bromobenzene is one product formed when benzene reacts with bromine in the presence of iron. This type of reaction is called __(50)__ .

51. Reacting benzene with the compound represented as RCl in the presence of anhydrous aluminum chloride introduces a(n) __(51)__ group into the benzene ring.

52. Knocking occurs in an automobile engine when the gasoline vapor and air within the cylinders does not burn at a(n) __(52)__ rate.

53. Gasoline composed of __(53)__ hydrocarbons tends to knock badly in automobiles.

54. The best known gasoline additive used to improve the antiknock properties is __(54)__ .

55. A gasoline that has the characteristics of a mixture of 87% iso-octane and 13% n-heptane has an octane rating of __(55)__ .

56–58. It is estimated that about 72% of the energy used in the United States is being supplied by petroleum and natural gas. The most abundant fuel remaining in the United States is __(56)__ . The two well-known methods by which it can be converted to fuel gases and petroleumlike liquids are the __(57)__ and the __(58)__ .

59–62. The simplest formula for natural rubber is __(59)__ . Considerable amounts of the substance __(60)__ are needed to increase the bulk and wearing qualities of automobile tires. The synthetic rubber that resists the action of hydrocarbons and therefore is used in gasoline delivery hoses is __(61)__ . *SBR* is made by churning styrene and __(62)__ in soapy water and a catalyst.

substitution _____ 50

alkyl _____ 51

uniform _____ 52

straight-chain _____ 53

lead tetraethyl _____ 54

87 _____ 55

coal _____ 56

Bergius process _____ 57

Fischer-Tropsch process _____ 58

$(C_5H_8)_x$ _____ 59

carbon black _____ 60

Neoprene _____ 61

butadiene _____ 62

DIRECTIONS: Draw structural formulas for the following compounds.

63–65. The three isomers of pentane.

66. propene

67. propyne

68. ethylbenzene

69. 1,1,2,2, tetrabromoethane

70. nitrobenzene

DIRECTIONS: Write balanced formula equations for the following reactions.

71. Laboratory preparation of methane $NaC_2H_3O_2(s) + NaOH(s) \rightarrow Na_2CO_3(s) + CH_4(g)$ ___ 71

72. The action of bromine on methane $CH_4 + Br_2 \rightarrow CH_3Br + HBr$ ___ 72

73. The action of bromine on ethene $C_2H_4 + Br_2 \rightarrow C_2H_4Br_2$ ___ 73

74. The preparation of ethyne from calcium carbide $CaC_2(s) + 2H_2O(l) \rightarrow Ca(OH)_2(aq) + C_2H_2(g)$ 74

75. The complete combustion of ethane $2C_2H_6 + 7O_2 \rightarrow 4CO_2(g) + 6H_2O$ ___ 75

76. Production of styrene from ethylbenzene $C_6H_5C_2H_5 \rightarrow C_6H_5CH{=}CH_2 + H_2$ ___ 76

77. The complete combustion of ethyne $2C_2H_2 + 5O_2 \rightarrow 4CO_2 + 2H_2O$ ___ 77

78. Formation of ethene from ethyl alcohol $C_2H_5OH \xrightarrow{H_2SO_4} C_2H_4 + H_2O$ ___ 78

79. Production of ethylbenzene ___ 79

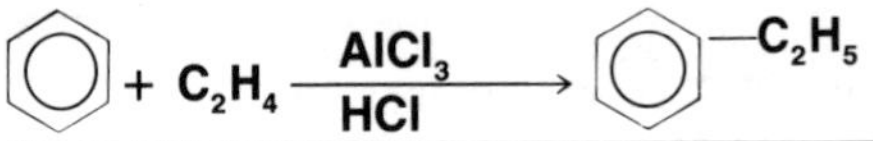

80. Production of chloroprene (use structural formulas)

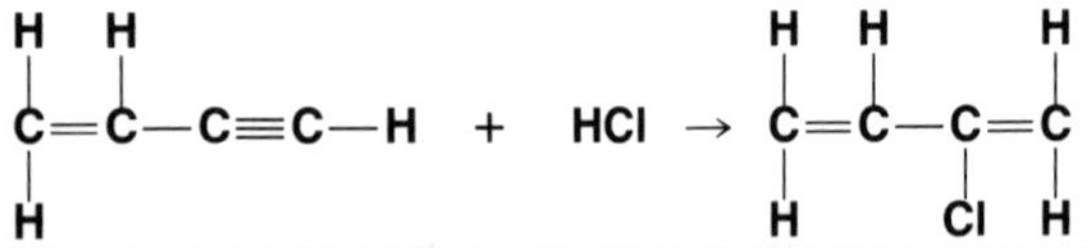

___ 80

Exercises and Experiments in Modern Chemistry
Holt, Rinehart and Winston, Publishers

Hydrocarbon Substitution Products

EXERCISE **19**

DIRECTIONS: In the parentheses at the right of each word or expression in the second column, write the letter of the expression in the first column that is *most closely* related. The expressions in the first column may be used more than once.

a. RX
b. RMgX
c. ROH
d. RCHO
e. ROR'
f. RCOR'
g. RCOOH
h. RCOOR'

acetic acid	(**g**)	1
methanol	(**c**)	2
methyl ethyl ether	(**e**)	3
ethyl acetate	(**h**)	4
ethyl chloride	(**a**)	5
carbon tetrachloride	(**a**)	6
acetaldehyde	(**d**)	7
propionic acid	(**g**)	8
ethyl methyl ketone	(**f**)	9
carboxyl group	(**g**)	10
Fehling's solution	(**d**)	11
acetone	(**f**)	12

DIRECTIONS: In the blank space at the right of each statement, write the word or expression that BEST completes the meaning when substituted for the corresponding number.

13–15. Alkyl halides may be formed from alkanes by the process of (13) ; from alkenes and alkynes by the process of (14) ; and from an alcohol by treatment with a(n) (15) .

substitution _____ 13

addition _____ 14

hydrogen halide _____ 15

16–18. Alkyl halides react with (16) in the Friedel-Crafts reaction in the presence of anhydrous aluminum chloride. They also react with aqueous solutions of strong hydroxides to yield (17) and (18) .

benzene _____ 16

alcohols _____ 17

halide ions _____ 18

19–23. Carbon tetrachloride is prepared commercially by the reaction between (19) and chlorine. CCl_2F_2 is one of a family of compounds called (20) . Tetrafluoroethene may be polymerized to produce the material called (21) . Most of ethylene dichloride is converted to (22) by heat. This substance is polymerized to form (23) .

methane _____ 19

Freons _____ 20

Teflon _____ 21

vinyl chloride _____ 22

polyvinyl chloride _____ 23

24. Alcohols may be produced by (24) of alkenes.

hydration _____ 24

25–26. Using a catalyst and high pressure, methanol is synthesized from (25) gas and (26) gas.

CO _____ 25

H₂ _____ 26

27–28. A mixture of 10% ethanol and 90% unleaded gasoline is being marketed as (27) . The addition of the ethanol is claimed to produce an increase in (28) .

gasohol _____ 27

octane number _____ 28

29–30. The molecular formula for ethylene glycol is (29) . The molecular formula for glycerol is (30) .

C₂H₄(OH)₂ _____ 29

C₃H₅(OH)₃ _____ 30

31. The reaction of sodium with ethanol is similar to its reaction with (31) .

water _____ 31

32–33. Ethanol may be dehydrated by hot concentrated sulfuric acid to yield water and either (32) or (33) .

ethene _____ 32

diethyl ether _____ 33

34. The oxidation of alcohols with the hydroxyl group attached to the end carbon in the presence of heated copper(II) oxide produces (34) .

35. Sulfation of lauryl alcohol with sulfuric acid and subsequent neutralization with sodium hydroxide yields the very effective detergent whose formula is (35) .

36. Acetaldehyde can be made by oxidation of (36) .

37. The mild oxidation of an aldehyde produces a(n) (37) having the same number of carbon atoms.

38–39. In the Fehling's test, Fehling's solutions are mixed with a(n) (38) and heated. The copper(II) ion is reduced to the copper(I) ion and precipitated as brick red (39) .

40. The addition of hydrogen to aldehydes, using nickel as a catalyst, produces (40) .

41–42. Ketones are organic compounds containing the (41) group. They may be prepared from alcohols that do not have the hydroxyl group attached to a(n) (42) atom.

43. The mild oxidation of 2-propanol can be used to prepare (43) .

44. A new method for preparing very pure acetic acid uses the catalytic reaction of (44) with carbon monoxide at moderate temperature and moderate pressure.

45. Formic acid can be produced from sodium formate by carefully heating with (45) .

46–50. Carboxylic acids generally are classified as (46) acids. They can be (47) by hydroxides, just as inorganic acids are. They react with alcohols to form (48) , in whose formation sulfuric acid is used as a(n) (49) agent. Experiments with alcohols containing oxygen-18 have shown that the oxygen of the water product comes from the (50) .

51–52. Fats and oils are esters of (51) and (52) acids.

53–55. The hydrolysis of a fat using a solution of a(n) (53) is called (54) . The products are soap and (55) .

aldehydes	34
$C_{12}H_{25}\,OSO_2ONa$	35
ethanol	36
organic acid	37
aldehyde	38
Cu_2O	39
alcohols	40
carbonyl	41
end-carbon	42
acetone	43
methanol	44
sulfuric acid	45
weak	46
neutralized	47
esters	48
catalytic	49
acid	50
glycerol	51
long-carbon-chain	52
strong hydroxide	53
saponification	54
glycerol	55

DIRECTIONS: Complete and balance the following equations.

56. $C_{12}H_{22}O_{11}$ + H_2O $\xrightarrow{enzymes}$ **4CO$_2$ + 4C$_2$H$_5$OH** _____ 56

57. C_2H_5ONa + CH_3Br → **C$_2$H$_5$OCH$_3$ + NaBr** _____ 57

58. CH_3OH + CuO → **HCHO + H$_2$O + Cu** _____ 58

59. C_2H_5OH + O_2 $\xrightarrow{enzymes}$ **CH$_3$COOH + H$_2$O** _____ 59

60. CH_3COOH + C_3H_7OH → **CH$_3$COOC$_3$H$_7$ + H$_2$O** _____ 60

Exercises and Experiments in Modern Chemistry
Holt, Rinehart and Winston, Publishers

Reaction Energy and Reaction Kinetics

EXERCISE  **20**

DIRECTIONS: In the blank space at the right of each statement, write the word or expression that BEST completes the meaning when substituted for the corresponding number.

1–2. Chemical kinetics is the branch of chemistry that deals with reaction __(1)__ and reaction pathways. The pathway from reactants to products may consist of a sequence of simple steps called the reaction __(2)__ .

3. The energy change in a chemical reaction is directly related to the change in number and strengths of __(3)__ as the reactants form products.

4–6. In most chemical reactions, the energy change can be measured in terms of the __(4)__ released or absorbed during the reaction. At constant pressure, the heat content is often called the __(5)__ of the substance and is represented by the symbol __(6)__ .

7. The products of a(n) __(7)__ reaction have a heat content higher than that of the reactants.

8. In a thermochemical equation, the __(8)__ of reactants and products should be shown along with their formulas.

9. Heats of reaction are commonly expressed in terms of __(9)__ of substance.

10. According to the equation $H_2O(l) + 68.32 \text{ kcal} \rightarrow H_2(g) + \frac{1}{2} O_2(g)$, when 1 mole of water is decomposed, the products have a heat content that is __(10)__ by 68.32 kcal.

11. The heat of reaction, ΔH, for an exothermic reaction has a(n) __(11)__ sign.

12. Chemical reactions in which elements combine to form compounds are generally __(12)__ .

13. Compounds with a(n) __(13)__ heat of formation are very stable.

14. Compounds with low positive or low negative heats of formation are generally (very stable, unstable, explosively unstable) __(14)__ .

15. The heat of combustion, ΔH_c, is defined in terms of 1 mole of __(15)__ .

16. The heat of formation of compound X equals the sum of heats of formation of products of combustion of compound X minus the heat of __(16)__ of compound X.

17. The $\Delta H_f(CO) = -26.41$ kcal/mole and the $\Delta H_c(CO) = -67.64$ kcal/mole. The $\Delta H_f(CO_2)$ is __(17)__ kcal/mole.

rates	1
mechanism	2
bonds	3
heat	4
enthalpy	5
H	6
endothermic	7
standard states	8
kcal/mole	9
higher	10
negative	11
exothermic	12
high negative	13
unstable	14
reactant	15
combustion	16
−94.05	17

18. In the water-gas reaction, the product gases carbon monoxide and hydrogen collectively have a(n) __(18)__ heat content than the reactants steam and carbon.

higher _____ 18

19. The property that describes the state of disorder of a system is called __(19)__ .

entropy _____ 19

20–21. The property of a system that makes a reaction go consists of two driving forces, a tendency toward the lowest __(20)__ and a tendency toward the highest __(21)__ .

energy _____ 20

entropy _____ 21

22. A chemical reaction proceeds if it is accompanied by a(n) __(22)__ in free energy.

decrease _____ 22

23–27. In endothermic reactions, ΔH has a __(23)__ value. From the expression for ΔG, we can see that the more __(24)__ ΔH is, the more __(25)__ ΔG is likely to be. Reaction systems that change from a high-energy to a low-energy state tend to proceed __(26)__ . The more positive ΔS is, the more __(27)__ ΔG is likely to be.

positive _____ 23

negative _____ 24

negative _____ 25

spontaneously _____ 26

negative _____ 27

28. Increases in temperature tend to favor __(28)__ in entropy.

increases _____ 28

29–30. When the temperature of a system is low, whether ΔS is positive or negative, the product $T\Delta S$ may be __(29)__ compared to the ΔH. In such cases, the reaction may proceed as the __(30)__ change predicts.

small _____ 29

energy _____ 30

DIRECTIONS: Write the answers to these questions in the space provided. Where appropriate, make complete statements.

31. What does a balanced chemical equation reveal about the reaction mechanism? _____
A balanced chemical equation reveals nothing about the reaction mechanism. ____ 31

32. What are the five factors or conditions that may affect the rate of a chemical reaction?
temperature, concentration of reactants and products, catalysts, nature of reactants, ____

surface area of contact for heterogeneous reactions _____ 32

33. What is a catalyst? **A catalyst is a substance or substances that** ____

increases the rate of a chemical reaction without itself being permanently consumed. ____ 33

34. What is meant by a homogeneous chemical system? **A homogeneous chemical system is** ____
one in which all reactants and products are in the same phase. ____ 34

35. What are the three equations that represent the complex reaction pathway for the reaction
between hydrogen gas and bromine vapor? **$Br_2 \rightleftarrows 2Br$; $Br + H_2 \rightleftarrows HBr + H$; $H + Br_2 \rightleftarrows HBr + Br$** ____

_____ 35

36. What are the equations for the two-step mechanism proposed for the reaction
$H_2(g) + I_2(g) \rightleftarrows 2HI(g)$? **$I_2 \rightleftarrows 2I$; $2I + H_2 \rightleftarrows 2HI$** ____

_____ 36

37. According to the collision theory, in order for reactions to occur between substances,
(a) what must their particles do, and (b) what must be the result of (a)? (a) **Their particles must** ____
collide. _____ (b) **These collisions must result in interactions.** ____ 37

Exercises and Experiments in Modern Chemistry
Holt, Rinehart and Winston, Publishers

38. According to the collision theory, give two reasons why a collision between reactant molecules may be ineffective. **The collision is not energetic enough to supply the required activation energy. The colliding molecules are not oriented in a way that enables them to react with each other.**

_____ 38

39. What is meant by the "activated complex"? **The activated complex is the transitional structure that results from effective collision and persists while old bonds are breaking and new bonds are forming.**

_____ 39

40. How is activation energy related to the activated complex? **Activation energy is the energy required to transform the reactants into the activated complex.**

_____ 40

41. What are the two possibilities to which the activated complex may respond during the brief interval of its existence? **The activated complex may re-form the original bonds and separate into reactant molecules, or it may form a new bond and separate into product molecules.**

_____ 41

42. How is the rate of a chemical reaction measured? **The rate of reaction is measured by the amount of reactants converted to products in a unit of time.**

_____ 42

43. According to the collision theory, on what two factors does the rate of a reaction (other than a simple decomposition) depend? **The rate of a reaction depends on the collision frequency of the reacting substances and the collision efficiency.**

_____ 43

44. One factor that influences the rate of chemical reaction is the nature of the reactants. At room temperature, which of the following elements combines most rapidly with oxygen? (a) chlorine; (b) iron; (c) sodium; (d) platinum. **(c) sodium**

_____ 44

45. In what type of reactions is the reaction rate proportional to the area of contact? **The reaction rate is proportional to the area of contact in heterogeneous reactions.**

_____ 45

46. In the reaction between charcoal and oxygen, the rate of reaction is proportional to (a) the concentration of the solid; (b) twice the concentration of the solid; (c) the concentration of the gas; (d) ten times the concentration of the gas. **(c) the concentration of the gas**

_____ 46

47. How must the specific effect of concentration changes in homogeneous reaction systems be determined? **The specific effect of concentration changes must be determined by experiment.**

_____ 47

48. What possible effects could increasing the concentration of substance A in reacting with substance B have on the reaction rate? **It could increase the rate, decrease the rate, or have no effect on the rate.**

_____ 48

49. When a complex chemical reaction takes place in a series of simple steps, which step determines the rate of the overall reaction? **The slowest step, which is called the rate-determining step.**

_____ 49

50. According to the collision theory, what are the two reasons why the rates of many reactions (at about room temperature) approximately double or triple with a 10 C° rise in temperature? **A rise in temperature produces an increase in collision efficiency**

(since a greater proportion of molecules reach the activation energy) as well as

collision frequency. _____ 50

51. How can a catalyst provide an alternate pathway by which the potential energy barrier between reactants and products may be lowered? **This could be accomplished by way**
of an alternate activated complex requiring lower activation energy that somehow

involves the catalyst. _____ 51

52. How may the reaction rate for the reaction $2H_2(g) + 2NO(g) \rightarrow N_2(g) + 2H_2O(g)$, carried out at an elevated constant temperature, be measured? **The rate may be measured by measuring**
the decrease in pressure with time since 4 reactant molecules change to 3 product molecules. 52

53–54. The rate law for the reaction in Question 52 is $R = k[H_2]^2[NO]^2$.

53. What is the specific rate constant for this reaction at a given temperature? _____
The specific rate constant is k. _____ 53

54. What effect does an increase in temperature have on the value of the specific rate constant? Why? **A temperature increase usually increases the value of k since an increase in**
temperature usually increases the rate of reaction. _____ 54

55. What is the simple relationship that exists between the chemical equation for a *step* in a reaction pathway and the rate law for that step? **The power to which the molar concentration**
of each reactant or product is raised in the rate law corresponds to the coefficient for

the reactant or product in the balanced equation for that step. 55

56. If a reaction proceeds in a series of steps, the rate law is simply that for the __(56)__ step.
slowest _____ 56

57. Assume that the reaction $2H_2(g) + 2NO(g) \rightarrow N_2(g) + 2H_2O(g)$ occurs in a single step by way of collision between two H_2 molecules and two NO molecules. What would the rate law be if this assumed reaction mechanism proved to be experimentally correct? _____
$R = k[H_2]^2[NO]^2$ _____ 57

58. The general form for a rate law is $R = k[A]^n[B]^m$ . . . . . . If n and m are appropriate powers to which the concentrations must be raised, what determines the value of these powers? **Experimental data** _____ 58

59. State the law of mass action. **The rate of a chemical reaction is directly**
proportional to the product of the concentrations of reacting substances, each raised

to the appropriate power. _____ 59

Exercises and Experiments in Modern Chemistry
Holt, Rinehart and Winston, Publishers

Chemical Equilibrium

EXERCISE **21**

DIRECTIONS: In the parentheses at the right of each word or expression in the second column, write the letter of the expression in the first column that is *most closely* related.

a. resistance to change in pH
b. opposing processes of equal rate
c. $\dfrac{[HI]^2}{[H_2][I_2]}$
d. $\dfrac{[HB][OH^-]}{[B^-]}$
e. $[H_3O^+][OH^-]$
f. $[Ca^{++}][F^-]^2$
g. pH greater than 7
h. reaction of an ion of a dissolved salt with water
i. pH less than 7
j. $Al(H_2O)_6^{+++}$
k. pH = 7
l. $[C_2H_3O_2^-][H_3O^+]$

hydrolysis	(**h**)	1
acid solution	(**i**) or (**j**)	2
buffer	(**a**)	3
ion product constant for water	(**e**)	4
equilibrium	(**b**)	5
an equilibrium constant for a gaseous system	(**c**)	6
alkaline solution	(**g**)	7
proton donor to water	(**j**)	8
hydrolysis constant	(**d**)	9
a solubility-product constant	(**f**)	10

DIRECTIONS: In the space at the right, place the letter or letters indicating each choice that forms a correct statement. More than one response may be correct.

11. When a state of equilibrium is reached between two opposing chemical reactions, (a) all chemical activity ceases, (b) both reactions continue but the net change is zero, (c) the rates of the two reactions are equal, (d) the quantities of reactants and products remain unchanged.

b, c, d _____ 11

12. Chemical equilibrium (a) occurs when a solution becomes saturated, (b) is a dynamic state, (c) occurs when a liquid evaporates in an enclosed space, (d) exists when opposing chemical reactions occur at equal rates.

b, d _____ 12

13. When an irregularly shaped crystal of sodium chloride is placed in a saturated solution of sodium chloride, (a) the shape of the crystal becomes more irregular, (b) the concentration of the solution increases, (c) the shape of the crystal becomes more regular, (d) the mass of the crystal in contact with the solution decreases.

c _____ 13

14. Ionic equilibrium occurs between (a) dissolved molecules and their hydrated ions, (b) undissolved and dissolved solute molecules, (c) a liquid and its vapor in a confined space, (d) undissolved crystals of an electrovalent solute and its dissociated ions.

a, d _____ 14

15. In an equilibrium in which the forward reaction runs well toward completion before the speed of the reverse reaction is high enough to establish equilibrium, (a) the products of the reverse reaction are favored, (b) the products of the forward reaction are favored, (c) neither set of products is favored, (d) both reactants and products exist in equal quantities.

b _____ 15

16. The rate of a homogeneous reaction may be increased by all of the following except (a) a rise in temperature, (b) the use of a catalyst, (c) an increase in surface area, (d) an increase in concentration.

c _____ 16

17. In a reaction between a gas and a solid, the speed of the reaction is proportional to (a) the concentration of the solid, (b) twice the concentration of the solid, (c) the concentration of the gas, (d) twice the concentration of the gas.

c _____ 17

18. In a bimolecular reaction between two gases, the speed of the reaction (a) is proportional to the concentrations of both gases, (b) is doubled if the concentrations of both gases are doubled, (c) is doubled if the concentration of one gas is doubled, (d) is independent of the gas concentrations.

a, c _____ 18

19. In the equilibrium reaction, $A + B \rightleftarrows C + D$, starting with $A + B$ (a) the speed of the forward reaction increases as A and B are used up, (b) the speed of the reverse reaction increases as A and B are used up, (c) the speed of the forward reaction decreases as A and B are used up, (d) the speeds of both forward and reverse reactions become equal.

b, c, d _____ 19

20. In the equilibrium reaction, $A + B \rightleftarrows C + D$, the ratio of the product [C] [D] to the product [A] [B] (a) is always equal to one, (b) is known as the equilibrium constant, (c) may be greater or less than one, (d) depends on the initial concentrations of A and B.

b, c _____ 20

21. If the equilibrium constant K for a given equilibrium reaction is very much less than one, (a) the original reactants are largely converted to products, (b) the forward reaction is barely underway when equilibrium is established, (c) its numerical value may be changed by increasing the concentration of either reactant, (d) its numerical value may be changed by altering the reaction temperature.

b, d _____ 21

22. For the reaction system at equilibrium shown by the equation
$3A + B \rightleftarrows 2C + 3D$, K is given by the expression

(a) $\dfrac{[2C] [3D]}{[3A] [B]}$, (b) $\dfrac{[C] [D]}{[A] [B]}$, (c) $\dfrac{[C]^2 [D]^3}{[A]^3 [B]}$, (d) $\dfrac{[C]^3 [D]^2}{[A] [B]^3}$

c _____ 22

23. The expression for the equilibrium constant K (a) may be written directly from the chemical equation, (b) requires information concerning the kinetics of the system, (c) may be derived from the appropriate rate laws for the forward and reverse reactions, (d) may be calculated from the equilibrium concentrations of reactants and products which are determined experimentally.

a, c, d _____ 23

24. For the equilibrium system given by the equation $2A_2 + 2BC \rightleftarrows B_2 + 2A_2C$, for which the reaction takes place in two steps (1) $A_2 + 2BC \rightleftarrows B_2 + A_2C_2$ (slow) (2) $A_2 + A_2C_2 \rightleftarrows 2A_2C$ (fast), (a) $R_f = k_f[A_2] [BC]^2$ (for step 1), (b) $R_r = k_r[2C]$ (for step 1), (c) at equilibrium $R_f = R_r$ (for step 1), (d) the equilibrium constant for both steps $= \dfrac{[B_2] [A_2C]^2}{[A_2]^2 [BC]^2}$

a, c, d _____ 24

Exercises and Experiments in Modern Chemistry
Holt, Rinehart and Winston, Publishers

25. For the hypothetical reaction A + B ⇌ C + D, an increase in the concentration of A (a) displaces the equilibrium to the *right,* (b) causes A and B to be used up faster, (c) causes more C and D to be formed, (d) results in a reestablished equilibrium in which the concentration of B will be lower.

a, b, c, d _____ 25

26. In the synthesis of ammonia, an increase in pressure results in a greater yield of ammonia because (a) the formation of ammonia molecules tends to relieve the pressure, (b) hydrogen has a lower molecular weight than nitrogen, (c) there are two molecules of ammonia formed for every four molecules of reactants used, (d) ammonia has a lower molecular weight than nitrogen.

a, c _____ 26

27. In equilibrium systems in which gases are involved, (a) pressure changes have the effect of altering the concentration of the gases, (b) pressure changes have no effect on the numerical value of the equilibrium constant, (c) an increase in pressure causes a shift in the equilibrium, (d) a decrease in pressure produces an undesirable shift in the equilibrium.

a, b, c _____ 27

28. A change in the operating temperature of an equilibrium reaction (a) always causes a change in the numerical value of the equilibrium constant, (b) favors the endothermic reaction, (c) favors the exothermic reaction, (d) alters the speeds of both reactions unequally.

a, d _____ 28

29. The addition of a catalyst to a system (a) does not affect the value of *K*, (b) accelerates both forward and reverse reactions, (c) accelerates the forward reaction more than the reverse reaction, (d) reduces the time required for a system to reach equilibrium.

a, b, d _____ 29

DIRECTIONS: In the blank space at the right of each statement, write the word or expression that BEST completes the meaning when substituted for the corresponding number.

30. We may drive an equilibrium in a desired direction by the proper application of the principle of __(30)__ .

Le Chatelier _____ 30

31. A reaction between solutions of barium chloride and sulfuric acid may be considered to run to completion because __(31)__ is practically insoluble.

$BaSO_4$ _____ 31

32–33. A reaction between hydrochloric acid and potassium hydroxide may be said to run to completion because __(32)__ is practically __(33)__ .

water _____ 32

un-ionized _____ 33

34. If a solution of $NaC_2H_3O_2$ is added to a solution of $HC_2H_3O_2$, the concentration of __(34)__ ions is reduced.

H_3O^+ _____ 34

35. The expression for K_a for the ionization of the typical weak acid HB is __(35)__ .

$\dfrac{[H_3O^+][B^-]}{[HB]}$ _____ 35

36. A solution of a weak acid may be buffered against changes in __(36)__ by the addition of a salt of the acid.

pH _____ 36

37. The hydronium-ion concentration in water at room temperature is __(37)__ mole per liter.

10^{-7} _____ 37

38. The hydroxide-ion concentration in water at room temperature is __(38)__ mole per liter.

10^{-7} _____ 38

39. In any water solution having a pH of 9, the $[OH^-]$ is __(39)__ .

40. If the solution of a salt in water has a pH less than 7, the salt is said to __(40)__ in water solution.

41–43. Aluminum chloride dissolves in water to produce the hydrated cation __(41)__ , which then reacts with water to yield the ions __(42)__ and __(43)__ .

44–45. The solubility product constant for the equilibrium system $BaCO_3(s) \rightleftarrows Ba^{++}(aq) + CO_3^{--}(aq)$ is __(44)__ . If mixing two solutions results in an ion product that exceeds the K_{sp} of $BaCO_3$, a __(45)__ will form.

10^{-5} mole/liter	39
hydrolyze	40
$Al(H_2O)_6{}^{+++}$	41
$Al(H_2O)_5 (OH)^{++}$	42
H_3O^+	43
$[Ba^{++}] [CO_3^{--}]$	44
precipitate	45

DIRECTIONS: Write the answers to the following problems in the space provided. Show calculations in the space below, or in your notebook.

46. The solubility of silver chloride at room temperature is 1.1×10^{-5} mole/liter. What is its K_{sp}?

47. What is the pH of a 0.001-M solution of NaOH?

48. Calculate the hydrolysis constant for an acid whose K_a is 2.0×10^{-5}.

49. The K_{sp} for $AgC_2H_3O_2$ is 2.5×10^{-3}. Calculate its solubility in moles/liter.

50. What is the solubility of $AgC_2H_3O_2$ in grams/liter of solution?

1.2×10^{-10}	46
11	47
5.0×10^{-10}	48
5×10^{-2}	49
8.3 g/L	50

Exercises and Experiments in Modern Chemistry
Holt, Rinehart and Winston, Publishers

Oxidation-Reduction Reactions

EXERCISE **22**

DIRECTIONS: Write the answers to the following in the space provided. Where appropriate, make complete statements.

1. What is the general definition of oxidation? **Oxidation is a chemical reaction in which the atoms or ions of an element attain a more positive oxidation state.**

1

2. What is the general definition of reduction? **Reduction is a chemical reaction in which the atoms or ions of an element attain a more negative oxidation state.**

2

3. What are the oxidation numbers of the respective elements in NaCl? Explain. **Na = +1, Cl = −1. The oxidation number of a monatomic ion is equal to its charge. NaCl is an ionic compound.**

3

4. What is the oxidation number of chlorine in Cl_2 and HCl, respectively? Explain. **In Cl_2, 0; in HCl, −1. In Cl_2, the oxidation number of a free element is zero. In HCl, the Cl is the more electronegative element, and the unequally shared electron pair in the polar molecule is more strongly attracted to the Cl than to the H.**

4

5. What is the oxidation number of each element in (a) nitric acid, HNO_3; (b) copper(II) nitrite, $Cu(NO_2)_2$; (c) ammonium chloride, NH_4Cl; (d) lead(II) chromate, $PbCrO_4$; (e) potassium dichromate, $K_2Cr_2O_7$; (f) nitrogen, N_2; (g) ammonia, NH_3?
(a) H = +1, N = + 5, O = −2;   (b) Cu = +2, N = +3, O = −2;
(c) N = −3, H = +1, Cl = −1;   (d) Pb = +2, Cr = +6, O = −2;
(e) K = +1, Cr = +6, O = −2;   (f) N = 0; (g) N = −3, H = +1.

5

6. What determines whether a chemical reaction is an oxidation-reduction reaction? **Reactions in which elements undergo a change in oxidation number are oxidation-reduction reactions.** 6

7. What effect do (a) oxidation and (b) reduction have on the oxidation number of a substance? **(a) a more positive oxidation state, (b) a more negative oxidation state**

7

8. What special conservation rule must be observed in balancing oxidation-reduction equations? **Conservation of electrons must be observed in addition to the other considerations in balancing oxidation-reduction reactions.**

8

9. How do you distinguish between an oxidizing agent and a reducing agent? **An oxidizing agent is a substance that attains a more negative oxidation state in an oxidation-reduction reaction; it is reduced. A reducing agent is a substance that attains a more positive oxidation state; it is oxidized.**

9

10. Why are the Group I elements very active reducing agents? **The relatively large atoms of Group I have a weak attraction for their valence electrons and form positive ions readily.**

10

11. Why are the elements of Group VII very active oxidizing agents? **Group VII elements have a strong attraction for electrons and form negative ions readily.**

_____ 11

12. What is the relationship between the strength of a reducing agent and its corresponding oxidizing agent? **The stronger a reducing agent, the weaker is its corresponding oxidizing agent.**

_____ 12

13. Write the electron-dot formula for the peroxide ion, and state the oxidation number of oxygen in the peroxide form. $\left[\;:\overset{..}{\underset{x.}{O}}:\overset{..}{\underset{x.}{O}}:\;\right]^{--}$ **; – 1.**

_____ 13

14. What is meant by the chemical equivalent of a reactant? **The mass of the reactant that loses or acquires the Avogadro number of electrons in a chemical reaction.**

_____ 14

15. What is the chemical equivalent for tin (atomic weight $= 118.7$) in the reaction $Sn^{++} \rightarrow Sn^{++++} + 2e^-$? Explain. **59.35 g. Each mole of Sn^{++} ions furnishes two times the Avogadro number of electrons. One equivalent therefore has one-half the mass of a mole.**

_____ 15

16. Explain the transfer of electrons that takes place in oxidation-reduction reactions. **Oxidation-reduction reactions involve the transfer of electrons from the substance being oxidized to the substance being reduced.**

_____ 16

17. What energy change occurs in spontaneous oxidation-reduction reactions when the reactants are in contact? **The energy is released during the electron transfer in the form of heat.**

_____ 17

18. What is an electrochemical cell? **An arrangement in which, by separating the reactants in an electrolytic solution, the spontaneous transfer of electrons may take place through a conducting wire joining them externally.**

_____ 18

19. Which materials serve as the cathode and the anode in the dry cell?
The zinc container is the cathode and the carbon rod is the anode.

_____ 19

20. When the external circuit of a dry cell is closed, what reaction occurs at the cathode?
$Zn \rightarrow Zn^{++} + 2e^-$

_____ 20

21. Write the equation for the reaction that would occur at the anode of a dry cell (external circuit closed) if MnO_2 were not present. **$2NH_4^+ + 2e^- \rightarrow 2NH_3 + H_2(g)$**

_____ 21

22. What are electrolytic cells? **Electrolytic cells are those in which oxidation-reduction reactions that are not spontaneous may be forced to occur by means of electric energy supplied externally.**

_____ 22

23. For the electrolysis of water, write equations for (a) the net cathode reaction, (b) the net anode reaction, and (c) net reaction for the cell. **(a) $2H_2O + 2e^- \rightarrow 2OH^- + H_2(g)$**
(b) $6H_2O \rightarrow 4H_3O^+ + O_2(g) + 4e^-$
(c) $2H_2O \rightarrow 2H_2(g) + O_2(g)$

_____ 23

Exercises and Experiments in Modern Chemistry
Holt, Rinehart and Winston, Publishers

24. For the electrolysis of an aqueous solution of NaCl, write the equations for (a) cathode reaction, (b) anode reaction, and (c) net reaction for the cell. **(a) 2H₂O + 2e⁻ → 2OH⁻ + H₂(g)**

(b) 2Cl⁻ → Cl₂(g) + 2e⁻

(c) 2H₂O + 2Cl⁻ → 2OH⁻ + H₂(g) + Cl₂(g)   24

25. In general, what type of metals yield (a) the metal; (b) hydrogen gas, when aqueous solutions of their ions are subjected to electrolysis? **(a) metals that are difficult**

to oxidize and form ions that are easily reduced; (b) metals that are strong reducing

agents (easily oxidized) and form ions that are not easily reduced.   25

DIRECTIONS: In the blank space at the right of each statement, write the word or expression that BEST completes the meaning when substituted for the corresponding number.

26–32. A silverplating cell consists essentially of a solution of a(n) (26) , an anode of (27) , and a cathode of (28) . Silver (29) are (30) at the cathode while silver (31) are (32) at the anode.

soluble silver salt	26
silver	27
the object to be plated	28
ions	29
reduced	30
atoms	31
oxidized	32

33–34. A consistent definition of electrodes defines the electron- (33) electrode as the cathode, and the electron- (34) electrode as the anode.

rich	33
poor	34

35–36. The chemical action at the cathode in electrochemical (spontaneous) cells is (35) , while in electrolytic (driven) cells it is (36) .

37–42. When the lead storage battery is being charged, the cells act as (37) cells. When it is being discharged, the cells act as (38) cells. When it is discharging, both electrodes in each cell are converted to (39) , and the electrolyte becomes (40) . In the electrolyte during charging, (41) is formed and (42) is decomposed.

oxidation	35
reduction	36
electrolytic	37
electrochemical	38
PbSO₄	39
dilute	40
sulfuric acid	41
water	42

43. In electrochemical cells, we may think of the potential difference as the (43) of the potentials produced at the cathode and at the anode.

44–48. The potential difference between an electrode and its solution in a half-reaction is known as its (44) . The standard hydrogen electrode consists of a(n) (45) electrode dipping in a(n) (46) solution of H_3O^+ ions and surrounded by hydrogen gas at (47) . It is assigned an electrode potential of (48) volt(s).

sum	43
electrode potential	44
platinum	45
1-molal	46
1 atmosphere pressure	47
zero	48

49–50. A copper half-cell coupled with the standard hydrogen electrode gives a potential difference measurement of $+0.34$ volt, indicating that copper ions are __(49)__ readily reduced than hydrogen ions. When a zinc half-cell (standard electrode potential $= -0.76$ volt) is coupled with a copper half-cell, the overall potential difference of the cell is __(50)__ volt(s).

more	49
$+1.10$	50

DIRECTIONS: Balance each oxidation-reduction equation in the space provided showing the various steps used to arrive at the final equation. Use the oxidation number (electron-transfer) method.

51. copper + nitric acid(dil) $\rightarrow$ copper(II) nitrate + water + nitrogen monoxide.

STEP 1: $Cu + HNO_3 \rightarrow Cu(NO_3)_2 + H_2O + NO$

STEP 2: $\overset{0}{Cu} + \overset{+1+5-2}{HNO_3} \rightarrow \overset{+2}{Cu}\overset{+5-2}{(NO_3)_2} + \overset{+1-2}{H_2O} + \overset{+2-2}{NO}$

STEP 3: $\overset{0}{Cu} \rightarrow \overset{+2}{Cu} + 2e^-$ (oxidation)

$\overset{+5}{N} + 3e^- \rightarrow \overset{+2}{N}$ (reduction)

STEP 4: $3\overset{0}{Cu} \rightarrow 3\overset{+2}{Cu} + 6e^-$

$2\overset{+5}{N} + 6e^- \rightarrow 2\overset{+2}{N}$

STEP 5: $3Cu + 2HNO_3 \rightarrow 3Cu(NO_3)_2 + H_2O + 2NO$

STEP 6: $3Cu + 8HNO_3 \rightarrow 3Cu(NO_3)_2 + 4H_2O + 2NO(g)$

51

52. hydrochloric acid + potassium permanganate $\rightarrow$ manganese(II) chloride + potassium chloride + water + chlorine.

STEP 1: $HCl + KMnO_4 \rightarrow MnCl_2 + KCl + H_2O + Cl_2$

STEP 2: $\overset{+1-1}{HCl} + \overset{+1+7-2}{KMnO_4} \rightarrow \overset{+2\ -1}{MnCl_2} + \overset{+1-1}{KCl} + \overset{+1-2}{H_2O} + \overset{0}{Cl_2}$

STEP 3: $\overset{-1}{Cl} \rightarrow \overset{0}{Cl} + 1e^- \quad 2\overset{-1}{Cl} \rightarrow \overset{0}{Cl_2} + 2e^-$ (oxidation)

$\overset{+7}{Mn} + 5e^- \rightarrow \overset{+2}{Mn}$ (reduction)

STEP 4: $10\overset{-1}{Cl} \rightarrow 5\overset{0}{Cl_2} + 10e^-$

$2\overset{+7}{Mn} + 10e^- \rightarrow 2\overset{+2}{Mn}$

STEP 5: $10HCl + 2KMnO_4 \rightarrow 2MnCl_2 + KCl + H_2O + 5Cl_2$

STEP 6: $16HCl + 2KMnO_4 \rightarrow 2MnCl_2 + 2KCl + 8H_2O + 5Cl_2(g)$

52

53. aluminum + copper(II) ions $\rightarrow$ aluminum ions + copper.

STEP 1: $Al + Cu^{++} \rightarrow Al^{+++} + Cu$

STEP 2: $\overset{0}{Al} + \overset{+2}{Cu^{++}} \rightarrow \overset{+3}{Al^{+++}} + \overset{0}{Cu}$

STEP 3: $\overset{0}{Al} \rightarrow \overset{+3}{Al^{+++}} + 3e^-$ (oxidation)

$\overset{+2}{Cu^{++}} + 2e^- \rightarrow \overset{0}{Cu}$ (reduction)

STEP 4: $2\overset{0}{Al} \rightarrow 2\overset{+3}{Al^{+++}} + 6e^-$

$3\overset{+2}{Cu^{++}} + 6e^- \rightarrow 3\overset{+2}{Cu^{++}}$

STEPS 5 & 6: $2Al + 3Cu^{++} \rightarrow 2Al^{+++} + 3Cu$

53

Exercises and Experiments in Modern Chemistry
Holt, Rinehart and Winston, Publishers

Elements of Period Three

DIRECTIONS: Write answers to the following in the space provided. Where appropriate, make complete statements.

1. Explain the similarity in properties between elements in a given column in the periodic table. **Elements in a given column have similar outer-electron arrangements.**

_____ 1

2. What type of element is the first element in a short period such as Period Three? _____
It is a highly active metal.

2

3. How do the rest of the elements in Period Three vary in type and character with increasing atomic number? **In order, there are metals of decreasing activity, a metalloid, nonmetals**

of increasing activity, and the last element, which is a noble gas.

3

4. Name and state the general characteristics of the element in Period Three that is classified as a metalloid. **Silicon is the hardest element. It is gray with a metallic luster and**

has properties between those of metals and nonmetals.

4

5. What are the common physical properties of metals in Period Three? **Each is a good**

conductor of heat and electricity, has a silvery luster, and is ductile and malleable.

5

6. What is the nature of the binding force in metallic crystal lattices? **It is the attraction**

between positive ions constituting the lattice and the negative electron "gas"

permeating the lattice. It is essentially uniform in all directions.

6

7. Which physical properties of the metals vary with the magnitude of this binding force?
The boiling and melting points and the degree of hardness, malleability, and

ductility depend on the magnitude of the binding force.

7

8. What does the wide temperature range over which these metals are liquid indicate about the forces existent in the liquid phase? **The forces holding the mobile ions together**

in the liquid phase are evidently quite strong.

8

9. Explain the increase in density as we go from sodium to magnesium to aluminum.
This increase in density is explained by the progressively heavier, yet smaller, atoms which may

be packed closer and closer together.

9

10. In which form does silicon exist in the cubic crystal structure? **It exists as a**
covalent network of atoms.

10

11. In terms of electron configuration and covalent bonds, explain how the pattern of arrangement in the silicon crystal is identical to diamond. **The electron configuration**
of Si is $1s^2\,2s^2\,2p^6\,3s^2\,3p^2$ which is analogous to that of C: $1s^2\,2s^2\,2p^2$. Hybridization

occurs in both elements, producing four equivalent sp^3 orbitals and, hence, four

equivalent covalent bonds.

11

12. Account for the great difference in melting points between the two consecutive elements aluminum and silicon. **The change from metallic (aluminum) to covalent network (silicon) structure between these two elements accounts for the difference in their melting points.**

_12_

13. Explain the low electric conductivity of silicon. **Some of the valence electrons in silicon crystals are free to move.**

_13_

14. Explain why phosphorus is capable of forming three covalent bonds. **Phosphorus atoms have three half-filled $3p$ orbitals. It exists as separate P_4 molecules.**

_14_

15. What physical properties of white phosphorus are typical of nonmetals? **It has no luster, is a poor conductor of heat, and a nonconductor of electricity. It lacks free electrons.**

_15_

16. Which characteristics of white phosphorus indicate the existence of only weak dispersion interaction forces between its P_4 molecules? **The low melting and boiling points of white phosphorus together with its brittleness indicate weak dispersion interaction forces.**

_16_

17. Describe the structure of the S_8 molecule. **Each sulfur atom forms two covalent bonds resulting in a molecule of 8 atoms joined together in a puckered ring.**

_17_

18. Explain the relatively low melting point of sulfur. **This is explained by weak dispersion interaction forces between the S_8 molecules.**

_18_

19. Explain why chlorine is a gas at room temperature. **The dispersion interaction forces between the chlorine molecules are very weak.**

_19_

20. Why does argon exist as single atoms? **Argon has no half-filled orbitals to use in bond formation.**

_20_

21. Complete the following table. Use the numbers 1 (smallest) to 8 (largest) to indicate the relative magnitudes of ionization energies and atomic radii, and thus the patterns of their variations within the period.

Symbol	Electron configuration	Principal oxidation states	Ionization energy (kcal/ mole atoms)	Atomic radius (Å)
$_{11}Na$	$1s^2 2s^2 2p^6 3s^1$	+1	1	8
$_{12}Mg$	$1s^2 2s^2 2p^6 3s^2$	+2	3	7
$_{13}Al$	$1s^2 2s^2 2p^6 3s^2 3p^1$	+3	2	6
$_{14}Si$	$1s^2 2s^2 2p^6 3s^2 3p^2$	+4	4	5
$_{15}P$	$1s^2 2s^2 2p^6 3s^2 3p^3$	+3, +5	6	4
$_{16}S$	$1s^2 2s^2 2p^6 3s^2 3p^4$	−2, +4, +6	5	3
$_{17}Cl$	$1s^2 2s^2 2p^6 3s^2 3p^5$	−1, +5, +7	7	2
$_{18}Ar$	$1s^2 2s^2 2p^6 3s^2 3p^6$	0	8	1

Exercises and Experiments in Modern Chemistry
Holt, Rinehart and Winston, Publishers

22. Complete the following table. Identify the type of compound according to the terms: ionic, covalent network, molecular. Indicate the nature of the reaction with water, if any, in terms of production of OH^- or H_3O^+ ions.

Element	Oxide formula	Type of compound	Nature of reaction with water
Na	Na_2O	ionic	forms OH^-
Mg	MgO	ionic	forms OH^-
Al	Al_2O_3	ionic	none: hydroxide is amphoteric
Si	SiO_2	covalent network	none
P	P_4O_{10}	molecular	forms $H^+(aq)$
S	SO_2	molecular	forms $H^+(aq)$
Cl	Cl_2O	molecular	forms $H^+(aq)$

DIRECTIONS: In the blank space at the right of each statement, write the word or expression that BEST completes the meaning when substituted for the corresponding number.

23. The outer sublevel electron in aluminum is in a (higher, lower) _(23)_ energy sublevel than an outer $3s$ electron in magnesium.

higher _____ 23

24. A half-filled $3p$ sublevel with three singly occupied orbitals is a (more, less) _(24)_ stable electron configuration than a $3p$ sublevel with one filled and two singly occupied orbitals.

more _____ 24

25. In the presence of hydroxide ions, aluminum hydroxide reacts as a(n) _(25)_.

acid _____ 25

26. With hot, concentrated solutions containing hydroxide ions, silicon dioxide acts as a(n) _(26)_.

acid _____ 26

27. Silicon dioxide does not react with common acids, but does react with _(27)_.

hydrofluoric acid _____ 27

28–30. Diphosphorus pentoxide reacts with water to form a solution containing _(28)_, whose equilibrium constant for its first ionization is of the order of _(29)_. This acid is a(n) _(30)_ acid.

phosphoric acid _____ 28

10^{-2} _____ 29

moderately strong _____ 30

31–33. Sulfur dioxide reacts with water to form a solution containing _(31)_, which is rated as _(32)_ with an equilibrium constant for its first ionization of the order of _(33)_.

sulfurous acid _____ 31

moderately strong _____ 32

10^{-2} _____ 33

34–37. Dichlorine monoxide is prepared by the moderate oxidation of chlorine with _(34)_. Its water solution contains _(35)_, which is a(n) _(36)_ acid whose ionization constant is of the order of _(37)_.

mercury(II) oxide _____ 34

hypochlorous acid _____ 35

very weak _____ 36

10^{-8} _____ 37

38. Sodium hydride is a(n) _(38)_ compound.

ionic _____ 38

39. The silicon hydrides such as SiH_4 are (more, less) _(39)_ reactive than the alkanes.

40. Phosphine dissolves in water to produce a solution that is _(40)_ .

41. The combustion of hydrogen sulfide produces sulfur or sulfur dioxide and _(41)_ .

42. The binary hydrogen compound of a Period Three non-metal that is almost completely ionized by water has the formula _(42)_ .

DIRECTIONS: Complete and balance the following equations.

43. $MgO + H_2O \rightarrow$ $Mg^{++} + 2OH^-$ _____ 43

44. $Al(OH)_3 + 3H_3O^+ \rightarrow$ $Al(H_2O)_6^{+++}$ _____ 44

45. $SO_2 + 2H_2O \rightleftharpoons$ $H_3O^+(aq) + HSO_3^-$ _____ 45

46. $Cl_2O + H_2O \rightarrow$ $2HClO$ _____ 46

47. $NaH + H_2O \rightarrow$ $Na^+ + OH^- + H_2(g)$ _____ 47

48. $SiH_4 + 2H_2O \rightarrow$ $SiO_2 + 4H_2(g)$ _____ 48

49. $H_2S + H_2O \rightleftharpoons$ $H_3O^+ + HS^-$ _____ 49

50. $NaCl + H_2SO_4 \rightarrow$ $NaHSO_4 + HCl\ (g)$ _____ 50

51. $SiO_2 + 4HF \rightarrow$ $SiF_4(g) + 2H_2O$ _____ 51

52. $HClO + H_2O \rightleftharpoons$ $H_3O^+(aq) + ClO^-$ _____ 52

53. $MgH_2 + 2H_2O \rightarrow$ $Mg(OH)_2 + 2H_2(g)$ _____ 53

54. $3LiH + AlCl_3 \rightarrow$ $AlH_3(s) + 3LiCl$ _____ 54

55. $Ca_3P_2 + 6H_2O \rightarrow$ $3Ca(OH)_2 + 2PH_3(g)$ _____ 55

Exercises and Experiments in Modern Chemistry
Holt, Rinehart and Winston, Publishers

The Metals of Group I

DIRECTIONS: In the blank space at the right of each statement, write the word or expression that BEST completes the meaning when substituted for the corresponding number.

1–5. The elements of the Sodium Family are chemically (active, inactive) __(1)__ and occur in nature only as ions with a(n) __(2)__ charge. Only trace quantities of the element __(3)__ have been produced in certain nuclear reactions. The Group I elements form hydroxides that are strongly __(4)__. They are relatively soft, have a silvery luster, and are __(5)__ conductors of electricity and heat.

active _____	1
+1 _____	2
francium _____	3
basic (alkaline) _____	4
good _____	5

6–9. The crystal lattice of Group I metals is built around a(n) __(6)__ unit cell made up of ions with a(n) __(7)__ charge. The valence electrons form a(n) __(8)__ that exists throughout the lattice structure. The silvery luster results from the __(9)__ in the crystal structure.

body-centered cubic _____	6
+1 _____	7
electron "gas" _____	8
free electrons _____	9

10. The electron configuration of the sodium ion is __(10)__.

$1s^2\ 2s^2\ 2p^6$ _____	10

11–14. The Group I elements are characterized by __(11)__ ionization energies. The ionization energy __(12)__ as the atom size increases going down the group. They are vigorous __(13)__ agents, the strongest being the __(14)__ atom.

low _____	11
decreases _____	12
reducing _____	13
lithium _____	14

15–17. These metals are usually stored under __(15)__ because they react so vigorously with water, releasing __(16)__ and forming solutions that are strongly __(17)__.

kerosene (liquid hydrocarbons) _____	15
hydrogen _____	16
basic _____	17

18–21. Metallic sodium is prepared by the electrolysis of fused __(18)__ in an apparatus called the __(19)__. The other product of this electrolysis is __(20)__. Sodium is used in the manufacture of __(21)__, the antiknock additive for gasoline.

sodium chloride _____	18
Downs cell _____	19
chlorine _____	20
tetraethyl lead _____	21

22–26. The starting material for many other sodium compounds is sodium __(22)__. Most commercial sodium hydroxide is produced as a byproduct of the __(23)__ of a(n) __(24)__. Sodium hydroxide has a destructive effect on skin, hair, and wool, and is described as a very __(25)__ substance. It reacts with __(26)__ to form soap.

chloride _____	22
electrolysis _____	23
aqueous NaCl solution _____	24
caustic _____	25
fats _____	26

27–30. In the Solvay process, the substance precipitated is __(27)__ . It is sold under the common name __(28)__ or converted into __(29)__ by thermal decomposition. The substance that is more valuable than these two products and must be recovered for reuse is __(30)__ .

31–32. The small annual production of potassium is by the reaction between potassium chloride and __(31)__ . The reaction proceeds to the right because __(32)__ .

33–36. Potassium hydroxide has the typical properties of a (strong, weak) __(33)__ alkali. For making black gunpowder, __(34)__ nitrate is preferred, since __(35)__ is hygroscopic. Sodium compounds (can, cannot) __(36)__ be substituted for potassium compounds in fertilizers.

37. When compounds of Group I elements are vaporized, the spectral lines observable through a spectroscope depend on the energy (absorbed, emitted) __(37)__ by excited electrons returning to their unexcited state.

sodium hydrogen carbonate	27
baking soda	28
sodium carbonate	29
ammonia	30
sodium	31
potassium is removed	32
strong	33
potassium	34
sodium nitrate	35
cannot	36
emitted	37

DIRECTIONS: In the flow chart for the Solvay process given below, the formulas for substances involved have been omitted. In the corresponding numbered spaces at the right, supply the proper formulas.

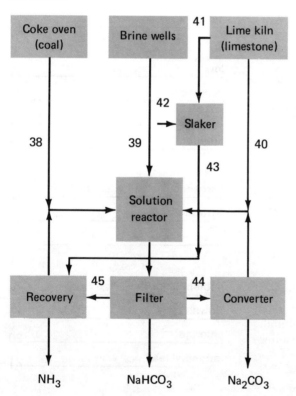

NH_3	38
$NaCl$	39
CO_2	40
CaO	41
H_2O	42
$Ca(OH)_2$	43
$NaHCO_3$	44
NH_4Cl	45

DIRECTIONS: Write the balanced chemical equations for the following:

46. Solvay process: the net reaction taking place in the production and precipitation of $NaHCO_3$ $\underline{CO_2(g) + NH_3(g) + H_2O + Na^+(aq) \rightarrow NH_4^+ + NaHCO_3(s)}$

_____ 46

47. Solvay process: the reaction producing Na_2CO_3 $\underline{2NaHCO_3(s) \rightarrow Na_2CO_3(s) + H_2O(g) + CO_2(g)}$

_____ 47

Exercises and Experiments in Modern Chemistry
Holt, Rinehart and Winston, Publishers

48. Solvay process: release of ammonia from the ammonium ion ———————
$NH_4^+(aq) + OH^-(aq) \rightarrow NH_3(g) + H_2O$ ———— 48

49. Hydrolysis of the carbonate ion $\underline{CO_3^{--} + H_2O \rightleftarrows HCO_3^- + OH^-}$ ———— 49

50. The reaction between sodium and water $\underline{2Na(s) + 2H_2O \rightarrow 2Na^+(aq) + 2OH^-(aq) + H_2(g)}$ 50

51. The reaction of slaked lime with sodium carbonate solution ——————
$Ca(OH)_2 + Na_2CO_3 \rightarrow 2NaOH + CaCO_3(s)$ ———— 51

52. Electrolysis of fused sodium chloride —————————————
$2Na^+ + 2Cl^- \rightarrow 2Na(l) + Cl_2(g)$ ———— 52

53. The cell reaction for the electrolysis of an aqueous solution of sodium chloride
$2H_2O + 2Cl^- \rightarrow H_2(g) + Cl_2(g) + 2OH^-(aq)$ ———— 53

54. Heating sodium hydroxide with sodium $\underline{2NaOH + 2Na \rightarrow 2Na_2O + H_2(g)}$ ———— 54

55. Mixing hot concentrated solutions of potassium chloride and sodium nitrate ——————
$KCl + NaNO_3 \rightarrow KNO_3 + NaCl(s)$ ———— 55

DIRECTIONS: Write the answers to the following questions in the space provided. Where appropriate, make complete statements.

56. Explain what happens when white light passes through a triangular prism. **A continuous** ——————
spectrum is produced because of the unequal bending of ——————
light of different wavelengths. ———— 56

57. Name the six elementary colors in order of their decreasing wavelengths. ——————
red, orange, yellow, green, blue, violet ———— 57

58. What phenomena give bright-line spectra? **Bright-line spectra are** ——————
produced by luminous gases and vapors under low pressure. ———— 58

59. What phenomena give continuous spectra? **Incandescent solids and gases** ——————
under high pressure give continuous spectra. ———— 59

60. Of what does the spectrum produced by vaporized sodium atoms consist? ——————
The spectrum of vaporized sodium atoms consists of two narrow yellow ——————
lines very close together. ———— 60

The Metals of Group II

DIRECTIONS: Write the answers to the following questions in the space provided. Where appropriate, make complete statements.

1. Why are the members of the Calcium Family denser, harder, and with higher melting and boiling points than the members of the Sodium Family? **There is a stronger**

force of attraction between the doubly charged metal ions and the electron

"gas" of the metallic crystals. _____ 1

2. Why are calcium atoms and ions smaller than potassium atoms and ions? **Calcium atoms and**

ions are smaller because of their higher nuclear charge, which attracts electrons more

strongly and results in smaller K, L, and M shells. _____ 2

3. Why does strontium form peroxides with oxygen? **Because of the large size of its ions.**

_____ 3

4. Why are solutions of calcium hydroxide and magnesium hydroxide weakly basic? _____
Although ionic, they are only slightly soluble in water. _____ 4

5. What is the most important source of magnesium? **sea water** _____ 5

6. How is magnesium produced from magnesium chloride? **Electrolysis of fused $MgCl_2$**

produces magnesium metal. _____ 6

7. Why is magnesium said to be a self-protective metal? **It forms a nonporous, nonscaling coat of**

tarnish (basic magnesium carbonate) in moist air. _____ 7

8. What are the two products of the combustion of magnesium in air? **MgO and Mg_3N_2**

(magnesium oxide and magnesium nitride) _____ 8

9. With what metal does magnesium form light, strong alloys? **aluminum**

_____ 9

10. How is chemical reduction employed today for recovering calcium? **Calcium oxide**

is heated with aluminum in a vacuum retort. The calcium metal is distilled off as a

gas at the high reaction temperature. _____ 10

11. In what *natural* forms does calcium carbonate exist? **limestone, calcite, marble, shells**

_____ 11

12. What are the two principal raw materials for making cement? **limestone and clay** ____ 12

13. What metallic ions commonly cause water to be hard? **Ca^{++}, Mg^{++}** _____ 13

14. Why can water that contains the metallic ions in Question 13 with (a) HCO_3^- ions be softened by boiling whereas with (b) SO_4^{--} ions cannot? (a) _____
These hydrogen carbonates decompose and form insoluble carbonates.

(b) **The sulfates are not decomposed by heating.** _____ 14

15. How does the addition of a basic solution soften temporary hard water? _____

The OH$^-$ ions neutralize the HCO$_3^-$ ions and precipitate the "hard" metal ions as carbonates.

15 _____

16. How is a zeolite water softener regenerated? By immersing the exhausted zeolite containing

Ca zeolite in a sodium chloride solution, the Ca^{++} ions are replaced.

16 _____

17. What principle is employed in the regeneration of a zeolite water softener? _____

The law of mass action.

17 _____

18. How may a synthetic base-exchange resin be regenerated? It can be regenerated

by running a basic solution through it.

18 _____

19. Why is it necessary to remove the CO$_2$ from the kiln in which CaO is produced?

To avoid a high concentration of CO$_2$, which would drive the reaction in the reverse

direction according to Le Chatelier's principle, the CO$_2$ is removed from

the kiln as it forms.

19 _____

20. How does lime mortar harden? First it hardens as water evaporates. Crystals

of Ca(OH)$_2$ form and cement the grains of sand together. The calcium hydroxide

is slowly converted to the carbonate by action of atmospheric carbon dioxide.

20 _____

21. How is plaster of paris produced? By gentle heating of gypsum resulting in partial dehydration.

_____

21 _____

DIRECTIONS: Write equations for these reactions.

22. Burning magnesium in oxygen $2Mg + O_2 \rightarrow 2MgO$

22 _____

23. Reaction of calcium with water $Ca + 2H_2O \rightarrow Ca(OH)_2 + H_2(g)$

23 _____

24. Production of precipitated chalk $Na_2CO_3 + CaCl_2 \rightarrow CaCO_3(s) + 2\,NaCl$

24 _____

25. Electrolysis of fused magnesium chloride $Mg^{++} + 2Cl^- \rightarrow Mg(l) + Cl_2(g)$

25 _____

26. Reaction of soap with calcium ions $Ca^{++} + 2C_{18}H_{35}O_2^- \rightarrow Ca(C_{18}H_{35}O_2)_2(s)$

26 _____

27. Boiling temporary hard water $Ca^{++} + 2HCO_3^- \rightarrow CaCO_3(s) + H_2O + CO_2(g)$

27 _____

28. Sodium zeolite and calcium ions $Ca^{++}(aq) + 2Na\ zeolite \rightleftarrows Ca(zeolite)_2 + 2Na^+(aq)$

28 _____

29. Calcium oxide and water $CaO(s) + H_2O \rightarrow Ca(OH)_2(s)$

29 _____

30. Heating calcium carbonate in a kiln $CaCO_3(s) \rightarrow CaO(s) + CO_2(g)$

30 _____

31. Slaked lime and carbon dioxide $Ca(OH)_2 + CO_2 \rightarrow CaCO_3 + H_2O$

31 _____

32. Magnesium hydroxide and hydrochloric acid $Mg(OH)_2 + 2HCl \rightarrow MgCl_2 + 2H_2O$

32 _____

33. Calcium oxide and aluminum $3CaO + 2Al \rightarrow Al_2O_3 + 3Ca(g)$

33 _____

34. Calcium and uranium hexafluoride $2Ca + UF_4 \rightarrow 2CaF_2 + U$

34 _____

35. Preparation of plaster of paris $2CaSO_4 \cdot 2H_2O(s) \rightarrow (CaSO_4)_2 \cdot H_2O(s) + 3H_2O(g)$

35' _____

Exercises and Experiments in Modern Chemistry
Holt, Rinehart and Winston, Publishers

The Transition Metals

EXERCISE **26**

DIRECTIONS: In the blank space at the right of each statement, write the word or expression that BEST completes the meaning when substituted for the corresponding number.

1. In the fourth period beyond calcium, the elements whose inner $3d$ sublevel is occupied by electrons before the occupation of the fourth energy level is resumed are called the __(1)__ elements.

2. In the sixth period, the buildup of the $4f$ sublevel gives rise to the __(2)__ series.

3–7. The important properties of the transition elements are their distinctly __(3)__ character, __(4)__ oxidation state(s), formation of compounds with strong __(5)__, tendency to form __(6)__ ions, and attraction into a(n) __(7)__ field.

8. Within the 6th, 7th, and 8th subgroups, the similarities across each period are __(8)__ than those down each subgroup.

9–10. The Fe^{++} ion is formed by the removal of __(9)__ electron(s) from the Fe atom. The Fe^{+++} ion is formed from the Fe^{++} ion by the further removal of a(n) __(10)__ electron.

11–13. The ferromagnetic nature of Fe, Co, and Ni is thought to be related to the similarities in the __(11)__ orientation of their __(12)__ $3d$ electrons. In these metals, groups of atoms may be so aligned as to form a small magnetized region called a(n) __(13)__.

14–15. Presently the most abundant iron ore is __(14)__, in which the two main minerals are __(15)__.

16–19. The reducing agent that actually reduces the iron ore in the blast furnace is __(16)__. The silica impurity combines with the __(17)__ produced from the added __(18)__ to form the slag whose formula is __(19)__.

20–21. The conversion of iron to steel is essentially a process of removing impurities by __(20)__. Iron ore may be added to supply __(21)__.

22–23. Dilute acids react readily with iron. However, dipping iron into concentrated __(22)__ acid makes the iron passive. Strong hydroxides (do, do not) __(23)__ react with iron.

24–25. The ion identified by the formation of a deep-blue precipitate in a solution to which $K_3Fe(CN)_6$ has been added is the __(24)__ ion. The composition of this precipitate is considered to be __(25)__.

transition	1
lanthanide	2
metallic	3
variable	4
color	5
complex	6
magnetic	7
greater	8
two 4s	9
3d	10
spin	11
unpaired	12
domain	13
taconite	14
hematite (Fe_2O_3), magnetite (Fe_3O_4)	15
carbon monoxide	16
calcium oxide	17
limestone	18
$CaSiO_3$	19
oxidation	20
oxygen	21
nitric	22
do not	23
Fe^{++}	24
$KFeFe(CN)_6 \cdot H_2O$	25

26–27. The addition of an excess of ammonia to a solution of copper(II) ions results in a __(26)__ color owing to the formation of the __(27)__ ion.

28. Copper reacts vigorously with cold __(28)__ acid.

deep-blue _____ 26

$Cu(NH_3)_4^{++}$ _____ 27

nitric _____ 28

DIRECTIONS: Complete and balance the following equations.

29. $Fe_2O_3 + 3CO \rightarrow$ __2Fe(l) + 3CO₂(g)__ _____ 29

30. $CaO + SiO_2 \rightarrow$ __CaSiO₃(l)__ _____ 30

31. $3Fe(NO_3)_2 + 4HNO_3 \rightarrow$ __3Fe(NO₃)₃ + 2H₂O + NO(g)__ _____ 31

32. $Fe^{+++} + K^+ + Fe(CN)_6^{----} + H_2O \rightarrow$ __KFeFe(CN)₆ · H₂O(s)__ _____ 32

33. $Cu^{++} + 4NH_3 \rightarrow$ __Cu(NH₃)₄⁺⁺__ _____ 33

34. $Cu(H_2O)_4^{++} + H_2O \rightarrow$ __Cu(H₂O)₃OH⁺ + H₃O⁺__ _____ 34

35. $Ag^+ + 2\ :\overset{\displaystyle H}{\underset{\displaystyle H}{N}}:\ H \rightarrow$
$$\left[\begin{array}{c} H \quad\quad H \\ H:N:Ag:N:H \\ H \quad\quad H \end{array} \right]^+$$
_____ 35

36. Complete the following table. The symbol $\uparrow$ represents an orbital occupied by a single electron: $\updownarrow$ an orbital with an electron pair: ___ an unoccupied orbital.

Atomic number	Element	Electron configuration $1s^2\ 2s^2\ 2p^6\ 3s^2\ 3p^6$	3d	4s
21	scandium	Each transition	↑ __ __ __ __	↑↓
22	titanium	element has all of	↑ ↑ __ __ __	↑↓
23	vanadium	these sublevels filled	↑ ↑ ↑ __ __	↑↓
24	chromium	in an argon	↑ ↑ ↑ ↑ ↑	↑
25	manganese	structure.	↑ ↑ ↑ ↑ ↑	↑↓
26	iron		↑↓ ↑ ↑ ↑ ↑	↑↓
27	cobalt		↑↓ ↑↓ ↑ ↑ ↑	↑↓
28	nickel		↑↓ ↑↓ ↑↓ ↑ ↑	↑↓
29	copper		↑↓ ↑↓ ↑↓ ↑↓ ↑↓	↑
30	zinc		↑↓ ↑↓ ↑↓ ↑↓ ↑↓	↑↓

37. Complete the following table by indicating the ground-state configurations of the valence electrons in titanium (atomic number = 22) for each of its common oxidation states.

	3d	4s
Ti	$3d^2$	$4s^2$
Ti⁺	$3d^2$	$4s^1$
Ti⁺⁺	$3d^2$	$4s^0$
Ti⁺⁺⁺	$3d^1$	
Ti⁺⁺⁺⁺	$3d^0$	

38. Complete the following table for members of the Iron Family. Paired and unpaired electrons of the 3d and 4s sublevels are to be represented by paired and unpaired dots.

Atomic numbers	Electron configurations of the Iron Family Sublevel 1s	2s	2p	3s	3p	3d	4s
	Maximum population 2	2	6	2	6	10	2
26 iron	2	2	6	2	6	∷···	:
27 cobalt	2	2	6	2	6	∷∷·	:
28 nickel	2	2	6	2	6	∷∷∷	:

Aluminum and the Metalloids

EXERCISE **27**

DIRECTIONS: In the blank space at the right of each statement, write the word or expression that BEST completes the meaning when substituted for the corresponding number.

1–5. Aluminum is _(1)_ metallic. Characteristics that tend to place it among the metalloids include: its union with four hydroxide ions in negative _(2)_ ions; its hydroxide is _(3)_, its oxide is _(4)_, and its hydride is _(5)_.

distinctly	1
aluminate	2
amphoteric	3
ionic	4
polymeric	5

6–7. With the development of the transistor, germanium has become an important _(6)_ material. It is chemically similar to _(7)_.

semiconductor	6
silicon	7

8–10. The chemistry of tellurium is typically _(8)_. It combines with hydrogen to form _(9)_. It combines with oxygen and the halogens to form compounds in which the oxidation states _(10)_ are observed.

metalloidal	8
hydrogen telluride	9
$+2, +4, +6$	10

11–12. Aluminum is extracted by electrolyzing _(11)_ dissolved in molten _(12)_.

anhydrous aluminum oxide (refined bauxite)	11
cryolite	12

13–16. Aluminum has a density of _(13)_; it (is, is not) _(14)_ ductile; it is a (good, poor) _(15)_ conductor of electricity; it (can, cannot) _(16)_ be cast.

2.70 g/cm³	13
is	14
good	15
can	16

17–20. Highly polished aluminum soon becomes covered with a thin layer of _(17)_. Aluminum is an excellent _(18)_ agent. The Al^{+++} ion is quite _(19)_ and hydrates _(20)_ in water solution.

aluminum oxide	17
reducing	18
small	19
vigorously	20

21. Hydrochloric acid (does, does not) _(21)_ react with aluminum.

does	21

22–23. Aluminum reacts in a basic solution to form the _(22)_ ion and release _(23)_.

aluminate	22
hydrogen	23

24–26. The formation of aluminum oxide is strongly _(24)_. In the thermite reaction, aluminum is used to _(25)_ oxides of (less, more) _(26)_ active metals.

exothermic	24
reduce	25
less	26

27–28. Synthetic rubies and sapphires are made by fusing pure _(27)_ with an oxyhydrogen torch. An aluminum rod incorporating sapphire _(28)_ is much stronger than aluminum.

aluminum oxide	27
"whiskers"	28

29–34. Among the Group III elements, boron has a relatively (29) ionization energy. It has the (30) electronegativity in the Group. These characteristics indicate that boron is a(n) (31) that forms only (32) bonds with other atoms. As the temperature is raised, the electric conductivity of boron (33) . This behavior is typical of a(n) (34) .

35–37. Silicon atoms crystallize with a(n) (35) bond arrangement similar to that of carbon atoms in (36) . Unlike carbon, silicon forms only (37) bonds.

38–39. Boron and silicon atoms have roughly (38) radii. This permits them to be substituted for one another in (39) .

40–41. Silicon resembles carbon in the ability of its atoms to form (40) . The silicon chains are formed by (41) bonds.

42–43. Silicones have silicon atoms bound together with (42) atoms. By using different (43) groups, a variety of silicones can be produced.

44–45. Silicones are (greatly, not greatly) (44) affected by heat. Water (does, does not) (45) penetrate cloth treated with a silicone.

46. Arsenic is used as a(n) (46) agent in certain alloys.

47. An alloy of lead and (47) is used to reduce friction between the surfaces of moving parts in machinery.

high	29
highest	30
metalloid	31
covalent	32
increases	33
semiconductor	34
tetrahedral	35
diamond	36
single	37
similar small	38
glass	39
chains	40
silicon-oxygen	41
oxygen	42
hydrocarbon	43
not greatly	44
does not	45
hardening	46
antimony	47

DIRECTIONS: Complete and balance the following equations.

48. $2Al(s) + 6H_3O^+ + 6H_2O \rightarrow$ $2Al(H_2O)_6^{+++} + 3H_2(g)$ _____ 48

49. $2Al(s) + 2NaOH + 6H_2O \rightarrow$ $2NaAl(OH)_4 + 3H_2(g)$ _____ 49

50. $2Al + Fe_2O_3 \rightarrow$ $2Fe + Al_2O_3$ _____ 50

51. $Al(H_2O)_6^{+++} + H_2O \rightarrow$ $Al(H_2O)_5(OH)^{++} + H_3O^+$ _____ 51

52. Hall process (a) cathode reaction $4Al^{+++} + 12e^- \rightarrow 4Al$ _____ 52a

  (b) two anode reactions _____ $6O^{--} \rightarrow 3O_2 + 12e^-$

  $3C + 3O_2 \rightarrow 3CO_2(g)$ _____ 52b

Exercises and Experiments in Modern Chemistry
Holt, Rinehart and Winston, Publishers

Nitrogen and Its Compounds

EXERCISE **28**

DIRECTIONS: In the parentheses at the right of each word or expression in the second column, write the letter of the expression in the first column that is *most closely* related.

a. strong triple covalent bond
b. moist blue litmus turns red
c. cleaning agent
d. nitrocellulose
e. nitrobenzene
f. proteins of plants and animals
g. hydrazine

natural combined nitrogen (**f**) 1
plastics (**d**) 2
nitrogen dioxide (**b**) 3
ammonia-water solution (**c**) 4
inactivity of nitrogen (**a**) 5

DIRECTIONS: Complete the following statements, which refer to the diagram at the left, forming accurate and complete sentences.

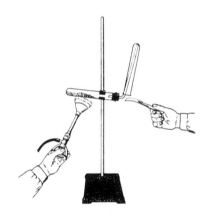

6. In preparing ammonia in the laboratory, a nitrogen-containing compound that might be placed in the test tube is ___ammonium chloride.___

_____ 6

7. The other reactant is ___calcium hydroxide.___

_____ 7

8. Ammonia is collected by downward displacement of air because it is ___soluble in water and less dense than air.___

_____ 8

9. When the test tube is filled with ammonia, the wet litmus test strip will change to ___blue.___ 9

10. The solid remaining in the test tube after the reaction is ___calcium chloride.___ 10

DIRECTIONS: In the blank space at the right of each statement, write the word or expression that BEST completes the meaning when substituted for the corresponding number.

11–14. The process of producing ammonia by direct combination of nitrogen and hydrogen is called the _(11)_ process. This process requires _(12)_ pressure, _(13)_ temperature, and the presence of a mixture of iron and the oxides of potassium and aluminum as a(n) _(14)_.

15–17. On a farm, ammonia and ammonium compounds may be used as _(15)_. In the home, ammonia may be used as a(n) _(16)_. In frozen food production and storage plants, it is used as a(n) _(17)_.

Haber _____ 11
high _____ 12
moderately high _____ 13
catalyst _____ 14
fertilizers _____ 15
cleaning agent _____ 16
refrigerant _____ 17

DIRECTIONS: Write the answers to the following in the space provided. Where appropriate, make complete statements.

18. Define nitrogen fixation. Nitrogen fixation is any process that converts free nitrogen to nitrogen compounds.

_____ 18

19. Explain how certain plants restore large amounts of nitrogen compounds to the soil. Legumes such as peas and beans have nodules on their roots in which nitrogen-fixing bacteria grow. In alkaline soil the bacteria convert nitrogen in air to nitrogen compounds.

_____ 19

20. Describe another natural method of nitrogen fixation. Lightning supplies energy which enables some of the nitrogen and oxygen of air to combine to form an oxide of nitrogen. After a series of changes, the nitrogen compounds are washed down into the soil in rain.

_____ 20

21. Why are the Haber process and the Ostwald process important and related processes? They make possible the production of nitric acid and nitrates from readily available raw materials. Ammonia produced by the Haber process is converted to nitric acid by the Ostwald process.

_____ 21

22. Why does nitric acid exhibit both the properties of acids and the properties of oxidizing agents? The hydronium ions give it its acid properties, while the nitrogen in the nitrate ions acts as an oxidizing agent.

_____ 22

23. What factors determine the nitrogen compounds produced by the action between metals and nitric acid? The concentration and temperature of the acid and the metal that reacts.

_____ 23

24. What gas is produced when very dilute nitric acid reacts with magnesium? _____
Hydrogen is produced.

_____ 24

25. With which metals does nitric acid *not* react? Why? _____
It does not react with gold or platinum because of their inactivity.

_____ 25

26. List four important uses for nitric acid. Making fertilizers, dyes, plastics, and explosives

_____ 26

DIRECTIONS: Complete and balance the following equations.

27. $4NH_3 + 3O_2 \rightarrow$ $2N_2 + 6H_2O$

_____ 27

28. $NaOH(s) + NH_4Cl(s) \rightarrow$ $NaCl(s) + NH_3(g) + H_2O(g)$

_____ 28

29. $N_2(g) + 3H_2(g) \rightleftarrows$ $2NH_3(g)$

_____ 29

30. $NaNO_3(s) + H_2SO_4(aq) \rightarrow$ $NaHSO_4(aq) + HNO_3(g)$

_____ 30

31. $4NH_3 + 5O_2 \rightarrow$ $4NO + 6H_2O$

_____ 31

32. $2NO + O_2 \rightarrow$ $2NO_2$

_____ 32

33. $3NO_2(g) + H_2O(l) \rightarrow$ $2HNO_3(aq) + NO(g)$

_____ 33

34. $3Cu(s) + 8H^+(aq) + 2NO_3^-(aq) \rightarrow$ $3Cu^{++}(aq) + 2NO(g) + 4H_2O(l)$

_____ 34

Sulfur and Its Compounds

EXERCISE

DIRECTIONS: In the parentheses at the right of each word or expression in the second column, write the letter of the expression in the first column that is *most closely* related.

a. SO_3	a weak acid	(**b**) 1
b. H_2SO_3	contact catalyst	(**e**) 2
c. SO_2	drying gases	(**f**) 3
d. $Ca_3(PO_4)_2$	fruit preservative	(**c**) 4
e. V_2O_5	roasting yields sulfur dioxide	(**g**) 5
f. H_2SO_4	pyrosulfuric acid	(**h**) 6
g. ZnS		
h. $H_2S_2O_7$		

DIRECTIONS: Write the answers to the following in the space provided. Where appropriate, make complete statements.

7. In what forms does sulfur occur in nature? **Sulfur occurs as the free element or combined with** **other elements in sulfides and sulfates.** _____ 7

8. What is superheated water? **Water that is heated under pressure to above its normal boiling point.** _____ 8

9. Why is superheated water used in the Frasch process? **The superheated water (170 °C) melts** **the sulfur (melting point 112.8 °C).** _____ 9

10. At what temperature does λ-sulfur form? **just above 112.8 °C** _____ 10

11. At what temperature does λ-sulfur change to μ-sulfur? **above 160 °C** _____ 11

12. What common oxidation numbers of sulfur are represented in the compounds SO_3, SO_2, and H_2S, respectively? **+6; +4; −2** _____ 12

13. By what method is sulfur dioxide collected in the laboratory? **upward displacement of air** _____ 13

14. Why is it collected by this method? **It is denser than air and very soluble in water.** _____ 14

15. How is sulfuric acid in acid rain formed? **Sulfur dioxide is formed by combustion** **of sulfur-containing coal or smelting of sulfide ores. The SO$_2$ dissolves in water** **drops in the air to form sulfurous acid, which is then oxidized by oxygen in** **the air to form sulfuric acid.** _____ 15

16. What is the role of the reagents (a) copper and (b) hot, concentrated sulfuric acid in the laboratory method for preparing sulfur dioxide? (a) **reducing agent** _____ (b) **oxidizing agent** _____ 16

17. What is the anhydride of (a) sulfurous acid, (b) sulfuric acid? (a) **sulfur dioxide** _____ (b) **sulfur trioxide** _____ 17

18. How, according to current belief, does sulfurous acid bleach colored materials? _____ **It converts the colored compounds to colorless sulfites.** _____ 18

19. How is sulfur dioxide converted to sulfur trioxide? by heating it with air in the presence of a catalyst such as divanadium pentoxide

_____ 19

20. How is sulfur trioxide converted to sulfuric acid in the contact process? It is dissolved in approximately 98% sulfuric acid forming pyrosulfuric acid, which, when diluted with water, yields sulfuric acid.

_____ 20

21. How is sulfuric acid safely diluted? Why is this precaution necessary? The acid is added to the water (you must never add water to sulfuric acid) because a great deal of heat is evolved as the hydrates $H_2SO_4 \cdot H_2O$ and $H_2SO_4 \cdot 2H_2O$ are formed.

_____ 21

22. Why does dilute sulfuric acid react more readily with metals above hydrogen (in the series of oxidizing and reducing agents) than does cold, concentrated sulfuric acid? _____
Because it is more highly ionized.

_____ 22

23. What kind of sulfuric acid acts as a vigorous oxidizing agent? _____
Hot, concentrated sulfuric acid is an oxidizing agent.

_____ 23

24. Why is sulfuric acid used in the manufacture of nitroglycerin? It acts as a dehydrating agent, absorbing water as fast as it is formed and thereby maintaining the rate of reaction.

_____ 24

DIRECTIONS: Complete and balance the following equations.

25. $S_8(s) + 8O_2(g) \rightarrow$ $8SO_2(g)$

_____ 25

26. $2ZnS(s) + 3O_2(g) \rightarrow$ $2ZnO(s) + 2SO_2(g)$

_____ 26

27. $Cu(s) + 2H_2SO_4(hot) \rightarrow$ $CuSO_4(aq) + 2H_2O(l) + SO_2(g)$

_____ 27

28. $Na_2SO_3(aq) + H_2SO_4(aq) \rightleftharpoons$ $Na_2SO_4(aq) + H_2O(l) + SO_2(g)$

_____ 28

29. $H_2O(l) + SO_2(aq) \rightleftharpoons$ $H_2SO_3(aq)$

_____ 29

30. $2SO_2(g) + O_2(g) \rightleftharpoons$ $2SO_3(g)$

_____ 30

31. $SO_3 + H_2SO_4 \rightarrow$ $H_2S_2O_7$

_____ 31

32. $H_2SO_4 + H_2O \rightleftharpoons$ $H_3O^+ + HSO_4^-$

_____ 32

33. $HSO_4^- + H_2O \rightleftharpoons$ $H_3O^+ + SO_4^{--}$

_____ 33

34. $C_{12}H_{22}O_{11} + 11H_2SO_4 \rightarrow$ $12C + 11H_2SO_4 \cdot H_2O$

_____ 34

35. $C_3H_5(OH)_3 + 3HNO_3 \rightarrow$ $C_3H_5(NO_3)_3 + 3H_2O$

_____ 35

DIRECTIONS: Solve the following problems. Show calculations in the space provided or on separate paper in your notebook. Enter your answer in the space provided.

36. (a) What volume of oxygen is required for the complete combustion of 15.8 liters of hydrogen sulfide at STP? (b) How many grams of sulfur dioxide are produced? (a) 23.7 liters O_2
(b) 45.1 g SO_2

_____ 36

37. The K_{sp} for CoS is 8.7×10^{-23}. Calculate the concentration of sulfide ion that must be exceeded in order for CoS to precipitate in a solution in which the Co^{++} concentration is 0.001 M. 8.7×10^{-20}

_____ 37

Exercises and Experiments in Modern Chemistry
Holt, Rinehart and Winston, Publishers

The Halogen Family

EXERCISE **30**

DIRECTIONS: In the blank space at the right of each statement, write the word or expression that BEST completes the meaning when substituted for the corresponding number.

1–5. The Halogen Family consists of the (metallic, non-metallic) (1) elements: fluorine, chlorine, bromine, iodine, and astatine. The atoms of each of these elements have (2) outershell electrons and commonly exhibit an oxidation number of (3) . The halogens are (active, inactive, inert) (4) elements that are (always, sometimes, rarely, never) (5) found free in nature.

6–10. Within the Halogen Family, electronegativity (6) with increasing atomic radius, so that (7) is the most electronegative halogen. The melting point, boiling point, and density of the members of the Halogen Family (8) with increasing atomic number. Compounds of the halogens and metals are formed by (9) bonding. Hydrogen halides are formed by (10) bonding.

11–17. The halogens are prepared commercially by different processes: fluorine by the (11) of a mixture of (12) and hydrogen fluoride; chlorine by the electrolysis of (13) ; bromine by (14) from (15) by chlorine; iodine by displacement from (16) by (17) .

18–21. The halogens are colorful elements. Fluorine is a(n) (18) gas; chlorine, a(n) (19) gas; bromine, a(n) (20) liquid; and iodine, a(n) (21) solid.

22–23. Hydrofluoric acid is used as a(n) (22) in the manufacture of high-octane gasoline, and in the production of synthetic (23) for aluminum production.

24–29. Hydrogen chloride may be prepared commercially by heating (24) with (25) . Liquid hydrogen chloride consists of (26) molecules and therefore (does, does not) (27) conduct electricity. Hydrochloric acid is used for (28) metals before they are galvanized or plated with other metals. It is a component of a secretion that promotes the body process of (29) .

nonmetallic	1
seven	2
−1	3
active	4
rarely	5
decreases	6
fluorine	7
increase	8
ionic	9
covalent	10
electrolysis	11
potassium fluoride	12
sodium chloride	13
displacement	14
brine	15
brine	16
chlorine	17
pale-yellow	18
greenish-yellow	19
reddish-brown	20
grayish-black	21
catalyst	22
cryolite	23
sodium chloride	24
sulfuric acid	25
polar covalent	26
does not	27
cleaning	28
digestion	29

DIRECTIONS: Write the answers to the following in the space provided. Where appropriate, make complete statements.

30. What is the formula, chemical name, and commercial name of the fluorine compound used as a refrigerant? CCl_2F_2, dichlorodifluoromethane, a Freon

30

31. What are the formulas of the fluorides of xenon that are white solids at ordinary temperatures? XeF_2, XeF_4, XeF_6

What are the products of their reaction with hydrogen? _____
elemental xenon and hydrogen fluoride

31

32. How do the compounds of Question 31 react with water? XeF_2 produces xenon,
oxygen, and hydrogen fluoride. The other two yield xenon trioxide, XeO_3.

32

33. Describe changes in the appearance of a freshly prepared solution of chlorine in water as it stands in sunlight for several days. The color changes from yellow-green to
colorless and the strong odor of chlorine disappears.

33

34. How is a dye bleached by a water solution of chlorine? The hypochlorous acid formed
liberates oxygen, which converts an oxidizable dye to a colorless compound.

34

35. What are three uses of bromine compounds? As sedatives in medicine; for making
photographic film and plates; as ethylene bromide, which is used to increase the
efficiency of lead tetraethyl in antiknock gasoline; as soil fumigants; for making polyurethane
and polystyrene plastics flame retardant; as disinfectants.

35

36. Why is iodine more soluble in solutions of iodides than it is in water? Because it
forms the complex I_3^- ion in solutions of iodides.

36

DIRECTIONS: Write complete and balanced equations for the following reactions.

37. $2NaCl(aq) + 2H_2O(l) \xrightarrow{\text{(electricity)}}$ $2NaOH(aq) + H_2(g) + Cl_2(g)$

37

38. $MnO_2(s) + 4HCl(aq) \rightarrow$ $MnCl_2(aq) + 2H_2O(l) + Cl_2(g)$

38

39. $2Sb(s) + 3Cl_2(g) \rightarrow$ $2SbCl_3(s)$

39

40. $NaCl(s) + H_2SO_4(aq) \rightarrow$ $NaHSO_4(aq) + HCl(g)$

40

41. $2Br^-(aq) + Cl_2(g) \rightarrow$ $2Cl^-(aq) + Br_2(l)$

41

42. $2NaI(s) + MnO_2(s) + 2H_2SO_4(aq) \rightarrow$ $Na_2SO_4(aq) + MnSO_4(aq) + 2H_2O(l) + I_2(g)$

42

43. $2NaCl(s) + 2H_2SO_4(aq) + MnO_2(s) \rightarrow$ $Na_2SO_4(aq) + MnSO_4(aq) + 2H_2O(l) + Cl_2(g)$

43

44. $H_2(g) + Cl_2(g) \rightarrow$ $2HCl(g)$

44

$2HClO(aq) + 2HCl(aq)$
                    ↘
45. $2H_2O(l) + 2Cl_2(g) \rightarrow$ _____ $2HCl(aq) + O_2(g)$

45

Exercises and Experiments in Modern Chemistry
Holt, Rinehart and Winston, Publishers

Radioactivity

EXERCISE **31**

DIRECTIONS: In the blank space at the right of each definition, write the name of the term defined.

1. The property of substances that give off invisible rays that affect an unexposed photographic plate in the same way as light.

radioactivity _____ 1

2. A device used to detect radiation by the ionization of low-pressure gas in a tube.

Geiger counter _____ 2

3. The glow that radium compounds produce when mixed with certain compounds such as zinc sulfide.

fluorescence _____ 3

4. The length of time required for the decay of one half of a given number of atoms of a radioactive nuclide.

half-life _____ 4

5. Helium nucleus emitted from the nucleus of a radioactive nuclide.

alpha particle _____ 5

6. Electron emitted from the nucleus of a radioactive nuclide.

beta particle _____ 6

7. High-energy electromagnetic waves emitted from the nucleus of a radioactive nuclide.

gamma rays _____ 7

8. The heaviest nuclide of a series of related radioactive nuclides.

parent nuclide _____ 8

9. A reaction in which the nucleus of an atom undergoes a change in the number of protons and, consequently, in its identity.

transmutation _____ 9

10. The difference between the measured mass of a nucleus and the sum of the masses of its constituent particles.

nuclear mass defect _____ 10

11. The energy released when a nucleus is formed from its component particles.

binding energy _____ 11

12. The emission of an alpha particle or a beta particle and gamma rays from a nucleus producing a slightly lighter, more stable nucleus.

radioactive decay _____ 12

13. The emission of a proton or neutron from a nucleus as a result of bombarding the nucleus with alpha particles, protons, deuterons, neutrons.

nuclear disintegration _____ 13

14. The splitting of a very heavy nucleus into medium-weight nuclei.

fission _____ 14

15. The combination of light-weight nuclei to form heavier, more stable nuclei.

fusion _____ 15

16. A particle with zero atomic number and a mass number of one.

neutron _____ 16

17. A device that accelerates electrons rather than positively charged particles as does the synchrotron.

betatron _____ 17

18. A device in which particles travel in a straight line through many stages of small potential difference and are thus accelerated.

19. Elements with more than 92 protons in their nuclei.

20. A radioactive isotope that is used to determine the course of chemical reactions.

21. A reaction in which the material or energy that starts the reaction is also one of the products.

22. A device in which the controlled fission of radioactive material produces new radioactive substances and energy.

23. A material that slows down fast neutrons and makes them more effective in producing nuclear changes.

24. A neutron-absorbing shaft inserted into a nuclear fuel lattice to limit the number of free neutrons.

25. The quantity of uranium necessary to maintain a chain reaction.

linear accelerator _____ 18

transuranium elements _____ 19

radioactive tracer _____ 20

chain reaction _____ 21

nuclear reactor _____ 22

moderator _____ 23

control rod _____ 24

critical mass _____ 25

DIRECTIONS: In the parentheses at the right of each name or pair of names in the second column, write the letter of the expression in the first column that is *most closely* related.

a. predicted relationship between matter and energy
b. produced first artificial radioactive nuclides
c. invented the cyclotron
d. built the first nuclear reactor
e. discovered neutrons
f. discovered polonium
g. produced first nuclear disintegration
h. isolated uranium
i. constructed a counter tube
j. verified Einstein's equation
k. studied fluorescence in minerals

Becquerel (**k**) 26
Chadwick (**e**) 27
Cockcroft and Walton (**j**) 28
Pierre and Marie Curie (**f**) 29
Geiger (**i**) 30
Einstein (**a**) 31
Frederic and Irene Joliot (**b**) 32
Lawrence (**c**) 33
Rutherford (**g**) 34

DIRECTIONS: In Questions 35–40, complete the nuclear equations that represent several steps in the disintegration of a $^{235}_{92}U$ nuclide. Use the product of one reaction as the reactant in the next one.

35. $^{235}_{92}U \rightarrow {}^{4}_{2}He + {}^{231}_{90}Th$ _____

36. $^{231}_{90}Th$ _____ $\rightarrow {}^{0}_{-1}e + {}^{231}_{91}Pa$

37. $^{231}_{91}Pa$ _____ $\rightarrow {}^{4}_{2}He + {}^{227}_{89}Ac$

38. $^{227}_{89}Ac$ _____ $\rightarrow {}^{0}_{-1}e + {}^{227}_{90}Th$

39. $^{227}_{90}Th$ _____ $\rightarrow {}^{4}_{2}He + {}^{223}_{88}Ra$

40. $^{223}_{88}Ra$ _____ $\rightarrow {}^{4}_{2}He + {}^{219}_{86}Rn$

DIRECTIONS: In Questions 41–46, complete the equations by supplying the missing information. Use the tables in the Appendix of MODERN CHEMISTRY for names, symbols, and atomic numbers of the elements.

41. $^{14}_{7}N + {}^{4}_{2}He \rightarrow {}^{1}_{1}H + {}^{17}_{8}O$ _____

42. $^{7}_{3}Li + {}^{1}_{1}H \rightarrow {}^{4}_{2}He + {}^{4}_{2}He$ _____

43. $^{9}_{4}Be + {}^{4}_{2}He \rightarrow {}^{12}_{6}C + {}^{1}_{0}n$ _____

44. $^{239}_{92}U \rightarrow {}^{0}_{-1}e + {}^{239}_{93}Np$ _____

45. $^{32}_{16}S + {}^{1}_{0}n \rightarrow {}^{1}_{1}H + {}^{32}_{15}P$ _____

46. $^{239}_{94}Pu + 2\,{}^{1}_{0}n \rightarrow {}^{0}_{-1}e + {}^{241}_{95}Am$ _____

Exercises and Experiments in Modern Chemistry
Holt, Rinehart and Winston, Publishers

A Special Message on Safety

SAFETY should be **FIRST** in the minds of administrators, teachers, and students actively involved in a science program. The responsibility for safety and the enforcement of safety regulations and laws are shared by everyone within the school community. With careful planning and instruction, a safe and healthful environment can be established within your science class.

You are encouraged to develop and maintain a safety program from the outset of this chemistry course. The information contained in the safety section will aid you in accomplishing this important task. The information is not intended to be all-inclusive, for no publication can be prepared to list safe practices for science in every situation. Nor should the information be read as legal requirements, but as suggestions and recommendations for the establishment of a safety base upon which to build. A bibliography lists several sources that give detailed coverage to individual or multiple topics on safety. See page 110. You are encouraged to review these publications on hand in your safety library.

Proper planning, prudent foresight, and care must be continuously exercised by everyone. By following the recommended safeguards and precautions written in this lab course, you will be practicing good safety skills.

Safety Regulations

To insure that a safe and healthful environment is maintained when taking the *Modern Chemistry* laboratory course, everyone should read and follow the safety regulations listed below. To indicate that you have completely read and understand the safety regulations, you are asked to give your signature and the date upon completion of this important task in the spaces provided on page 98. You should check to see that your lab partner has likewise completed the safety regulations, for you will be allied closely while working together in the laboratory.

1. Safety goggles, apron, and gloves should be worn by everyone (including visitors) upon entering the science laboratory.
2. Contact lenses should not be worn in the laboratory because there is a distinct possibility that chemicals may infuse under the contact lenses and cause irreparable eye damage.
3. You should prepare for each laboratory lesson by reading all instructions before you come to class. Follow all directions and review with your teacher the safety precautions needed to conduct the experiment safely before you begin. Only materials and equipment authorized by your teacher should be used.
4. Everyone should be alert and proceed with caution at all times in the laboratory. Take care not to bump another student, and remain in your lab station while performing an experiment. An unattended experiment can produce an accident.
5. Your apparel should be appropriate for laboratory work. Long hanging necklaces, bulky jewelry, and excessive and bulky clothing should not be worn in the laboratory. Cotton clothing is preferred over nylon, polyesters, or wool.
6. Only lab manuals and lab notebooks are permitted in the working areas. Other books, purses, and such items should be placed in your desk or storage area.

7. No food, beverage, or smoking is permitted in any science laboratory.

8. **NEVER** taste chemicals. **NEVER** touch chemicals with your hands.

9. Extreme caution should be exercised when using a burner. Keep your head and clothing away from the flame and turn off the burner when not in use. Gas burners should be lighted only with a sparker in accordance with your teacher's instructions. Check to see that all gas valves and hot plates are turned off before leaving the laboratory.

10. You should know the proper fire drill procedures and the location of fire exits.

11. Work areas and apparatus should be kept clean and tidy. You should always clean, and wipe dry, all apparatus, desks, tables, or laboratory work areas at the conclusion of each laboratory experiment.

12. Hands should be washed thoroughly with soap at the conclusion of each laboratory.

13. You should know the locations and operations of all Safety Control Equipment listed on pages 100 to 102.

14. You should study and examine the Safety Sketches and Techniques on pages 104 to 107 and review them with your teacher.

15. Experiment 1 should be performed and each part completed as instructed by your teacher before you do any other experiment. The safety precautions stressed in each part should be discussed and followed by everyone when working in the laboratory.

16. Everyone should recognize and heed all safety symbols and cautions incorporated into the procedures of the laboratory experiments.

17. All accidents should be reported to the teacher immediately, no matter how minor.

18. **NEVER WORK ALONE IN THE LABORATORY.**
You should only work in the laboratory while under the supervision of your teacher and with your assigned class.

I, _____,
have read and agree to abide by the safety regulations as set forth above and also any additional printed instructions provided by the teacher and/or district. I further agree to follow all other written and verbal instructions given in class.

_____
Signature

_____
Date

You should not be afraid to do experiments or to use chemicals and equipment, but should respect them as potential hazards. To alert you to procedures in which added caution may be necessary, each lab experiment contains a **SAFETY** paragraph at the beginning. You and your teacher should review the safety rules and regulations needed to conduct the experiment safely before you begin.

Safety Symbols

During the course of an experiment you are also reminded to work cautiously by the use of **safety symbols.** These symbols frequently appear within the procedures of an experiment. The figure below shows you the safety symbols that will be used in the *Modern Chemistry* lab course. A line is drawn from the person in the center to a safety symbol. The line connects the symbol (the area for concern) with the area of the body most likely affected, should an accident occur. If you observe the safety precaution indicated by the symbol, accidents and injuries will be prevented.

SAFETY SYMBOLS

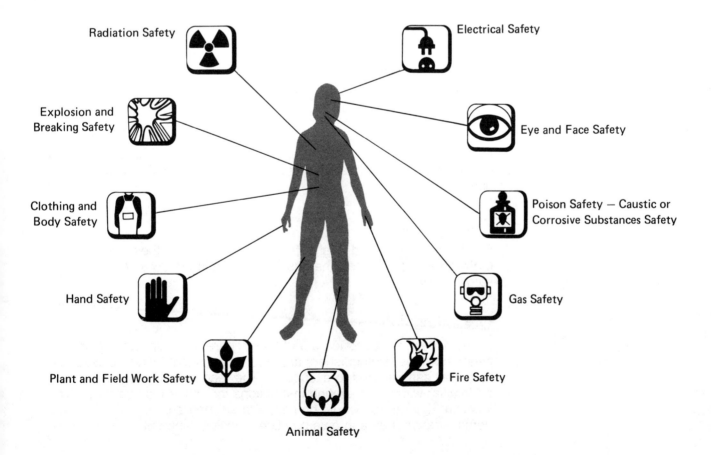

Radiation Safety

Electrical Safety

Explosion and Breaking Safety

Eye and Face Safety

Clothing and Body Safety

Poison Safety — Caustic or Corrosive Substances Safety

Hand Safety

Gas Safety

Plant and Field Work Safety

Fire Safety

Animal Safety

The symbols are designed to help you and your teacher make quick references to the safety precautions and safety equipment necessary for the experiment. The symbols are followed by the word **CAUTION** with specific safety instructions that should be observed.

Example

 CAUTION
Before you light the burner, check to see that long hair and loose clothing have been confined.

Safety Control Equipment

Instruments and tools play an important part in the safety program of your chemistry course. Throughout this course references are made to equipment and devices used to prevent accidents from occurring in the science classroom and laboratory. Before experimenting in the laboratory, you should become familiar with the safety equipment listed below, know their locations, and gain experience in actually using these items. All equipment should be easily accessible to everyone, and should be checked periodically to assure proper operation and cleanliness.

Eye and Face Wash Fountains

Fountains prevent or reduce injuries from chemicals splashing in or near the eyes. The fountain is designed to provide a gentle flow of aerated water to cleanse the eye and surrounding areas of foreign substances for at least 15 minutes at a time. They should be checked daily for proper operation.

Safety Showers

Showers prevent or reduce injuries from caustic chemicals or acid burns, from contact with toxic chemical reagents, or from clothing fires. A good water supply is essential for a safety shower. The shower heads must be a nonclogging, deluge-type capable of covering a contaminated area of skin with a flood of water that is sufficient to dilute material to a safe level in 15 seconds. They should be checked daily for proper operation.

Fire Blankets

Fire blankets are used to smother flaming hair or clothes. **If the clothing is a polyester,** the best way of putting out the fire is to use the safety shower.

Fire Extinguishers

Extinguishers are used to put out fires. There are four recognized classes of fires; extinguishers are labeled to indicate which classes of fires they can be used to extinguish. The teacher and students should be familiar with the operating instructions for all fire extinguishers. Your local fire department would be happy to arrange a series of demonstration fires and give practice in extinguishment.

First Aid Kits

First Aid Kits are used to give emergency treatment for burns, cuts, and so on; treatment should be administered only by your teacher. It is also recommended that a chart that shows proper treatment for specific injuries should be posted prominently next to the kit.

Lab Aprons

Aprons are used to protect body and clothing from chemical hazards. The front side of the apron should be coded so that you always know which side may have caustic chemicals on it. Remember to clean the apron frequently.

Lab Gloves

Gloves protect your hands from laboratory hazards. Everyone should have a pair to wear when handling chemicals, glass tubing, or heated materials.

Safety Goggles

Goggles protect your eyes from chemical and particle injuries. Everyone should have his/her own pair and the goggles must meet the ANSI standard. The type most commonly used in the school laboratory is a flexible soft-sided plastic model with a single large plastic lens. The goggles are available with baffled vents on the sides, so that air can flow through but liquids will not enter. Goggles should be worn over prescription spectacles (glasses). The goggles should be washed frequently and stored in a protected place. See the special note on prohibiting the wearing of contact lenses in the lab, page 97, *Safety Regulations.*

Face Shields

Face shields protect head, face, and neck from chemical and particle injuries. One or two face shields should be available for the teacher to wear when working separately in the storage room with large quantities and highly reactive chemicals.

Sand Buckets

The *sand* is used to smother small fires such as one contained in a beaker. A scoop or hand shovel should be used to apply the sand.

Tongs

Tongs protect the hands from burns and chemical injuries. Always remember to use them when handling heated materials, especially in glass or porcelain containers.

Waste Containers

The *waste containers* prevent fires, explosions, and pollution. Separate waste containers or receptacles should be provided for each of the following: chemicals, matches, broken glass. **NEVER** use the wastepaper basket for disposal of materials.

Ventilation Hood

Ventilation hoods prevent the spreading of poisonous gases evolved in an experiment. Ventilation-hood-escape outlets and fans should be checked frequently to assure proper operation.

Heat-Resistant Mat

A *heat-resistant mat* should be placed under hot apparatus that needs to cool. This action will prevent the breakage of glass and porcelain containers that might otherwise shatter when they come in contact with the cool surface of the lab bench.

Spill Control Packages

These *packages* are designed to minimize the harmful effects of a chemical spill by absorbing the chemical and restricting its movement across the laboratory bench or floor. Some chemical manufacturers are producing spill control kits that can be ordered. Many spill control packages consist of a pail containing a mixture of sand and soda ash. Floor-drying compounds such as those used by garages are also cheap and effective for spill absorption.

Safety Evaluation Equipment

Many classrooms contain *accessory equipment* that is used to evaluate the safety conditions of the laboratory and classroom. This equipment helps to insure that a safe and healthful environment is being maintained. Following is a list of equipment with a brief description of their purposes.

SAFETY EVALUATION EQUIPMENT

Item	Purpose
Combustible Gas Meter	Take air measurements.
Detector Tube System	Indicate presence of hazardous gases and vapors.
Electric Hazard Tester	Evaluate static charge, current leaks, and electrical outlets.
Geiger-Müller Counter	Measure radioactivity.
Light Meter	Measure levels of illumination.
Noise Meter	Measure sound levels.
Radiation Detector	Measure radiation.
Velometer	Measure air flow.
Ventilation Smoke Tube	Measure air flow direction and rate.
Wind Chimes or Mobiles	Indicate air flow.

Holt, Rinehart and Winston, Publishers

In any science laboratory the *labeling* of chemical containers, reagent bottles, and equipment is essential for safe operations. Proper labeling can lower the potential for accidents occurring that result in personal injury due to misuse, spills, and so on. Labels and equipment instructions should be read several times before using. Be sure that you are using the correct items and that you know how to use them.

All chemical containers and reagent bottles should be labeled prominently and accurately with labeling materials that are not affected by the chemical. The label should make you readily familiar with characteristics of the chemical regarded as hazardous. Chemical labels should contain the following information:

1. *Name of chemical* and the *chemical composition* (formula).

2. *Statement of Possible Hazards.* This is indicated by the use of an appropriate signal word, such as **DANGER, WARNING,** or **CAUTION.** This signal word usually is accompanied by a word that indicates the type of hazard present such as **POISON, CAUSES BURNS, EXPLOSIVE, FLAMMABLE.**

LABELING

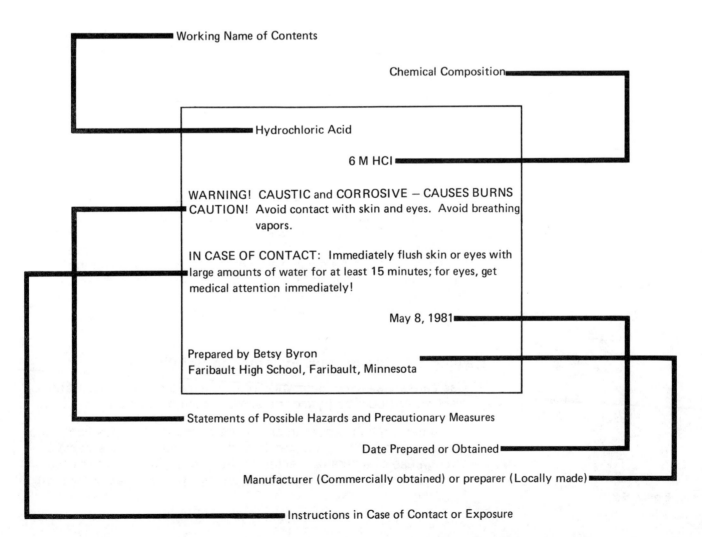

Working Name of Contents

Chemical Composition

Hydrochloric Acid

6 M HCl

WARNING! CAUSTIC and CORROSIVE — CAUSES BURNS
CAUTION! Avoid contact with skin and eyes. Avoid breathing vapors.

IN CASE OF CONTACT: Immediately flush skin or eyes with large amounts of water for at least 15 minutes; for eyes, get medical attention immediately!

May 8, 1981

Prepared by Betsy Byron
Faribault High School, Faribault, Minnesota

Statements of Possible Hazards and Precautionary Measures

Date Prepared or Obtained

Manufacturer (Commercially obtained) or preparer (Locally made)

Instructions in Case of Contact or Exposure

3. *Precautionary measures.* Precautionary measures are intended to be instructions that describe how users can avoid injury from the hazards listed on the label. Examples include: Use only with adequate ventilation; Do not get in eyes, on skin, or clothing.

4. *Instructions in case of contact or exposure.* If accidental contact or exposure does occur, immediate treatment is often necessary to minimize injury. Such treatment usually consists of proper first-aid measures that can be used before a physician can administer treatment. For example: In case of contact, flush with large amounts of water; for eyes, rinse freely with water for 15 minutes and get medical attention immediately.

5. The *date of preparation and the name of the person who prepared the chemical* is important for inventory. The *location of preparation,* such as the manufacturer's address or the name of the school (locally made) should also appear on the label.

Techniques and Safety Sketches

Decanting and Transferring Liquids

1. The safest way of transferring a liquid from one test tube to another is shown in Figure S-1. The liquid is transferred at arm's length with the elbows slightly bent in a position that enables you to see what you are doing and still maintain steady control.

Figure S-1

2. Sometimes liquids contain particles of insoluble solids that soon sink to the bottom of a test tube or beaker and you want to separate the two.

   (a) Figure S-2 shows the proper method of decanting a supernatant liquid in a test tube.

   (b) Figure S-3 shows the proper method of decanting a supernatant liquid in a beaker by using a stirring rod. The rod should touch the wall of the receiving vessel.

   Hold the stirring rod against the lip of the beaker containing the supernatant liquid. As you pour, the liquid will run down the rod and drop off into the beaker resting below. In this way the liquid will not run down the side of the beaker from which you are pouring.

Settled precipitate

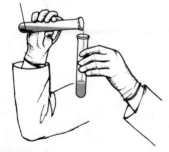

Figure S-2

Heating Substances and Evaporating Solutions

1. Use care in selecting glassware for high-temperature heating. The glassware should be Pyrex or a similar heat-treated type.

2. When heating substances in glassware by means of a gas flame, the glassware should be protected from direct contact with the flame through use of a ceramic-centered wire gauze. These wire gauzes have safer high-heating capabilities and will prevent glassware from breaking.

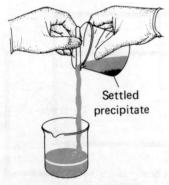

Settled precipitate

Figure S-3

Holt, Rinehart and Winston, Publishers

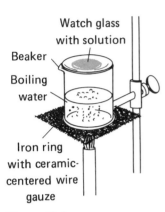

Figure S-4

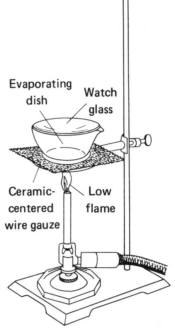

Figure S-5

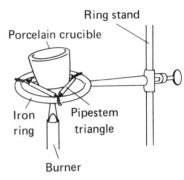

Figure S-6

3. Figure S-4 shows the proper setup for evaporating a solution over a water bath.

4. Figure S-5 shows the proper setup for evaporating a solution in a porcelain evaporating dish with a watch glass cover that prevents spattering.

5. In some experiments you are required to heat a substance strongly in a porcelain crucible. Figure S-6 shows the proper apparatus setup used to accomplish this task.

6. Heated glassware, porcelain, and iron rings look cool several seconds after heating, but can still burn for several minutes. Use heat-safety items such as safety tongs, heat-resistant mittens and pads, aprons, rubber gloves, and safety goggles whenever you handle this apparatus.

7. You can test the temperature of questionable beakers, ring stands, wire gauze, or other pieces of apparatus that have been heated by holding the back of your hand close to their surfaces before grasping them. Any heat generated from the hot surfaces will be felt—**DO NOT TOUCH.** Allow plenty of time for the apparatus to cool before handling.

How to Pour Liquid from a Reagent Bottle

1. Read the label at least three times before using the contents of a reagent bottle.

2. Never lay the reagent bottle's stopper on the lab table. Remove the stopper by grasping the stopper between two fingers, as shown in Figure S-7.

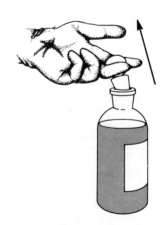

Figure S-7

Figure S-8

3. Pick up the reagent bottle making sure the label is toward the palm of your hand. Note the stopper is still between the fingers. See Figure S-8.

4. When pouring a caustic or corrosive liquid into a beaker, use a stirring rod to avoid drips and spills. Hold the stirring rod against the lip of the reagent bottle. Estimate the amount of liquid you need and pour this along the rod into the beaker. See Figure S-9.

5. Extra precaution should be taken when handling a bottle of acid. Remember these two important rules: (a) Never add water to any concentrated acid, particularly sulfuric acid, because of splashing and heat generation. (b) To dilute any acid, add the acid to water in small quantities, stirring slowly and constantly. Remember the "triple A's"— **Always Add Acid to water.**

6. Replace the stopper on the reagent bottle once you are finished pouring. See Figure S-10.

7. Examine the outside of the reagent bottle for any liquid that has dripped down the bottle or spilled on the counter top. Your teacher will show you the proper procedures for cleaning up a chemical spill.

8. Never pour reagents back into stock bottles. At the end of the experiment, any excess chemicals should be properly discarded under the direction of your teacher.

How to Heat Material in a Test Tube

1. Check to see that the test tube is Pyrex or a similar heat-treated type.

2. Always use a test tube holder or clamp when heating the test tube.

3. Never point a heated test tube at anyone, because the liquid may splash out of the test tube.

4. Never look down into the test tube while heating it.

5. Do not heat any one spot on the test tube. Heat the test tube from the upper portions of the tube downward and continuously move the test tube as shown in Figure S-11. Otherwise vapor meeting a head of liquid above it may cause the bottom of the tube to be blown out.

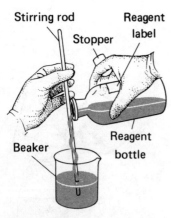

Figure S-9

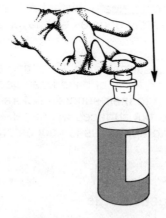

Figure S-10

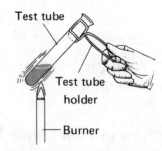

Figure S-11

Holt, Rinehart and Winston, Publishers

Figure S-12

How to Use a Mortar and Pestle

1. A mortar and pestle should be used only for grinding **one** substance. See Figures S-12 to S-14.
2. Never use a mortar and pestle for mixing different substances.
3. Place the one substance to be broken up into the mortar.
4. Pound the substance with the pestle and grind to pulverize.
5. Remove the powdered substance with a porcelain spoon. **CAUTION:** Do not blow into the mortar to remove any remaining powder, for dust may enter into your eyes and nasal passages.

Testing an Odor Safely

1. Test for the odor of gases by wafting your hand over the test tube and cautiously sniffing the fumes as shown in Figure S-15.
2. Do not inhale any fumes directly.
3. Use a fume hood whenever poisonous or irritating fumes are evolved and **DO NOT waft in this case.**

Figure S-13

Figure S-14

Figure S-15

LIST OF APPARATUS FOR STUDENT USE

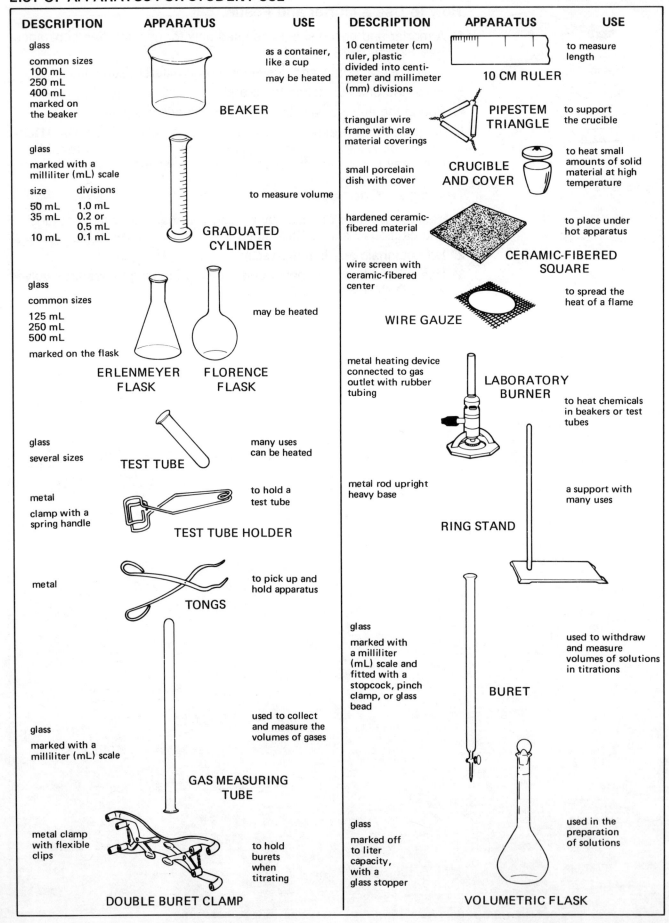

DESCRIPTION	APPARATUS	USE

glass

common sizes
100 mL
250 mL
400 mL
marked on
the beaker

BEAKER

as a container,
like a cup

may be heated

glass

marked with a
milliliter (mL) scale

size	divisions
50 mL	1.0 mL
35 mL	0.2 or
	0.5 mL
10 mL	0.1 mL

**GRADUATED
CYLINDER**

to measure volume

glass

common sizes

125 mL
250 mL
500 mL

marked on the flask

**ERLENMEYER
FLASK**

**FLORENCE
FLASK**

may be heated

glass

several sizes

TEST TUBE

many uses
can be heated

metal

clamp with a
spring handle

TEST TUBE HOLDER

to hold a
test tube

metal

TONGS

to pick up and
hold apparatus

glass

marked with a
milliliter (mL) scale

**GAS MEASURING
TUBE**

used to collect
and measure the
volumes of gases

**metal clamp
with flexible
clips**

DOUBLE BURET CLAMP

to hold
burets
when
titrating

**10 centimeter (cm)
ruler, plastic
divided into centi-
meter and millimeter
(mm) divisions**

10 CM RULER

to measure
length

**triangular wire
frame with clay
material coverings**

**PIPESTEM
TRIANGLE**

to support
the crucible

**small porcelain
dish with cover**

**CRUCIBLE
AND COVER**

to heat small
amounts of solid
material at high
temperature

**hardened ceramic-
fibered material**

**CERAMIC-FIBERED
SQUARE**

to place under
hot apparatus

**wire screen with
ceramic-fibered
center**

WIRE GAUZE

to spread the
heat of a flame

**metal heating device
connected to gas
outlet with rubber
tubing**

**LABORATORY
BURNER**

to heat chemicals
in beakers or test
tubes

**metal rod upright
heavy base**

RING STAND

a support with
many uses

glass

marked with
a milliliter
(mL) scale and
fitted with a
stopcock, pinch
clamp, or glass
bead

BURET

used to withdraw
and measure
volumes of solutions
in titrations

glass

marked off
to liter
capacity,
with a
glass stopper

VOLUMETRIC FLASK

used in the
preparation
of solutions

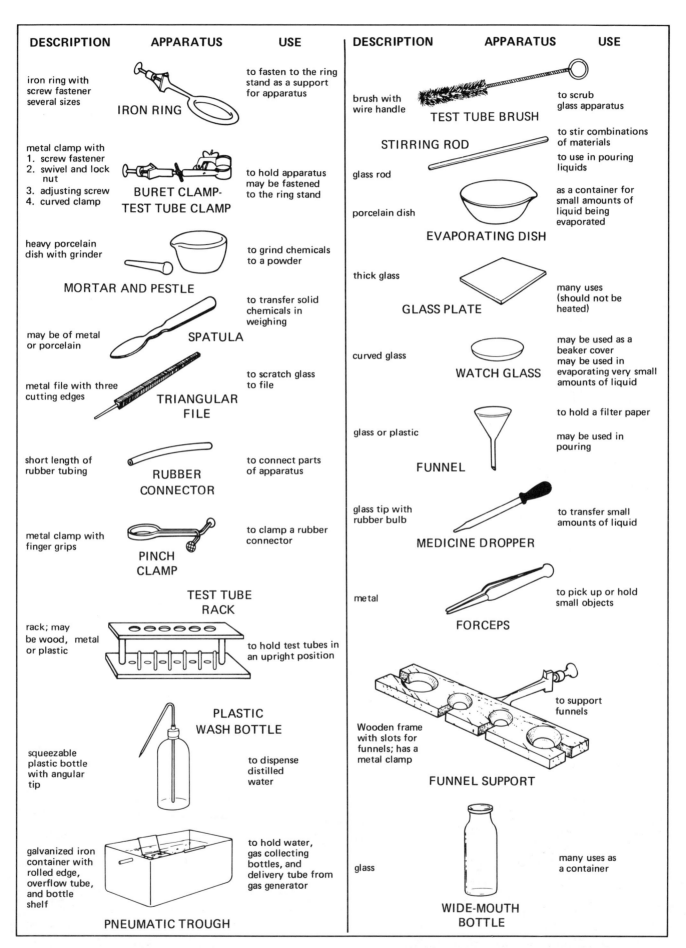

DESCRIPTION	APPARATUS	USE
iron ring with screw fastener several sizes	IRON RING	to fasten to the ring stand as a support for apparatus
metal clamp with 1. screw fastener 2. swivel and lock nut 3. adjusting screw 4. curved clamp	BURET CLAMP-TEST TUBE CLAMP	to hold apparatus may be fastened to the ring stand
heavy porcelain dish with grinder	MORTAR AND PESTLE	to grind chemicals to a powder
may be of metal or porcelain	SPATULA	to transfer solid chemicals in weighing
metal file with three cutting edges	TRIANGULAR FILE	to scratch glass to file
short length of rubber tubing	RUBBER CONNECTOR	to connect parts of apparatus
metal clamp with finger grips	PINCH CLAMP	to clamp a rubber connector
rack; may be wood, metal or plastic	TEST TUBE RACK	to hold test tubes in an upright position
squeezable plastic bottle with angular tip	PLASTIC WASH BOTTLE	to dispense distilled water
galvanized iron container with rolled edge, overflow tube, and bottle shelf	PNEUMATIC TROUGH	to hold water, gas collecting bottles, and delivery tube from gas generator

DESCRIPTION	APPARATUS	USE
brush with wire handle	TEST TUBE BRUSH	to scrub glass apparatus
glass rod	STIRRING ROD	to stir combinations of materials to use in pouring liquids
porcelain dish	EVAPORATING DISH	as a container for small amounts of liquid being evaporated
thick glass	GLASS PLATE	many uses (should not be heated)
curved glass	WATCH GLASS	may be used as a beaker cover may be used in evaporating very small amounts of liquid
glass or plastic	FUNNEL	to hold a filter paper may be used in pouring
glass tip with rubber bulb	MEDICINE DROPPER	to transfer small amounts of liquid
metal	FORCEPS	to pick up or hold small objects
Wooden frame with slots for funnels; has a metal clamp	FUNNEL SUPPORT	to support funnels
glass	WIDE-MOUTH BOTTLE	many uses as a container

SAFETY BIBLIOGRAPHY

Aldrich Chemical Co. Catalogue. Aldrich Chemical Co., 940 W. St. Paul Ave., Milwaukee, WI 53233

American National Safety Standard Practice for Occupational and Educational Eye and Face Protection. ANSI Z87. 1-1968. American National Standards Institute, New York, NY

Chemical and Biological Safety Guide. U.S. Department of Health, Education and Welfare, National Institutes of Health. Superintendent of Documents, U.S. Government Printing Office, Washington, DC Stock No. 174000383

Chemical Catalog Reference Manual. Flinn Scientific, Inc., P.O. Box 231, 910 W. Wilson St., Batavia, IL 60510

Code of Federal Regulations. Title 29, Part 1910. "Occupational Safety and Health Standards." U.S. Occupational Safety and Health Administration. Superintendent of Documents, U.S. Government Printing Office, Washington, DC 20402

Condensed Chemical Dictionary, Ninth Edition. Van Nostrand Reinhold Company, 450 West 33 St., New York, NY 10001

Deadly Harvest—A Guide to Common Poisonous Plants. John M. Kingsbury; Holt, Rinehart and Winston, New York, NY 10017

Disposing of Small Batches of Hazardous Wastes. U.S. Environmental Protection Agency. No. SW-562. Available from Solid Waste Information, U.S. Environmental Protection Agency, Cincinnati, OH 45268

Fire Protection Guide on Hazardous Materials. Seventh Edition. National Fire Protection Association, 470 Atlantic Avenue, Boston, MA 02210

Fisher Safety Manual. Fisher Scientific Co., 711 Forbes Ave., Pittsburgh, PA 15219

Guide for Safety in the Chemical Laboratory. Second Edition. Manufacturing Chemists' Association: Van Nostrand Reinhold Company, New York, NY 10001

Handbook of the National Electric Code. NFPA, Watt and Summers, Fourth Edition, McGraw/Hill, New York, NY

Human Poisoning from Native and Cultivated Plants. Second Edition. James W. Hardin and Jay M. Arena, M.D.; Duke University Press, Durham, NC

Laboratory Waste Disposal Manual. Manufacturing Chemists Association, 1825 Connecticut Ave., Washington, DC 20009

Manual of Hazardous Chemical Reactions. NFPA No. 491M. National Fire Protection Association, Boston, MA

Radiation Protection in Educational Institutions. National Council on Radiation Protection and Measurements; 7910 Woodmont Avenue, Washington, DC 20014

Safety in Academic Chemistry Laboratories. American Chemical Society, 1155 16 St., N.W., Washington, DC 20036

Safety in the Chemical Laboratory. Norman V. Steere, Ed., reprints in three volumes. Division of Chemical Education, American Chemical Society, Easton, PA 18042

Safety in the Secondary Science Classroom. National Science Teachers Association, 1742 Connecticut Avenue, N.W., Washington, DC 20009

U.S. Occupational Safety and Health Act of 1970. Public Law 91-596, 91st Congress, S. 2193 (December 29, 1970)

Laboratory Procedures

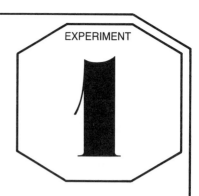

EXPERIMENT

1

The best way to become familiar with chemical apparatus is to actually handle the pieces yourself in the laboratory. This experiment is divided into several parts in which you will learn how to adjust the gas burner, insert glass tubing, use a balance, handle solids, measure liquids, filter a mixture, and measure temperature and heat. Great emphasis is placed on safety precautions that should be observed whenever you perform an experiment and use this apparatus. Several useful manipulative techniques are also illustrated on pages 104–107 under the heading Techniques and Safety Sketches. In many of the later experiments, references will be made to these Techniques and Safety Sketches. You will also be referred to many of the safety precautions and procedures explained in all parts of this experiment. It is important that everyone develop a positive approach to a safe and healthful environment in the laboratory.

OBJECTIVE
After completing this experiment, you should be able to use laboratory equipment safely and skillfully.

SAFETY

Begin each part of this experiment by taking the necessary safety precautions. Wear safety goggles, apron, and gloves. Get into the "good habit" of always putting on this standard safety equipment as soon as you enter the lab. It is important that you and your partner conduct all experiments by using good safety techniques. See pages 97 to 107. Read all safety cautions in your procedures and discuss them with your teacher.

Recording Your Observations
Record your observations in the spaces provided in each part of this experiment.

PART 1   THE BURNER

APPARATUS
heat-resistant mat   burner and tubing   forceps   evaporating dish
sparker

MATERIALS
copper wire, 18 gauge

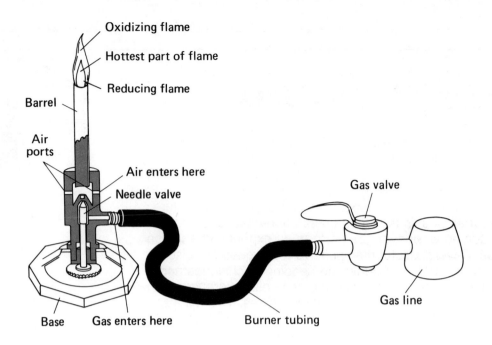

Oxidizing flame

Hottest part of flame

Reducing flame

Barrel

Air ports

Air enters here

Needle valve

Gas valve

Gas line

Base

Gas enters here

Burner tubing

Figure 1-1

PROCEDURES

1. The Bunsen or Tirrell burner is commonly used as a source of heat in the laboratory. While the details of construction vary among burners, each has a gas inlet located in the base, a vertical tube or barrel in which the gas is mixed with air, and adjustable openings or ports in the base of the barrel. These ports admit air to the gas stream. The burner may have an adjustable needle valve to regulate the flow of gas. In some models the gas flow is regulated simply by adjusting the gas valve on the supply line. The burner is always turned off at the gas valve, never at the needle valve. See Figure 1-1 and examine your Bunsen burner by locating these parts.

CAUTION
Before you light the burner, check to see that you and your partner have taken the following safety precautions against fires: You both are wearing safety goggles, aprons, and gloves. Confine long hair and loose clothing; long hair is tied in back of the head and away from the front of the face. Long sleeves on shirts, blouses, and sweaters are rolled up away from the wrists. You should also know the locations of fire extinguishers, fire blankets, safety showers, and sand buckets and how to use them in case of a fire.

2. In lighting the burner, partially close the ports at the base of the barrel, turn the gas full on, hold the sparker about 5 cm above the top of the burner and proceed to light. The gas flow may then be regulated by adjusting the gas valve until the flame has the desired height. If a very low flame is needed, remember that the ports should be partially closed when the gas pressure is reduced. Otherwise the flame may burn inside the base of the barrel. When improperly burning in this way, the barrel will get very hot and the flame will produce a poisonous gas, carbon monoxide.

Exercises and Experiments in Modern Chemistry
Holt, Rinehart and Winston, Publishers

CAUTION
Carbon monoxide is a poisonous gas. If the flame is burning inside the base of the barrel, immediately turn off the gas at the gas valve. Do not touch the barrel of the burner, for it is extremely hot! Allow the barrel of the burner to cool off and then proceed as follows:

Begin again, but first decrease the amount of air admitted to the burner by partly closing the ports. Turn the gas full on and then relight the burner. Control the height of the flame by adjusting the gas valve. By taking these steps, you should acquire a flame that is burning safely and is easily regulated throughout the experiment.

3. Once you have a flame that is burning safely and steadily, you can experiment by completely closing the holes (ports) at the base of the burner. What is the result?
When the holes at the base are closed, a yellow flame

results.

Using the forceps, hold an evaporating dish in the tip of the flame for about three minutes. Place the dish on a heat-resistant mat, allow the dish to cool and then examine its underside. Describe the results and suggest a possible explanation.
The yellow flame leaves a black deposit on the evaporating

dish. The lack of air results in incomplete combustion, the

luminous flame, and the deposit of soot.

Such a flame is seldom used in the laboratory. For laboratory work, you should adjust the burner so that the flame will be free of yellow color, nonluminous, and also free from the "roaring" sound caused by admitting too much air.

4. Regulate the flow of gas to give a flame extending roughly 8 cm above the barrel. Now adjust the supply of air until you have a quiet, steady flame with a sharply defined, light blue inner cone. This adjustment gives the highest temperature possible with your burner. Using the forceps, insert a 10-cm piece of copper wire into the flame just above the barrel. Lift the wire slowly up through the flame. Where is the hottest portion of the flame located?

The hottest portion of the nonluminous flame is just above the tip of the light blue cone.

Hold the wire in this part of the flame for a few seconds. Result?
The copper wire gets red hot and begins to soften (melt).

5. Shut off the gas burner. Now think about what you have just observed in procedures 3 and 4. Why is the nonluminous flame preferred over the yellow luminous flame in the laboratory? (Hint: The melting point of copper is 1083°C.)
The nonluminous flame burns hotter and cleaner than the yellow flame.

6. At the end of this part of the experiment, all the equipment you store in the lab locker or drawer should be completely cool, clean, dry, and arranged in an orderly fashion for the next lab experiment. Check to see that the valve on the gas jet is completely shut off. Remember that hands should be washed thoroughly with soap at the conclusion of each laboratory period.

PART 2   GLASS MANIPULATIONS

1. **Inserting glass tubing.** Inserting glass tubing into rubber stoppers can be very dangerous. The following precautions should be observed to prevent injuries:
   a. Never attempt to insert glass tubing having a jagged end. All glass tubing should be fire polished or have the edges beveled with emery paper before inserting it into a rubber stopper.
   b. Use water, soap solution, glycerin, or Vaseline as a lubricant on the ends of the glass tubing before inserting it into a rubber stopper. Ask your teacher for the proper lubricant.

   CAUTION
   Make certain you are wearing gloves, preferably leather ones, when handling the glass tubing. If leather gloves are not available, then rubber gloves should be worn and a layer of cloth should be wrapped around the glass tubing before inserting it into the stopper. See Figure 1-2.

   c. Hold the glass tubing as close as possible to the part where it is entering the rubber stopper. Remember, always aim the glass tubing away from the palm of the hand that holds the stopper. By using a twisting motion, gently insert the tube into the hole of the stopper. See Figure 1-2.

Figure 1-2

Exercises and Experiments in Modern Chemistry
Holt, Rinehart and Winston, Publishers

d. At the end of the experiment, rubber stoppers should be immediately removed from the tubing to keep them from sticking or "freezing" to the glass tube. Use a lubricant as mentioned in (b) if the stopper or tubing won't budge. Follow the same precautions in (b) and (c) when removing the stopper.

2. When **inserting glass tubing into a rubber or plastic hose,** the same precautions discussed in (a) to (d) should be observed. The glass tubing should be lubricated before insertion into the rubber or plastic hose. The rubber hose should be cut at an angle before the insertion of the glass piece. The angled cut allows the rubber to stretch more readily.

CAUTION
You should wear gloves and wrap a layer of cloth around the glass tubing before inserting it into the rubber or plastic hose.

At the end of an experiment, immediately disassemble the glass tubing in contact with the hose. Follow the same precautions in (a) to (d) above when disassembling.

In many experiments you are required to insert glass tubing in both a rubber stopper and a rubber hose. Carefully follow these precautions and techniques when inserting glass tubing. You will be referred to these safety precautions throughout the entire lab course.

PART 3   HANDLING SOLIDS

APPARATUS
test tube   glazed paper   porcelain or plastic spoon (or spatula)

MATERIALS
sodium chloride

PROCEDURES

1. Solids are usually kept in wide-mouthed bottles. A porcelain or plastic spoon (or spatula) should be used to dip out the solid. See Figure 1-3.

CAUTION
Do not touch chemicals with your hands. Some chemical reagents readily pass through the skin barrier into the bloodstream and can cause serious health problems. Some chemicals are extremely corrosive. Always wear gloves, apron, and safety goggles when handling chemicals. Carefully check the label on the reagent bottle or container before removing any of the contents. Never

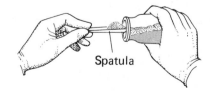
Spatula

Figure 1-3

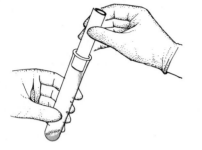

Figure 1-4

use more of a chemical than directed. You should also know the locations of the lab shower and eyewash and how to use them in case of an accident.

2. Obtain a spoonful of sodium chloride from its reagent bottle. In order to transfer the sodium chloride to a test tube, first place it on a piece of glazed paper about 10 cm square. Roll the paper into a cylinder and slide it into the test tube as it lies flat on the table. When you lift the tube to a vertical position and tap the paper gently, the solid will slide down into the test tube. See Figure 1-4.

 CAUTION
Never try to pour a solid from a bottle into a test tube. As a precaution against contamination, never pour unused chemicals back into the reagent bottles.

3. Throw away the solid sodium chloride and glazed paper into the appropriate waste jars or containers provided by your teacher in the lab.

   CAUTION
Never throw away chemicals or broken glassware in the wastepaper basket. This is an important safety precaution against fires and personal injuries (such as hand cuts) to anyone who empties the wastepaper basket.

4. Remember to clean up the lab and wash your hands thoroughly at the end of this part of the experiment.

PART 4   THE BALANCE

APPARATUS
centigram balance

weighing paper

spoon or spatula that are porcelain or plastic

MATERIALS
sodium chloride

PROCEDURES

1. When a balance is required for determining mass, you will use a centigram balance. See Figure 1-5. The centigram balance is sensitive to 0.01 g. This means that your mass readings should all be recorded to the nearest 0.01 g.

2. Before using the balance, always check to see if the pointer is resting at zero. If the pointer is not at zero, check the slider weights. If all the slider weights are at zero, then turn the zero adjust knob until the pointer rests at zero. The zero adjust knob is usually located at the far

Exercises and Experiments in Modern Chemistry
Holt, Rinehart and Winston, Publishers

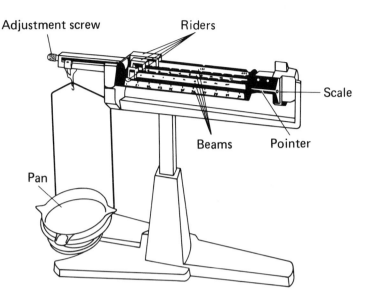

Figure 1-5

left end of the balance beam. See Figure 1-5. Note: The balance will not adjust to zero if the movable pan has been removed. Whenever weighing chemicals, always use weighing paper or a glass container. **Never place chemicals or hot objects directly on the balance pan.** They can permanently damage the surface of the balance pan and affect the mass weighing.

3. In many experiments you will be asked to weigh out a specified amount of a chemical solid.

CAUTION
Do not touch chemicals with your hands. Always wear gloves, apron, and safety goggles when handling chemicals. Carefully check the label on the reagent bottle or container before removing any of the contents. Never use more of a chemical than directed. You should know the locations of the safety shower and eyewash and how to use them in case of an accident.

Use the following procedures to obtain 23 grams of sodium chloride.
a. Make sure the pointer on the balance is set at zero. Obtain a piece of weighing paper and place it on the balance pan. Determine the mass of the paper by adjusting the weights on the various scales. Record the mass of the weighing paper to the nearest 0.01 g.

Student answer
_____

b. Add 23 grams to the balance by sliding over the weight of the 10 gram scale to 20 and the weight of the 1 gram scale to 3.
c. Using a porcelain spoon, obtain a quantity of sodium chloride from a reagent bottle and place it on a separate piece of glazed paper.
d. Now carefully pour the sodium chloride from the glazed paper onto the balance's weighing paper, until the balance's pointer once again comes to zero.

In most cases, you will only have to be close to the specified value. Do not waste time by trying to obtain exactly 23.00 g. Instead, read the mass when the pointer swings close to zero. For example, suppose you slightly overshot the zero point. Adjust the appropriate weights and read the value. The mass might be 23.18 g. This value would be just as satisfactory as 23.00 g. Record your mass of sodium chloride to the nearest 0.01 g.

Student answer

_____

4. Throw away the sodium chloride and weighing paper in the appropriate waste jars or containers provided by your teacher in the lab.

CAUTION
Never throw away chemicals, weighing papers, broken glassware, matches, etc. in the wastepaper basket. This is an important safety precaution against fires and personal injuries (such as hand cuts) to anyone who empties the wastepaper basket. As a precaution against contamination, never pour unused chemicals back into the reagent bottles.

5. Hands should be washed thoroughly with soap and water at the conclusion of this part of the experiment.

PART 5   MEASURING LIQUIDS

APPARATUS
graduated cylinder
ring stand

pipet
buret

buret clamp
beakers, 50 mL, 250 mL

MATERIALS
water

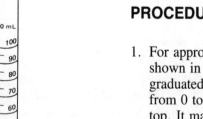

Figure 1-6

PROCEDURES

1. For approximate measurements of liquids, a graduated cylinder, as shown in Figure 1-6, is generally used. These cylinders are usually graduated in milliliters (mL). Such a graduated cylinder may read from 0 to 10 mL, 0 to 25 mL, 0 to 50 mL, or more, from bottom to top. It may also have a second row of graduations reading from top to bottom. Examine a cylinder for these markings.

2. For more accurate measurements, either the pipet or the buret is used. Pipets are made in many sizes and are used to deliver measured volumes of liquids. A pipet is fitted with a suction bulb used to withdraw air from the pipet while drawing up the liquid to be measured. See Figure 1-7. **Always use the suction bulb—NEVER pipet by mouth.**

Exercises and Experiments in Modern Chemistry
Holt, Rinehart and Winston, Publishers

3. Burets, fitted with either a stopcock, a pinch clamp, or a glass bead, are used for withdrawing any desired quantity of liquid to the capacity of the buret. Many burets are graduated in tenths of milliliters. See Figures 1-8 and 1-9. When using a buret, follow these steps:

   a. Clamp the buret in position on a ring stand. See Figure 1-10.
   b. Place a beaker, 250-mL, at the bottom of the buret. The beaker serves to catch any liquid that will be drawn off.
   c. Using a 50-mL beaker, obtain a quantity of the liquid you want to measure from the liquid's reagent bottle. (NOTE: In this first trial you will be using water.) Remember to carefully check the label of the reagent bottle before removing any liquid.

CAUTION
Safety goggles, gloves, and apron should be worn whenever you measure chemicals. Never pour a liquid directly from its reagent bottle into the buret. You should first pour the liquid into a small beaker (50-mL) that is easy to handle. Then pour the liquid from the small beaker into the buret. This simple method will prevent unnecessary spillage. Never pour any unused liquid back into the reagent bottle.

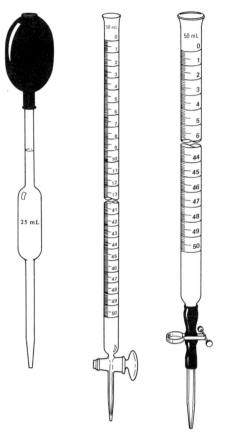

   d. Fill the buret with the liquid and then draw off enough liquid to fill the tip below the stopcock and bring the level of the liquid down to the scale. The height at which the liquid stands is then read accurately. Practice this procedure several times by pouring water into the buret.

Figure 1-7   Figure 1-8   Figure 1-9

4. Observe that the surface of such a liquid is slightly curved, concave if it wets the glass, and convex if it does not wet the glass. Such a curved surface is called a meniscus. If the liquid wets the glass, you read to the bottom of the meniscus, as shown in Figure 1-11. Your eye must be looking along the horizontal line AC at the bottom of the curve. If you look along the line BC or DC, you will get an incorrect reading. Locate the meniscus when reading the water level in the buret.

5. After you have taken your first buret reading, as directed, open the stopcock and draw off as many milliliters of the liquid as you wish. The exact amount drawn off is equal to the difference between your first and final buret readings. Practice measuring liquids by measuring 10 mL of water, first using a graduated cylinder, then a pipet, and finally a buret.

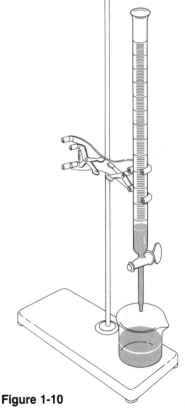

6. At the end of this part of the experiment, the equipment you store in the lab locker or drawer should be clean, dry, and arranged in an orderly fashion for the next lab experiment.

Figure 1-10

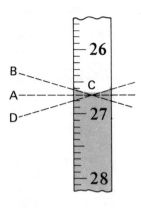

Figure 1-11

APPARATUS
ring stand
iron ring
evaporating dish
funnel

MATERIALS
sodium chloride

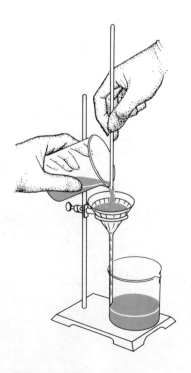

Figure 1-12

CAUTION
In many experiments you will have to dispose of a liquid chemical at the end of a lab. Always ask your teacher for the correct method of disposal. In many instances liquid chemicals can be washed down the sink's drain by diluting them with plenty of tapwater. Very toxic chemicals should be handled only by your teacher. All apparatus should be washed, rinsed, and dried.

7. Remember to wash your hands thoroughly at the end of this part of the experiment.

PART 6 FILTRATION

filter paper		stirring rod
ceramic-centered wire gauze		burner and tubing
two beakers, 250 mL		sparker
wash bottle		

fine sand		water

PROCEDURES

1. Sometimes liquids contain particles of insoluble solids, either present as impurities or as precipitates formed by the interaction of the chemicals used in the experiment. If they are denser than water, they soon sink to the bottom. Most of the clear, supernatant (swimming above) liquid may be poured off without disturbing the precipitate. Such a method of separation is known as decantation. See page 105 for the proper techniques.

2. Fine particles, or particles that settle slowly, are often separated from a liquid by filtration. Support a funnel on a small ring on the ring stand as shown in Figure 1-12, with the stem of the funnel just touching the inside wall of the beaker. Use a beaker to collect the filtrate.

3. Fold a circular piece of filter paper along its diameter, and then fold it again to form a quadrant. See Figure 1-13. Separate the folds of the filter, with three thicknesses on one side and one on the other; then place in the funnel. The funnel should be wet before the paper is added. Use your plastic wash bottle. Then wet the filter paper with a little water and press the edges firmly against the sides of the funnel so no air can get between the funnel and the filter paper while the liquid is being filtered. *EXCEPTION: A filter should not be wet with water when the liquid to be filtered does not mix with water.* Why? **Since the liquid does not mix with water, a filter paper wet with water will prevent the liquid from going through the filter paper.**

4. Dissolve 2 or 3 g of salt in a beaker containing 50 mL of water, and stir into the solution an equal bulk of fine sand. Then filter out the sand by pouring the mixture into the filter, observing the following suggestions:

   a. The filter paper should not extend above the edge of the funnel. It is better to use a filter disc that leaves about 1 cm of the funnel exposed.

   b. Do not fill the filter. It must never overflow.

   c. Try to establish a water column in the stem of the funnel, thus excluding air bubbles, and then add the liquid just fast enough to keep the level about 1 cm from the top of the filter.

   d. When a liquid is poured from a beaker or other container, it may adhere to the glass and run down the outside wall. This may be avoided by holding a stirring rod against the lip of the beaker, as shown in Figure 1-12. The liquid will run down the rod and drop off into the funnel without running down the side of the beaker.

The sand suspended from the liquid is retained on the filter paper. What property of the sand enables it to be separated from the liquid by filtration?

The insolubility of sand enables it to be separated by

filtration.

Filter folded along diameter

Folded filter

Filter ready for funnel

Filter in funnel

Figure 1-13

What does the filtrate contain?
The filtrate contains salt mixed in water.

5. The salt may be recovered from the filtrate by pouring the filtrate into an evaporating dish and evaporating it nearly to dryness. See Figure 1-14 for the correct setup.

   CAUTION
When using the burner, make certain that you confine loose clothing and that long hair is securely tied back. Wear your safety goggles, apron, and gloves!

6. Remove the flame as soon as the liquid begins to spatter. Shut off the gas burner. What property of salt prevents it from being separated from the water by filtration?
The filtrate contains salt that cannot be removed by

filtration, since salt is soluble in water.

7. At the end of this part of the experiment, all equipment you store in the lab locker or drawer should be completely cool, clean, dry, and arranged in an orderly fashion for the next lab experiment. Check to see that the valve on the gas jet is completely turned off. Make certain that filter papers and sand are thrown into waste jars or containers and not down the sink! Wash your hands thoroughly before leaving the lab.

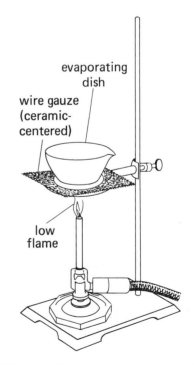

evaporating dish

wire gauze (ceramic-centered)

low flame

Figure 1-14

PART 7 MEASURING TEMPERATURE AND HEAT

APPARATUS

calorimeter (plastic cups and lid)
graduated cylinder
thermometer
ring stand

buret clamp
burner and tubing
sparker
iron ring

ceramic-centered wire gauze
beaker, 250 mL
beaker tongs

MATERIALS

water

PROCEDURES

1. A thermometer is used to measure temperature and temperature changes. Examine your thermometer and the temperature range for the Celsius temperature scale. Compare the Celsius temperatures with those on the Fahrenheit scale that appear on the thermometer in Figure 1-15.

CAUTION
If your mercury thermometer should ever break, immediately notify your teacher. Your teacher will clean up the spill.

2. Examine the calorimeter pictured in Figure 1-16. A calorimeter is an apparatus used in measurements involving heat and heat transfer. For approximate measurements, the simple calorimeter that is shown may be used. The small quantities of heat that may be transferred to or from the calorimeter by its contents may be disregarded because of the insulating characteristics of the plastic material of which it is composed.

3. Adjust the position of the thermometer in the calorimeter lid so that the bottom of the thermometer is approximately 1.0 cm above the bottom of the inside cup.

4. Pour 50 mL of tapwater, measured in a graduated cylinder, into your calorimeter and record its temperature in the data table on page 123.

5. Pour 50 mL of water into a 250-mL beaker. Warm the water to 60 °C, using the apparatus setup as in Figure 1-17.

CAUTION
When using the burner, make certain that you confine loose clothing and that long hair is securely tied back. You should know the locations of fire extinguishers and how to operate them. The beaker becomes hot after heating. Use beaker tongs when handling the beaker of hot water. Gloves should be worn!

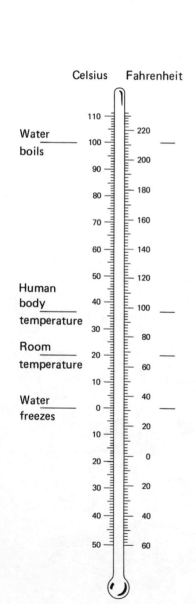

Figure 1-15

Exercises and Experiments in Modern Chemistry
Holt, Rinehart and Winston, Publishers

6. Turn off the gas burner as soon as the temperature reaches around the 60 °C mark. Record the temperature of the hot water. Then, using beaker tongs, immediately transfer the hot water into the calorimeter cup. Replace the lid, insert the thermometer, and stir the contents gently until a fixed temperature is reached. Record this final temperature of the mixture of hot and cold water in the data table.

7. At the end of this experiment, all the equipment you store in the lab locker or drawer should be completely cool, clean, dry, and arranged in an orderly fashion for the next lab experiment. Check to see that the valve on the gas jet is completely turned off. Remember to wash your hands before leaving the lab.

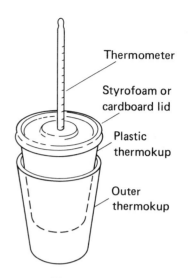

Figure 1-16

DATA AND CALCULATIONS TABLES

DATA

Mass of cold water	50.0	g
Temperature of cold water	24.0	°C
Mass of hot water	50.0	g
Temperature of hot water	66.2	°C
Fixed temperature of mixture	44.2	°C

CALCULATIONS

Temperature change of cold water	20.2	°C
Temperature change of hot water	22.0	°C
Heat gained by cold water	1010	cal
Heat lost by hot water	1100	cal

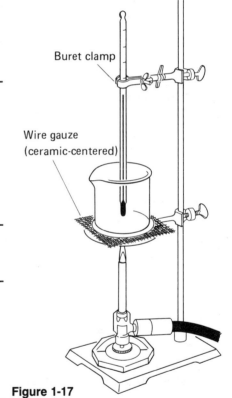

Figure 1-17

CALCULATIONS

Show your computations in the spaces provided. Place your answers in the calculations table.

1. Calculate the temperature change of the cold water.

Fixed temperature − initial temperature = temperature change of cold water

44.2 °C − 24.0 °C = 20.2 °C

2. Calculate the temperature change of the hot water.

Initial temperature − fixed temperature = temperature change of hot water

66.2 °C − 44.2 °C = 22.0 °C

3. The quantities of heat, Q, in calories, gained by the cold water and lost by the hot water may each be calculated from the following equation:

$$Q = temperature\ change\ (°C) \times mass(g) \times 1.0\ cal/g\ °C$$

a. Using this equation, calculate Q for the heat gained by the 50 g of cold water.

50.0 g × 20.2 °C × 1 cal/g °C = 1010 cal

b. Using this equation, calculate Q for the heat lost by the hot water.

50.0 g × 22.0 °C × 1 cal/g °C = 1100 cal

c. How do these two quantities of heat compare?
   The two quantities of heat are equal or nearly equal.

QUESTIONS

Answer the following questions in complete sentences.

1. As soon as you enter the lab, what standard safety equipment should you put on immediately?
   Wear safety goggles, apron, and gloves.

2. Before doing an experiment, what should you read and discuss with your teacher?
   One should read all safety precautions in the procedures and discuss them with the teacher.

3. Before you light a burner, what safety precautions should always be followed?
   Safety goggles, apron, and gloves should be worn. In addition, long hair and loose clothing should be confined. One should know the locations of fire extinguishers, fire blankets, and sand buckets and how to use them in case of a fire.

Exercises and Experiments in Modern Chemistry
Holt, Rinehart and Winston, Publishers

4. What immediate action should you take when the flame of your burner is burning inside the base of the burner's barrel?
Immediately turn off the gas at the gas valve.

5. What type of flame is preferred for laboratory work and why?
The nonluminous flame with the light blue inner cone is preferred because it burns

hotter and cleaner than the yellow luminous flame.

6. Why is it important that you use safety goggles, gloves, and a protective cloth layer when inserting glass tubing?
To prevent personal injuries such as hand cuts and to prevent glass objects from entering

the eye, this safety equipment should be worn.

7. What is a common cause of fires in lab drawers or lockers?
Putting away hot apparatus before it has had a chance to cool creates a serious fire hazard.

8. Why are broken glassware, chemicals, matches, etc. never thrown into a wastepaper basket?
This is an important safety precaution against fires and personal injuries, such as

hand cuts or chemical poisoning, to anyone who empties the wastepaper basket.

9. List the safety precautions that should be observed when inserting glass tubing into a stopper or rubber hose.
The ends of the glass tubing should be fire polished.

A lubricant should be used on the ends of the tubing.

Always aim the glass tubing away from the palm of the hand that holds the stopper

or hose.

Use a gentle twisting motion when inserting the tubing.

Immediately remove the tubing at the end of an experiment. Follow the same precautions

for removal as specified for insertion.

10. Why should you never touch chemicals with your hands?
Some chemicals readily pass through the skin barrier into the bloodstream. Some chemicals are extremely corrosive.

11. What precaution can you take against chemical contamination in reagent bottles?
Never pour unused chemicals back into the reagent bottles.

12. Why are chemicals and hot objects never placed directly on a balance pan?
They can permanently damage the surface of the balance pan and affect the mass weighing.

13. List three instruments used in the laboratory for measuring small quantities of liquids. What precaution should be taken when filling a buret with a liquid?
Liquids are measured into graduated cylinders, pipets, and burets. First pour the liquid into a small beaker that is easy to handle. Then pour the liquid from the small beaker into the buret.

14. What is the rule about size of filter paper for use with a given funnel?
The filter paper should not extend above the edge of the funnel. Use a filter disc that leaves about 1 cm of the funnel exposed above the edge of the filter cone.

15. How can a liquid be transferred from a beaker to a funnel without spattering and without running down the outside wall of the beaker?
A stirring rod may be held against the lip of the beaker, and the liquid will cling to the rod as it drops down into the funnel.

16. How should a thermometer be positioned in a calorimeter lid?
The bottom of the thermometer should be approximately 1.0 cm above the bottom of the inside cup.

17. In what condition should all lab equipment be stored at the end of an experiment? What else should be checked?
All the equipment you store in the lab locker or drawer should be completely cool, clean, dry, and arranged in an orderly fashion for the next lab experiment. Check to see that the valve on the gas jet is completely turned off.

Exercises and Experiments in Modern Chemistry
Holt, Rinehart and Winston, Publishers

SAFETY CHECK

Identify the following safety symbols:

 Eye and Face Safety _____

 Clothing and Body Safety _____

 Hand Safety _____

 Fire Safety _____

 Poison Safety _____

 Explosion and Breaking Safety _____

 Gas Safety _____

 Electrical Safety _____

 Radiation Safety _____

Practice labeling a chemical container or bottle by filling in the appropriate information missing on the label pictured below. Use 6 M sodium hydroxide (NaOH) as the solution to be labeled. Hint: 6 M sodium hydroxide is a caustic and corrosive solution and can be considered as potentially hazardous as 6 M HCl. See page 103.

LABELING

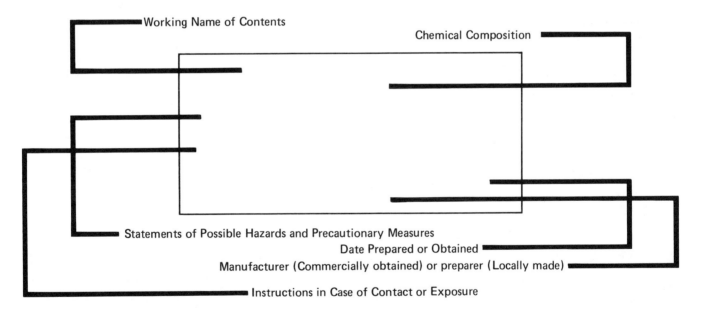

Working Name of Contents

Chemical Composition

Statements of Possible Hazards and Precautionary Measures
Date Prepared or Obtained
Manufacturer (Commercially obtained) or preparer (Locally made)
Instructions in Case of Contact or Exposure

True or False
Read the following statements and indicate whether they are true or false.
Place your answer in the space next to the statement.

1. Never work alone in the laboratory. _____**True**_____ 1.

2. Never lay a reagent bottle's stopper on the lab table. _____**True**_____ 2.

3. At the end of an experiment, save all excess chemicals and pour them back into their stock bottles. _____**False**_____ 3.

4. The quickest and safest way to heat a material in a test tube is by concentrating the flame on the bottom of the test tube. _____**False**_____ 4.

5. _____**True**_____ 5. Use care in selecting glassware for high temperature heating. Glassware should be Pyrex or a similar heat-treated type.

6. _____**True**_____ 6. A mortar and pestle should be used only for grinding one substance at a time.

7. _____**False**_____ 7. Safety goggles protect your eyes from particle and chemical injuries. It is completely safe to wear contact lenses under them while performing experiments.

8. _____**True**_____ 8. Never use the wastepaper basket for disposal of chemicals.

9. _____**False**_____ 9. First Aid Kits are used to give emergency treatment after an accident and can be administered by anyone.

10. _____**True**_____ 10. Eye and face wash fountains and safety showers should be checked daily for proper operation.

Chemical Apparatus

Identify each piece of apparatus. Place your answers in the spaces provided.

a. _____**beaker**_____

b. _____**graduated cylinder**_____

c. _____**spatula**_____

d. _____**pipestem triangle**_____

e. _____**funnel**_____

f. _____**evaporating dish**_____

g. _____**Erlenmeyer flask**_____

h. _____**burner**_____

i. _____**test tube**_____

j. _____**ceramic-centered wire gauze**_____

k. _____**crucible and cover**_____

l. _____**mortar and pestle**_____

a.

b.

c.

d.

e.

f.

g.

h.

i.

j.

k.

l.

Exercises and Experiments in Modern Chemistry
Holt, Rinehart and Winston, Publishers

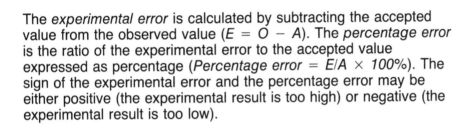

EXPERIMENT
2

Accuracy and Precision in Measurements

In this experiment, the volume of the graduated cylinder to the 50-mL graduation will be calculated from measurements of its internal diameter and height to the graduation. The *mass* of a measured volume of water will be calculated from its density ($m = V \times D$) and then determined by weighing. The *density* of a metal will then be calculated from measurements of its mass and volume ($D = m/V$). You will calculate the error and percentage error in each part of the experiment on the basis of accepted values.

The *experimental error* is calculated by subtracting the accepted value from the observed value ($E = O - A$). The *percentage error* is the ratio of the experimental error to the accepted value expressed as percentage (*Percentage error* = $E/A \times 100\%$). The sign of the experimental error and the percentage error may be either positive (the experimental result is too high) or negative (the experimental result is too low).

In procedure 4 the results of the entire class will be compiled for the density of the same metal. The *average deviation* of these data will then be calculated. The average deviation will be expressed as the *uncertainty* of the measurements. Review Chapter 1, Sections 1.13 and 1.17 in your textbook, for additional information.

OBJECTIVE
After completing this experiment, you should be able to measure several physical properties and calculate the density of a metal, the experimental error, the percentage error, and the uncertainty of the data.

APPARATUS
balance, centigram
beaker, 100 mL

graduated cylinders, 100 mL, 25 mL
plastic ruler, 15 cm

thermometer

MATERIALS
metal shot (aluminum, copper, lead)

water

SAFETY

Begin this experiment by taking the necessary safety precautions. Wear safety goggles, apron, and gloves. Get into the "good habit" of always putting on this standard safety equipment as soon as you enter the lab. It is important that you and your partner conduct all experiments by using good safety techniques. See pages 97 to 102.

RECORDING YOUR DATA AND CALCULATIONS
After completing each procedure, record your results in the data table.

PROCEDURE 1

Examine the centimeter scale of the plastic ruler. What are the smallest divisions?

The smallest divisions on the ruler are millimeters.

To what fraction of a centimeter are you expected to be able to make a measurement with such a ruler?

You should be able to measure to ± 0.05 cm.

Measure the inside diameter of the graduated cylinder using the ruler. Similarly, measure the inside height of the cylinder to the 50-mL graduation. Record these measurements in Data Table I.

DATA AND CALCULATIONS TABLES

DATA TABLE I

Inside diameter of cylinder	**2.5**	cm
Inside height of cylinder	**9.3**	cm
Volume of cylinder (accepted)	**50.0**	cm³

CALCULATIONS TABLE I

Volume of cylinder (computed)	**46**	cm³
Error	**4**	cm³
Percentage error	**8**	%

CALCULATIONS
Show your computations in the spaces provided below. Place your answers in Calculations Table I.

1. Calculate the volume of the cylinder to the 50-mL graduation ($V = 3.14\ r^2 \times h$).

$$V = \pi\ r^2 h = 3.14 \times \left(\frac{2.5\ cm}{2}\right)^2 \times 9.3\ cm = 46\ cm^3$$

2. Assume the capacity in mL of the cylinder (to the top graduation) to be equal to that numerical value in cm³. Using this value in cm³ as the *accepted value,* calculate the error and percentage error.

Error

$46\ cm^3 - 50\ cm^3 = 4\ cm^3$

Percentage Error

$\dfrac{4\ cm^3}{50\ cm^3} \times 100\% = 8\%$

Exercises and Experiments in Modern Chemistry
Holt, Rinehart and Winston, Publishers

PROCEDURE 2

Examine the gram scale of the centigram balance. What are the smallest divisions? **The smallest divisions are centigrams.** To what fraction of a gram may you make measurements with a centigram balance? **You should be able to measure to ± 0.01 g.**

Similarly examine the graduations on a 25-mL graduated cylinder and determine the smallest fraction of a milliliter to which you could make a measurement. Is this compatible with the uncertainty of a 100-mL graduated cylinder? **Most 25-mL cylinders are subdivided by 0.5-mL graduations, whereas 100-mL cylinders are subdivided by 1-mL graduations. The uncertainties involved when measuring with the two cylinders are, therefore, not compatible (± 0.25 mL for the 25-mL cylinder and ±0.5 mL for the 100-mL cylinder).**

Using the balance, determine the mass of the dry cylinder. Record the mass in Data Table II. Fill the beaker half-full of water and determine its temperature to the nearest degree. Look up the density of water for this temperature and record both the temperature and water density. Fill your graduated cylinder to some value between 10 and 15 mL; accurately read and record the volume. Determine the mass of this volume of water plus that of the cylinder by weighing. Then record this value in Data Table II. Save the water in the graduated cylinder for use in Procedure 3.

DATA AND CALCULATIONS TABLES

DATA TABLE II

Mass of empty cylinder	42.39	g
Mass of cylinder + water	55.98	g
Volume of water	13.8	mL
Temperature of water	25.0	°C
Density of water	0.997	g/cm³

CALCULATIONS TABLE II

Mass of water (from balance)	13.59	g
Mass of water (calculated: $m = D \times V$)	13.8	g
Error	0.2	g
Percentage error	1	%

CALCULATIONS

Show your computations in the spaces provided below. Place your answers in Calculations Table II.

1. Calculate the mass of the water as determined by use of the balance.

$$55.98 \text{ g} - 42.39 \text{ g} = 13.59 \text{ g}$$

2. Calculate the mass of the water from its measured volume and its density ($m = D \times V$).

$$m = D \times V = 0.997 \text{ g/cm}^3 \times 13.8 \text{ cm}^3 = 13.8 \text{ g}$$

3. Using the mass determined by the use of the balance as the *accepted value,* calculate the error and percentage error.

Error

$$13.8 - 13.6 = 0.2 \text{ g}$$

Percentage Error

$$\frac{0.2 \text{ g}}{13.59 \text{ g}} \times 100\% = 1\%$$

PROCEDURE 3

Add a sufficient quantity of the assigned metal shot (aluminum, copper, or lead) to the cylinder containing the water (saved from Procedure 2) to increase the volume by at least 5 mL. Determine the volume and then the mass of the shot, water, and cylinder, and record your measurements in Data Table III.

DATA AND CALCULATIONS TABLES

DATA TABLE III

Volume of water	13.8	mL
Mass of water + cylinder	55.98	g
Volume of metal and water	20.2	mL
Mass of metal + water + cylinder	73.98	g
Density of metal (accepted)	2.70	g/cm³

CALCULATIONS TABLE III

Volume of metal	6.4	cm³
Mass of metal	18.00	g
Density of metal (computed: 1 mL = 1 cm³)	2.8	g/cm³
Error	0.1	g/cm³
Percentage error	3.7	%

Exercises and Experiments in Modern Chemistry
Holt, Rinehart and Winston, Publishers

CALCULATIONS
Show your computations in the spaces provided below. Place your answers in Calculations Table III.

1. (a) Calculate the volume of the metal shot, its mass, and its density.

Volume of metal

20.2 mL − 13.8 mL = 6.4 mL = 6.4 cm³

Mass of metal

73.98 g − 55.98 g = 18.00 g

Density of metal

$$\frac{18.00\ g}{6.4\ mL} = 2.8\ g/cm^3$$

(b) Look up the specific gravity of the metal in a handbook or your textbook appendix. The density of liquids and solids in the metric system is numerically equal to the specific gravity. Record this accepted value in Data Table III. Then calculate the error and percentage error for the density of the metal shot that you determined in (a) above.

Error

2.8 g/cm³ − 2.7 g/cm³ = 0.1 g/cm³

Percentage error

$$\frac{0.1\ g/cm^3}{2.7\ g/cm^3} \times 100\% = 3.7\%$$

PROCEDURE 4

Precision is the agreement between the numerical values of two or more measurements that have been made in the same way. It is expressed in terms of *deviation*. An absolute deviation D_a is the difference between an observed value O and the arithmetic mean (average) M for a set of identical measurements.

$$D_a = O - M$$

In Data Table IV, record at least five results compiled by you and your classmates for the density of the same metal.

At the end of this experiment, all the equipment you store in the lab locker or drawer should be clean, dry, and arranged in an orderly fashion for the next lab experiment. Ask your teacher for the proper waste container for the metal shot. Wash your hands before leaving the lab.

DATA AND CALCULATIONS TABLES

DATA TABLE IV

Group Number	Density (g/cm³)
1	2.8
2	3.0
3	2.9
4	2.7
5	2.8

CALCULATIONS TABLE IV

Average: $M = 2.8$ g/cm^3	
Group Number 1	Absolute Deviation (D_a) 0.0 g/cm^3
2	0.2
3	0.1
4	0.1
5	0.0
Average Deviation = **0.1 g/cm³** Uncertainty = **±0.1 g/cm³**	
Expression for set of experimental results = $M \pm$ av. deviation = **2.8 ± 0.1 g/cm³**	

CALCULATIONS

Show your computations in the spaces provided below. Place your answers in Calculations Table IV.

1. Calculate the average density of the five results compiled by you and your classmates for the density of the same metal.

$$M = \frac{2.8 + 3.0 + 2.9 + 2.7 + 2.8}{5} = 2.8 \text{ g/cm}^3$$

2. Compute the absolute deviation D_a for each of the five measurements and enter these quantities in Calculations Table IV. Do not enter the sign of the deviation. Deviation ($D_a = O - M$):

(1) 2.8 − 2.8 = 0.0 g/cm³   (4) 2.7 − 2.8 = 0.1 g/cm³
(2) 3.0 − 2.8 = 0.2 g/cm³   (5) 2.8 − 2.8 = 0.0 g/cm³
(3) 2.9 − 2.8 = 0.1 g/cm³

3. Calculate the average value of the deviations and enter this quantity at the bottom of the Deviation column in Calculations Table IV.

$$\frac{0.2 + 0.1 + 0.1}{5} = 0.1 \text{ g/cm}^3 \qquad Uncertainty = \pm\ 0.1 \text{ g/cm}^3$$

This quantity with a $\pm$ sign before it is the *uncertainty* in the measurements data. Enter this value into Calculations Table IV. In the appropriate place in the table, express the result of this set of experimental measurements as $M \pm$ average deviation.

QUESTIONS

1. What value of a measurement must be available if the accuracy of a measurement is to be determined?
   The accepted value of a measurement must be available.

2. What are the possible sources of experimental errors in this experiment?
   Sources of experimental error include inaccurate observation and imperfections

   in apparatus design, which makes the use of measuring devices difficult

   (as in Procedure 1).

Exercises and Experiments in Modern Chemistry
Holt, Rinehart and Winston, Publishers

Energy and Entropy: Phase Changes

As a solid is heated, its temperature rises. The continuous addition of energy finally results in a phase change, and the solid melts at its melting point. Further addition of energy causes the temperature of the liquid to increase. Acetamide is a solid at room temperature. Its melting point is well below 100°C. In this experiment, you will melt a sample of acetamide and record the temperature at certain time intervals. As the solid melts and the liquid cools, solidification (crystallization) occurs, and the resultant solid undergoes subsequent cooling. The results of the experiment permit you to determine the melting and freezing point of the substance and to interpret the changes in energy and entropy that have taken place. Review Chapter 2, Section 2.14, and Chapter 20, Section 20.7, for additional information.

OBJECTIVE

After completing this experiment, you should be able to determine the melting point of a substance and plot a time–temperature graph of the phase change.

APPARATUS

balance, centigram
beakers, 600 mL, 400 mL
burner and tubing
sparker

clock
iron ring
ring stand
buret clamp

Pyrex test tube, 25 × 100 mm
thermometer
wire gauze, ceramic-centered

MATERIAL

acetamide (practical grade)   See safety warning below.

SAFETY

Begin this experiment by taking the necessary safety precautions. Wear safety goggles, apron, and gloves. Read all safety cautions in your procedures and discuss them with your teacher. Conduct this experiment by using good safety techniques. See pages 112 and 122.

WARNING: Due to recent research on the toxicity of acetamide, this experiment at the discretion of the teacher should be performed as **a teacher demonstration only.** See Teacher Notes, pages T-19 and T-24, and consult a recent *NIOSH Registry of Toxic Effects of Chemical Substances*.

PROCEDURES

Part I: the melting of a solid

1. Place a 600-mL beaker three-fourths full of water on a ring stand and heat the water to boiling.

CAUTION
Before you light the burner, check to see that long hair and loose clothing have been confined. Remember to work cautiously with the heated apparatus.

Also fill a 400-mL beaker three-fourths full with tapwater and set aside for Part II. While the water is heating, measure out approximately 10 grams of acetamide. Place the acetamide and a thermometer in a clean, dry, 25 × 100-mm Pyrex test tube. Clamp the test tube above the hot-water bath as shown in Figure 3-1.

2. When the water bath begins to boil, reduce the burner to a low flame. Read and record the temperature of the acetamide to the nearest 0.1°C. Immediately immerse the test tube into the hot-water bath by lowering the buret clamp on the ring stand. Record the temperature of the acetamide at 15-second intervals. Indicate on the data table when the crystals begin to dissolve. Continuously stir the liquid acetamide very gently with the thermometer.

CAUTION
If your mercury thermometer should ever break, immediately notify your teacher, who will clean up the spill.

Indicate on the data table when all the crystals have dissolved. Continue taking readings until the temperature of the acetamide reaches 90°C.

Part II: the freezing of a liquid

3. When the temperature of the acetamide exceeds 90°C, turn off the burner. Remove the test tube from the boiling water and clamp it opposite the hot-water bath. See Figure 3-2. Immediately read and record the temperature of the liquid acetamide. Take temperature readings at 15-second intervals. Continuously stir the liquid acetamide with the thermometer. If crystals form on the sides of the test tube above the liquid, use the thermometer and gently scrape the crystals down into the liquid. Record on the data table when crystallization in the liquid begins. If the temperature drops below 75°C without crystallizing, drop a few seed crystals of acetamide in the liquid. After the first crystals appear in the liquid, immerse the test tube in the cold-water bath you prepared in Part I. Continue taking temperature readings, but at 30-second intervals, until the acetamide cools below 70°C. Indicate on the data table when all the liquid acetamide has crystallized.

Exercises and Experiments in Modern Chemistry
Holt, Rinehart and Winston, Publishers

4. Reheat the solid acetamide in the hot-water bath. When the solid has
   melted, remove the thermometer and dispose of the acetamide as
   directed by your instructor. Clean all apparatus, wash your hands
   thoroughly at the end of this experiment, and check to see that the gas
   valve is completely turned off before leaving the laboratory.

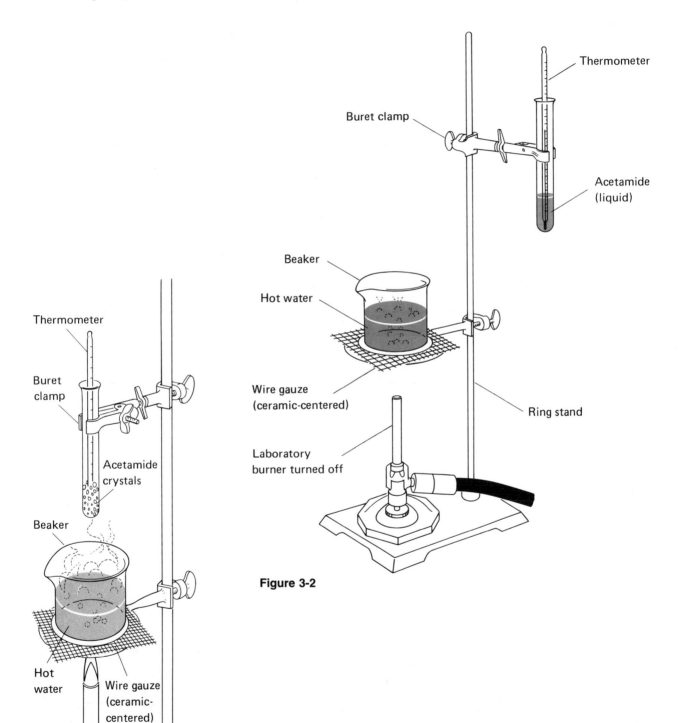

Figure 3-2

Figure 3-1

DATA TABLE

Warming Data			Cooling Data		
Time (s)	Temp (°C)	Observations	Time (s)	Temp (°C)	Observations
0	32.5		0	88.0	
15	36.0		15	83.0	
30	42.0		30	81.5	
45	75.0		45	79.8	crystallization begins
60	79.8	crystals melting	60	79.8	
75	79.8		90	79.8	test tube immersed in
90	79.8		120	79.8	cold water bath
105	79.8	all crystals melted	150	79.8	
120	82.0		180	79.8	crystallized
135	84.5		210	79.3	all of the liquid
150	87.0		240	76.0	
165	89.0		270	69.0	
180	91.0				

Exercises and Experiments in Modern Chemistry
Holt, Rinehart and Winston, Publishers

Plotting Your Results

Plot both the warming and cooling data on the same graph. Place the
time on the horizontal axis and the temperature on the vertical axis.

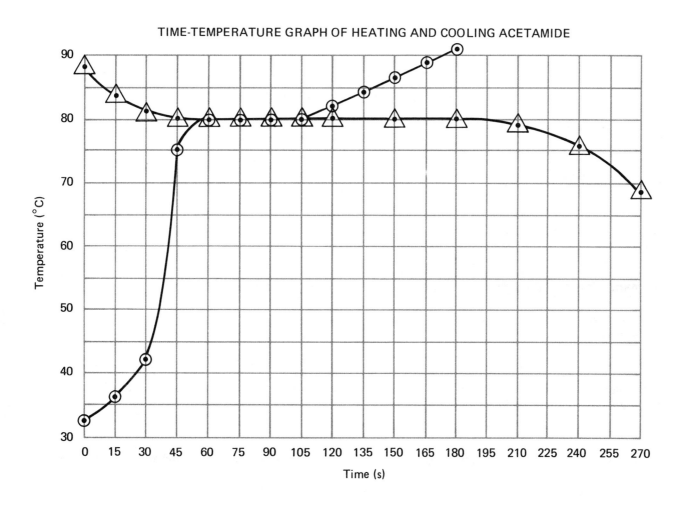

TIME-TEMPERATURE GRAPH OF HEATING AND COOLING ACETAMIDE

QUESTIONS

1. What is the shape of the part of the graph that represents the cooling of the liquid?
   It slopes downward.

2. What is happening to the kinetic energy of the acetamide molecules as the liquid cools?
   Kinetic energy (average) decreases.

3. How does the temperature of the acetamide sample compare with the temperature of the room (its external environment) while (a) the liquid is cooling, (b) very little, if any, change in temperature occurs, (c) the solid is cooling?
   (a) **above room temperature**
   (b) **above room temperature**
   (c) **may go down to room temperature**

4. In terms of the temperature differentials in question 3, are the changes taking place exothermic or endothermic?
   (a) **exothermic**
   (b) **exothermic, although little evidence of temperature change**

   (c) **exothermic**

5. What happens to the average kinetic energy of the molecules of a substance as the temperature falls?
   The average kinetic energy decreases.

6. How would you describe the temperature change(s) that you recorded while the liquid was freezing to the solid?
   The temperature remained relatively constant.

7. What happens to the entropy of acetamide as it changes from a liquid to a solid?
   The entropy decreases.

8. What is the melting temperature of acetamide?
   It is 79.8°C.

9. What is the freezing temperature of acetamide?
   It is 79.8°C.

Exercises and Experiments in Modern Chemistry
Holt, Rinehart and Winston, Publishers

Developing a Logical Model

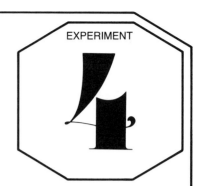

EXPERIMENT

The development of a model of the atom is perhaps the finest example of man's ability to construct a logical model in order to explain the behavior of something that has never been directly observed. Rutherford, for example, was able to conclude that an atom is mostly space and the mass is concentrated in a very small space called the nucleus. He made this conclusion after performing his scattering experiment. Rutherford aimed very small alpha particles through a very thin piece of gold foil. He found that the vast majority of the particles passed through the foil without any deflection, as though the foil was not even there. However, a few particles were deflected at large angles. Thus, Rutherford concluded, most of the particles passed only through empty space, while a few collided with the very tiny nucleus.

You will perform an experiment not unlike Rutherford's. An enclosed box contains a marble which will act as a probe. You will use this probe to determine the approximate location, size, and shape of an object located in the box. You most likely have performed this experiment before, when you tried to guess what was inside a gift-wrapped present. Review Chapter 3, Sections 3.2 and 3.3, for additional information.

OBJECTIVE

After completing this experiment, you should be able to construct a logical model by making indirect observations and drawing conclusions (inferences) from these observations.

APPARATUS

black box

Recording Your Results

Record your results in the space provided immediately following the procedure.

PROCEDURE

Develop your own procedure. Write the procedure in the space provided. As you complete each part of your procedure, record your observations in the space provided. Remember, you are not trying to determine exactly what is inside the box, but only its approximate size, shape, and location. Write a detailed conclusion of your results, describing the object in your black box.

YOUR PROCEDURE

_____

_____

_____

_____

_____

_____

_____

_____

_____

OBSERVATIONS

_____

_____

_____

_____

_____

_____

_____

_____

_____

CONCLUSIONS

_____

_____

_____

_____

_____

Exercises and Experiments in Modern Chemistry
Holt, Rinehart and Winston, Publishers

Flame Tests

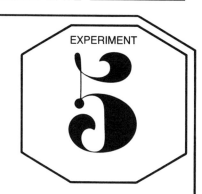

EXPERIMENT
5

Compounds of the Group I and II metals impart characteristic colors to a Bunsen flame. These flame tests are often used as confirmatory tests in identifying an unknown metal. In this experiment you will observe and record the flame colors of several metals of Group I and II. Review Chapter 4, Sections 4.1 to 4.3, and Chapter 24, Sections 24.2 and 24.12 in your textbook, for additional information.

OBJECTIVE
After completing this experiment you should be able to identify certain metal compounds (salts) by the color they give to a flame.

APPARATUS
burner and tubing
sparker
2 cobalt glass plates
test tubes (10)
forceps

5-cm length of No. 24 platinum wire, sealed at the opening of a glass tube 10 cm long. If platinum wire is not available, nichrome wire (not as satisfactory as platinum) may be used. Nichrome wire should be held with forceps.

MATERIALS
hydrochloric acid, 6 *M*
unknown solutions

0.5-*M* solutions in distilled water of the A. R. grade of sodium chloride and 0.5-*M* solutions of the nitrates of barium, calcium, lithium, potassium, sodium, strontium

SAFETY

Begin this experiment by taking the necessary safety precautions. Wear safety goggles, apron, and gloves. Read all safety cautions in your procedures and discuss them with your teacher. Conduct this experiment by using good safety techniques. See pages 112 and 103.

Recording Your Results
Record the colors of all flame tests in the data table at the end of the procedures.

PROCEDURES

1. In order to obtain good results in this experiment, your test tubes must be exceptionally clean to avoid contamination. To clean the ten test tubes, a 6 *M* HCl solution can be used.

CAUTION
Hydrochloric acid is caustic and corrosive. Avoid contact with skin and eyes. Make certain that you wear gloves, safety goggles, and an apron when working with acids. If any should spill on you, immediately flush the area with water and then notify your teacher.

Place a few mL of 6 *M* HCl into each test tube and use a test tube brush to thoroughly clean the ten test tubes. Rinse the test tubes with tapwater and then distilled water.

CAUTION
Before you use the burner in the next four procedures, check to see that long hair and loose clothing have been confined.

2. Clean a platinum wire by dipping it first into some 6 *M* hydrochloric acid in a test tube and then holding it in the colorless flame of your burner. Repeat until the wire imparts no color to the flame. Pour 4 mL of sodium nitrate solution into a clean test tube, dip the tip of the clean platinum wire into the solution, and then hold it in the flame. Observe the color of the flame just above the wire. Heat only the tip of the wire. If you heat the glass tube into which the wire is sealed, you will break the glass.

Clean the wire as before and then test a solution of sodium chloride in the same manner. Repeat the test, dipping the wire into a little dry sodium chloride. Describe what you observed.

Sodium nitrate solution, sodium chloride solution, and dry

sodium chloride all impart a yellow color to the flame.

3. Repeat Step 2, using in turn 4 mL of the solutions of the nitrates of lithium, strontium, calcium, barium, and potassium. Clean the wire thoroughly after each test. In the cases of lithium and strontium, observe which flame is more persistent and takes longer to burn off the wire. Also note the difference in the shades of color produced. When you have tested the calcium flame and then dipped the wire into hydrochloric acid and back into the flame when cleaning it, you often get an excellent flame of calcium momentarily. Record the color of the flame for each metal compound.

4. If two metals are present in the same solution, the color of one flame may obscure that of the other. If cobalt glass plates are used, it is sometimes possible to absorb one color and not the other. Examine the sodium nitrate flame through at least two thicknesses of cobalt glass. Repeat, using the potassium nitrate flame with the cobalt glasses. Record the colors of the flames in the data table.

Flame-test a mixture of the solutions of the nitrates of sodium and potassium with a clean wire. Observe the color the mixture imparts to the flame when viewed without the cobalt glasses. Repeat the test, but observe the flame as seen through the cobalt glasses. Record the colors of the flames in the data table.

5. Secure an unknown solution from your instructor. Test it in the flame as in this experiment in order to identify the metallic ion present. Place your answer in the data table.

6. Clean all apparatus at the end of this experiment. Ask your teacher how to dispose of all waste materials. Check to see that the gas valve is completely shut off and wash your hands before leaving the laboratory.

Exercises and Experiments in Modern Chemistry
Holt, Rinehart and Winston, Publishers

DATA TABLE

Metal in Compound	Color of Flame
sodium	yellow
lithium	red (carmine)
strontium	scarlet
calcium	yellowish-red
barium	yellowish-green
potassium	violet
sodium (cobalt glass)	blue of the glass
potassium (cobalt glass)	violet (purple)
sodium and potassium	yellow
sodium and potassium (cobalt glass)	violet
unknown metal	student answer

QUESTIONS

1. Is the flame coloration a test for the metal or for the nitrate ion?
   It is a test for the metal.

2. Why do dry sodium chloride and the solutions of sodium nitrate and sodium chloride all impart the same color to the flame?
   They all contain sodium.

3. Describe the test for sodium and potassium when both are present.
   Observe the flame directly. It will be yellow because of sodium. The violet color of the potassium is obscured. Next view through cobalt glass. The yellow color of sodium is absorbed, and the violet color of the potassium is visible.

4. How would you characterize the flame test with respect to its sensitivity?
   The test is extremely sensitive and very small amounts can be identified.

QUESTIONS (continued)

5. What difficulties may be encountered in the use of the flame test for identification?

The yellow sodium may be found in most things because traces of sodium are often present as impurities. The shades of red produced by lithium and strontium are somewhat hard to distinguish. The calcium flame is not satisfactory partly because almost all calcium compounds contain sodium compounds as an impurity.

CORRELATING YOUR FACTS

Review Chapter 24, Sections 24.11 and 24.12, and correlate what you have read with what you have learned by performing this experiment.

Describe the activity of electrons when a substance is vaporized in a flame. What is viewed through a spectroscope and how does this instrument serve in identifying substances?

When substances are vaporized in a flame, electrons are raised to higher energy levels by heat energy. When these electrons fall back into the lower energy levels available to them, energy is released. The energy released by any substance has wavelengths characteristic of that substance. Different wavelengths produce different spectral lines in a spectroscope. The spectra produced by excited atoms of different elements are as distinct as fingerprints.

Exercises and Experiments in Modern Chemistry
Holt, Rinehart and Winston, Publishers

Tests for Iron(II) and Iron(III) Ions

In the identification tests for the Fe^{++} and Fe^{+++} ions we shall use the complex *ferro*cyanide, $Fe(CN)_6^{----}$, and *ferri*cyanide, $Fe(CN)_6^{---}$, ions. The complex ion charges clearly indicate the difference in the oxidation number of the iron present in the two complexes. The (CN) group in each complex has a charge of -1. Thus, iron(II) is present in the *ferro*cyanide group, $[Fe^{++}(CN^-)_6]^{----}$. Iron(III) is present in the *ferri*cyanide group, $[Fe^{+++}(CN^-)_6]^{---}$. A deep-blue precipitate results when either complex ion combines with iron in a different oxidation state from that present in the complex. The deep-blue color of the precipitate is due to the presence of iron in *both* oxidation states. This provides us with the means of identifying either iron ion. If the deep-blue precipitate is formed on addition of the $[Fe^{++}(CN^-)_6]^{----}$ complex, the iron ion responsible must be the iron(III) ion. Similarly, the deep-blue precipitate formed with the $[Fe^{+++}(CN^-)_6]^{---}$ complex indicates the presence of the iron(II) ion.

Both deep-blue precipitates are now recognized as having the same composition. The potassium salts of the complex ions are commonly used, in which case the deep-blue precipitate may be considered to have the composition, $KFeFe(CN)_6 \cdot H_2O$.

The thiocyanate ion, SCN^-, provides an excellent confirming test for the Fe^{+++} ion. The soluble $FeSCN^{++}$ complex is formed, imparting a rich blood-red color to the solution. Review Chapter 6, Section 6.7, for additional information.

OBJECTIVE
After completing this experiment, you should be able to identify iron(II) and iron(III) ions in solution.

APPARATUS
graduated cylinder, 10 mL   6 test tubes, 18 × 150 mm

MATERIALS
0.1 *M* iron(III) chloride   0.2 *M* potassium thiocyanate   0.1 *M* potassium ferricyanide
0.1 *M* potassium ferrocyanide   0.1 *M* iron(II) ammonium sulfate

SAFETY

Begin this experiment by taking the necessary safety precautions. Wear safety goggles, apron, and gloves. During the procedures of this experiment, you are required to handle various chemicals. Do not touch the chemicals with your hands. Carefully check the labels on the reagent bottles before removing any of their contents. Conduct this experiment by using good safety techniques. See pages 103 and 115.

Recording Your Results

After completing each of the procedures, record your results in the data table and in the spaces provided below.

PROCEDURES

1. To a 5-mL test solution of freshly prepared $Fe(NH_4)_2(SO_4)_2$, add 1 mL of $K_4Fe(CN)_6$ solution. Observe the color of the precipitate that first forms. Allow the precipitate to stand a few minutes and observe the color once more.

   Observation: **Initially the precipitate is white, but in a few minutes changes to blue.**

2. To a second 5-mL test solution of iron(II) ammonium sulfate, add 3 or 4 drops of a solution of potassium thiocyanate, KSCN.

   Observation: **No color or precipitate forms.**

3. To a third 5-mL test solution of iron(II) ammonium sulfate, add 1 mL of $K_3Fe(CN)_6$ solution ($[Fe^{+++}(CN^-)_6]^{---}$ ion).

   Observation: **A deep-blue precipitate forms.**

4. To a 5-mL test solution of iron(III) chloride, add 1 mL of the $K_3Fe(CN)_6$ solution.

   Observation: **No precipitate forms.**

5. Add to a second 5-mL test solution of iron(III) chloride 1 mL of the $K_4Fe(CN)_6$ solution ($[Fe^{++}(CN^-)_6]^{----}$ ion).

   Observation: **A dark-blue precipitate forms.**

6. To a third 5-mL test solution of iron(III) chloride, add 2 or 3 drops of the KSCN solution.

   Observation: **A blood-red solution of the $FeSCN^{++}$ ion results.**

7. Clean all apparatus at the end of this experiment. Ask your teacher how to dispose of all solid residues and solutions. Remember to clean your hands thoroughly before leaving the laboratory.

Exercises and Experiments in Modern Chemistry
Holt, Rinehart and Winston, Publishers

DATA TABLE

Iron ion	Ferrocyanide ion $[Fe^{++}(CN^-)_6]^{----}$	Ferricyanide ion $[Fe^{+++}(CN^-)_6]^{---}$	Thiocyanate ion SCN^-
Fe^{++}	white precipitate	dark-blue precipitate	no visible result
Fe^{+++}	dark-blue precipitate	brown solution	blood-red solution

QUESTIONS

1. State specifically how you would make a decisive test for an iron(III) salt.

   Add $K_4Fe(CN)_6$ to the solution. The formation of a deep-blue precipitate identifies the

   iron(III) ion. Confirm by adding KSCN to a second test solution. Formation of a blood-red

   solution confirms the presence of an iron(III) salt.

2. Which test for iron(II) ions is decisive?

   The formation of a dark-blue precipitate on addition of $K_3Fe(CN)_6$ to a solution containing

   iron(II) ions is the decisive test.

3. When the iron(II) ammonium sulfate was mixed with the $[Fe^{++}(CN^-)_6]^{----}$ ion, the precipitate was initially white, but turned blue upon exposure to air. What happened to the iron(II) ion when the precipitate turned blue?

   Iron(II) oxidized in the presence of air to iron(III).

4. Suppose you have a solution containing both an iron(II) salt and an iron(III) salt. How would you proceed to identify both Fe^{++} and Fe^{+++} ions in this solution?

   $K_3Fe(CN)_6$ would be used to detect the iron(II) ion, and $K_4Fe(CN)_6$ would be used to identify

   the iron(III) ion without interference.

CORRELATING YOUR FACTS

Review Chapter 6, Sections 6.4 to 6.7, and correlate what you have read in the textbook with what you have learned by performing this experiment.

Complete the following data table on atoms and ions:

DATA ON ATOMS AND IONS

	number of protons	number of electrons	net charge	oxidation number	symbol
magnesium atom	**12**	12	**0**	0	Mg
magnesium ion	12	**10**	+2	**+2**	**Mg^{++}**
iron atom	26	**26**	0	0	Fe
iron(II) ion	**26**	24	**+2**	+2	Fe^{++}
iron(III) ion	26	**23**	+3	**+3**	**Fe^{+++}**
sodium atom	11	11	0	0	**Na**
sodium ion	11	10	+1	+1	Na$^+$

Complete the following sentences. Place your written answer in the space to the right of the statement.

1. Any chemical reaction in which an element attains a more positive oxidation state is called (1).

   _____**oxidation**_____ 1.

2. The particle whose oxidation state becomes more positive is said to be (2) .

   _____**oxidized**_____ 2.

3. The oxidation state of an element is represented by a signed number called an (3) .

   _____**oxidation number**_____ 3.

4. The above table indicates that the oxidation number of an atom of a free element is (4) .

   _____**zero**_____ 4.

5. The table also indicates that the oxidation number of a monatomic (one-atomed) ion is equal to its (5) .

   _____**net charge**_____ 5.

6. According to the table, the element (6) exhibits more than one oxidation state.

   _____**iron**_____ 6.

7. Iron is placed with the (7) elements in the periodic table.

   _____**transition**_____ 7.

Exercises and Experiments in Modern Chemistry
Holt, Rinehart and Winston, Publishers

Water of Crystallization and Empirical Formula of a Hydrate

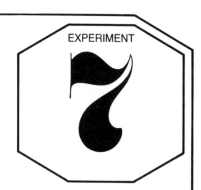

EXPERIMENT

7

Many ionic compounds, when crystallized from water solution, take up definite proportions of water as an integral part of their crystal structures. This water of crystallization may be driven off by the application of heat. Since the law of definite composition holds for crystalline hydrates, the number of moles of water of crystallization driven off per mole of the anhydrous compound is some simple number. If the formula of the anhydrous compound is known, you can then determine the formula of the hydrate. Review Chapter 7, Sections 7.9 to 7.12, for additional information.

OBJECTIVE

After completing this experiment, you will be able to determine the empirical formula of a hydrate.

APPARATUS

balance, centigram
iron ring
ring stand
burner and tubing

sparker
tongs
spatula

crucible and cover
pipestem triangle
desiccator

MATERIALS

barium chloride, C. P., crystals
calcium chloride, anhydrous, granular
crystals of potassium chloride, sodium aluminum
  sulfate, sodium chloride

clear crystals of magnesium chloride, potassium
  nitrate, sodium carbonate, sodium sulfate

SAFETY

Begin this experiment by taking the necessary safety precautions. Wear safety goggles, apron, and gloves. Read all safety cautions in your procedures and discuss them with your teacher. Conduct this experiment by using good safety techniques. See pages 105 and 117.

Recording Your Data

Where indicated in the procedures, record your data in the table that immediately follows the procedures.

PROCEDURES

1. Throughout the experiment handle the crucible and cover with clean crucible tongs only. Why?

   Clean tongs are used so that dirt or debris will not add

   to the mass of the crucible and cover.

   _____

   _____

2. Place the crucible and cover on the pipestem triangle as shown in Figure 7-1. Position the cover slightly askew (tipped), leaving only a small opening for any gases to escape. Preheat the crucible and cover to redness.

    CAUTION
   Before lighting the burner, remember to confine loose clothing and long hair. Remember to handle the crucible and cover only with tongs. The crucible and cover are very hot after each heating!

   Using the tongs, transfer the crucible and cover to a desiccator. Allow them to cool 5 minutes in the desiccator. _Never place a hot crucible on a balance._ When cool, determine the mass of the crucible and cover to the nearest 0.01 g. Record this mass in the data table.

3. Using a spatula, add approximately 5 g of fine barium chloride crystals to the crucible. Determine the mass of the covered crucible and crystals to the nearest 0.01 g. Record this mass in the data table.

4. Place the crucible with the barium chloride hydrate on the triangle and again position the cover so there is only a small opening. Too large an opening may allow the hydrate to spatter out of the crucible. Heat the crucible very gently on a low flame to avoid spattering any of the hydrate. Increase the temperature gradually for 2 or 3 minutes. Then heat strongly (red-hot) for at least 5 minutes. Allow the crucible, cover, and contents to cool for 5 minutes in the desiccator and then determine their mass. Keep a labeled record of each weighing.

5. Heat the covered crucible and contents again to redness for 5 minutes. Allow the crucible, cover, and contents to cool in the desiccator and then determine their mass. If the last two mass determinations differ by no more than 0.01 g, you may assume that the water has all been driven off. Otherwise repeat the process, heating to constant mass. Record this mass in the data table. The dehydrated compound left in the crucible should be returned to your instructor, since it can be used in the preparation of solutions.

6. At the end of this experiment, clean all apparatus. Check to see that the gas valve is completely shut off before leaving the laboratory and remember to wash your hands.

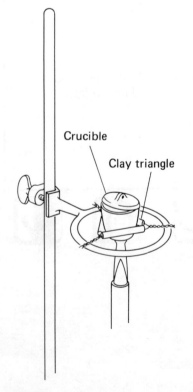

Figure 7-1

Crucible

Clay triangle

Exercises and Experiments in Modern Chemistry
Holt, Rinehart and Winston, Publishers

DATA AND CALCULATIONS TABLES

DATA

Mass of empty crucible and cover	32.18	g
Mass of crucible, cover and barium chloride hydrate	37.14	g
Mass of crucible, cover, and anhydrous barium chloride after 1st heating	36.38	g
Mass of crucible, cover, and anhydrous barium chloride after 2nd heating	36.37	g

CALCULATIONS

Mass of anhydrous barium chloride	4.20	g
Moles of anhydrous barium chloride	0.020	moles
Mass of water driven from hydrate	0.76	g
Moles of water driven from hydrate	0.042	moles
Mole ratio of water to anhydrous barium chloride	$\dfrac{2.1}{1.0}$	$\dfrac{\text{mol } H_2O}{\text{mol } BaCl_2}$

Empirical Formula . . . $BaCl_2 \cdot 2H_2O$

CALCULATIONS

Show your computations in the spaces provided below. Place your answers in the calculations table.

1. Calculate the mass of the anhydrous barium chloride (residue after driving off the water).

$$36.38 \text{ g} - 32.18 \text{ g} = 4.20 \text{ g}$$

2. Calculate the moles of anhydrous barium chloride.

$$4.20 \text{ g} \times \frac{1 \text{ mole } BaCl_2}{208.2 \text{ g}} = 0.020 \text{ mol}$$

3. Calculate the mass and moles of water driven from the hydrate.

$$\text{mass } H_2O = 37.14 \text{ g} - 36.38 \text{ g} = 0.76 \text{ g}$$

$$\text{moles } H_2O = 0.76 \text{ g} \times \frac{1 \text{ mole } H_2O}{18.0 \text{ g}} = 0.042 \text{ mol}$$

4. The reaction for this experiment is:

$$BaCl_2 \cdot xH_2O_{(s)} \rightarrow \underset{\substack{\text{anhydrous} \\ \text{salt}}}{BaCl_{2(s)}} + xH_2O$$
$$\underset{\text{hydrate}}{}$$

x = the number of moles of water driven off per mole of anhydrous barium chloride. Determine this mole ratio to the nearest whole number, and write the empirical formula for the barium chloride hydrate.

$$\text{mole ratio: } \frac{H_2O}{BaCl_2} = \frac{0.042 \text{ mol}}{0.020 \text{ mol}} = \frac{2.1 \text{ mol } H_2O}{1.0 \text{ mol } BaCl_2}$$

empirical formula: $BaCl_2 \cdot 2H_2O$

QUESTION

How does this experiment exemplify the law of definite composition?
Every compound has a definite composition by mass. Pure crystallized barium chloride always has the same composition.

FURTHER EXPERIMENTATION

In the table below, investigate the specific properties of several familiar crystalline hydrates to determine others that lend themselves to this method of determining percentage hydration.

Collect data on some representative substances and verify their hydrate formulas.

Undertake an explanation of any large deviations from the correct hydrate formulas that your data may yield.

Name of compound	Water of crystallization present?	Description of residue
sodium carbonate	**yes**	**white powder**
sodium sulfate	**yes**	**white powder**
sodium chloride	**no**	**unchanged**
sodium aluminum sulfate	**yes**	**white powder**
potassium chloride	**no**	**unchanged**
magnesium chloride	**no**	**unchanged**
potassium nitrate	**no**	**may melt**

Exercises and Experiments in Modern Chemistry
Holt, Rinehart and Winston, Publishers

Mass and Mole Relationships in a Chemical Reaction

EXPERIMENT

8

In this experiment, you will measure the mass of the solid reactant, $NaHCO_3$, and that of the solid product, $NaCl$. The experimental determination of these relative masses will enable you to determine the relative number of moles of this reactant and this product. As a result of your observations and calculations, you will determine the mass and mole relationships of the solid reactant and product. Review Chapter 8, Sections 8.1 to 8.3, 8.9, and 8.10, for further information.

OBJECTIVE

After completing this experiment, you should be able to verify experimentally the mass relationships and the mole relationships between reactants and products of a chemical reaction.

APPARATUS

balance, centigram
burner and tubing
sparker
evaporating dish

eye dropper
graduated cylinder, 25 mL
iron ring

ring stand
spatula
wire gauze, ceramic-centered

MATERIALS

sodium hydrogen carbonate

hydrochloric acid, 3 M

SAFETY

Begin this experiment by taking the necessary safety precautions. Wear safety goggles, apron, and gloves. Read all safety cautions in your procedures and discuss them with your teacher. Conduct this experiment by using good safety techniques. See pages 105 and 106.

Recording Your Data

After completing each procedure, record your results in the data table at the end of the procedures.

PROCEDURES

1. Place an evaporating dish on top of a watch glass. Measure the mass of the dry evaporating dish and the dry watch glass. Record this mass in the data table.

2. Add 2–3 g of sodium hydrogen carbonate to the evaporating dish. Measure the mass of the sodium hydrogen carbonate, evaporating dish, and watch glass. Record this mass in the data table.

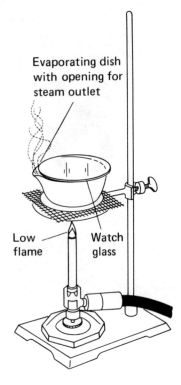

Figure 8-1

Evaporating dish with opening for steam outlet

Low flame

Watch glass

3. Slowly add about 10 mL of hydrochloric acid to the sodium hydrogen carbonate in the evaporating dish. Then carefully add hydrochloric acid from the medicine dropper until the bubbling stops.

CAUTION
Hydrochloric acid is caustic and corrosive. Avoid contact with skin and eyes. Avoid breathing vapors. Make certain that you wear safety goggles, apron, and gloves when working with acids. If any acid should spill on you, immediately flush the area with water and then notify your teacher.

4. Place the evaporating dish on the ceramic-centered wire gauze that has been placed on the iron ring attached to the ring stand. Place the watch glass on top of the dish, but tipped slightly so steam can escape. See Figure 8-1.

5. Gently heat the evaporating dish with a small flame until only a dry solid remains.

CAUTION
Before you light the burner, check to see that long hair and loose clothing have been confined. Remember to allow all apparatus to cool before you handle it again.

6. Turn off the gas burner. Allow the apparatus to cool for at least 15 minutes. Determine the mass of the cooled assembly. Record the mass of the dish, residue, and watch glass in the data table.

7. Ask your teacher how to dispose of the solid residue at the end of this lab. Wash your hands and check to see that the gas valve is turned off before leaving the laboratory.

DATA AND CALCULATIONS TABLES

DATA TABLE

Mass of evaporating dish and watch glass	**71.17**	g
Mass of dish, glass, and $NaHCO_3$	**73.27**	g
Mass of dish, glass, and residue (NaCl)	**72.65**	g

Exercises and Experiments in Modern Chemistry
Holt, Rinehart and Winston, Publishers

CALCULATIONS TABLE

Mass of reactant, $NaHCO_3$	**2.10**	g
Moles of $NaHCO_3$ reacted	**0.0250**	mol
Mass of product, NaCl	**1.48**	g
Moles of NaCl produced	**0.0253**	mol
Experimental mole ratio—NaCl to $NaHCO_3$	**1.01**	
Theoretical mole ratio—NaCl to $NaHCO_3$	**1**	
Percentage error of experimental mole ratio	**1**	%

Balanced reaction **$NaHCO_3$ + HCl → NaCl + H_2O + CO_2**

CALCULATIONS

Show your computations in the spaces provided below. Place your answers in the calculations table.

1. Calculate the mass of the reactant, $NaHCO_3$.

$$73.27 \text{ g} - 71.17 \text{ g} = 2.10 \text{ g}$$

2. Calculate the number of moles of $NaHCO_3$ reacted.

$$\textbf{Moles NaCl} = \frac{\textbf{1.48 g}}{\textbf{58.5 g/mol}} = \textbf{0.0253 mol}$$

3. Calculate the mass of the product, NaCl.

$$72.65 \text{ g} - 71.17 \text{ g} = 1.48 \text{ g}$$

4. Calculate the moles of NaCl produced.

$$\textbf{Moles NaCl} = \frac{\textbf{1.48 g}}{\textbf{58.5 g/mol}} = \textbf{0.0253 mol}$$

5. Calculate the experimental mole ratio of NaCl to $NaHCO_3$.

$$\frac{\textbf{0.0253 mol NaCl}}{\textbf{0.0250 mol NaHCO}_3} = \textbf{1.01}$$

6. Assuming the products are NaCl, CO_2, and H_2O, write a balanced equation for the reaction in this experiment.

$$NaHCO_3 + HCl \rightarrow NaCl + H_2O + CO_2$$

7. Using the reaction balanced in #6, determine the theoretical mole ratio of NaCl to $NaHCO_3$.

$$\frac{1 \text{ mole NaCl}}{1 \text{ mole NaHCO}_3} = 1$$

8. Determine the percentage error for your experimental mole ratio.

$$\frac{1.01 - 1.00}{1.00} \times 100\% = 1\%$$

CORRELATING YOUR FACTS

Review Chapter 8, Section 8.1, and correlate what you have read in the textbook with what you have learned by performing this experiment.

The balanced equation for a known chemical reaction shows the substances that react, the products that are formed, and the relative mass quantities of the reactants and products. Complete the following equations based on the balanced formula equation.

2 H$_2$	+	O$_2$	→	2 H$_2$O
2 molecules of hydrogen	+	1 molecule of oxygen	→	2 molecules of water
2 moles of hydrogen	+	**1 mole of oxygen**	→	**2 moles of water**
4 grams of hydrogen	+	**32 grams of oxygen**	→	36 grams of water
any mass quantity of hydrogen	+	mass of oxygen in ratio 8:1 with mass of hydrogen	→	mass of water in ratio 9:1 with mass of hydrogen

Exercises and Experiments in Modern Chemistry
Holt, Rinehart and Winston, Publishers

Boyle's Law

EXPERIMENT

9

According to Boyle's law, the volume of a fixed amount of dry gas is inversely proportional to the pressure, if the temperature remains constant. Boyle's law may be stated mathematically as $p \propto 1/V$ or $pV = k$ (where k is a constant). In this experiment, you will vary the pressure of air contained in a syringe, and measure the corresponding change in volume. You will then plot graphs of pressure versus volume and pressure versus the inverse of the volume. Review Chapter 10, Sections 10.7, 10.8, 10.12, and 10.15, for further information.

OBJECTIVES

After completing this experiment, you should be able to measure changes in volume of a fixed mass of gas as the pressure changes. You should be able to interpret a pressure–volume graph.

APPARATUS

Boyle's law apparatus

4 objects of equal mass (approximately 500 g each)

MATERIAL

carpet thread

SAFETY

Begin this experiment by taking the necessary safety precautions. Wear safety goggles, apron, and gloves. Conduct this experiment by using good safety techniques.

Recording Your Results
Record your results in the data table that follows the procedures.

PROCEDURES

1. Adjust the piston head so that it reads between 30 and 35 cc. To adjust, pull the piston head all the way out of the syringe, insert a piece of carpet thread in the barrel, and position the piston head at the desired location. See Figure 9-1.

   Note: Depending on the Boyle's law apparatus that is used, you may find the volume on the syringe abbreviated in cc or cm^3. Both abbreviations stand for cubic centimeters. The apparatus pictured in Figure 9-1 is marked in cc (cubic centimeters).

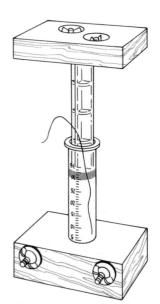

Figure 9-1

While holding the piston in place, carefully remove the thread. Twist the piston several times to allow the head to overcome any frictional forces. Read the volume to the nearest 0.1 cc. Record this value as the initial volume for zero weights in your data table.

2. Place one of the weights on the piston. Give the piston several twists to overcome any frictional forces. When the piston comes to rest, read and record the volume to the nearest 0.1 cc.

3. Repeat procedure 2 for 2, 3, and 4 weights.

4. Repeat procedures 2 and 3 for at least two more trials.

DATA AND CALCULATIONS TABLES

	DATA				CALCULATIONS	
	TRIAL 1	TRIAL 2	TRIAL 3			$\dfrac{1}{\text{Volume}}$
Pressure (weights)	Volume (cc)	Volume (cc)	Volume (cc)		Average Volume (cc)	(x 10^{-2}) (cc^{-1})
0	33.0	33.0	33.0		33.0	3.03
1	29.7	29.5	29.0		29.4	3.40
2	26.8	26.8	26.0		26.5	3.77
3	24.3	24.1	23.5		24.0	4.17
4	22.0	21.8	21.2		21.7	4.61

Exercises and Experiments in Modern Chemistry
Holt, Rinehart and Winston, Publishers

CALCULATIONS

Show your computations in the spaces provided below. Place your answers in the calculations table.

1. Calculate the average volumes of the three trials for weights 0–4. Record in the calculations table.

$$0 \text{ wts} = \frac{33.0 + 33.0 + 33.0}{3} = 33.0$$

$$1 \text{ wt} = \frac{29.7 + 29.5 + 29.0}{3} = 29.4$$

$$2 \text{ wts} = \frac{26.8 + 26.8 + 26.0}{3} = 26.5$$

$$3 \text{ wts} = \frac{24.3 + 24.1 + 23.5}{3} = 24.0$$

$$4 \text{ wts} = \frac{22.0 + 21.8 + 21.2}{3} = 21.7$$

2. Calculate the inverse for each of the average volumes. Multiply each value by 100 and record.
   Example: If the average volume for two weights is 26.5 cc, then
   $1/V = 1/26.5 \text{ cc} = 0.0377 \text{ cc}^{-1} \times 100 = 3.77 \times 10^{-2} \text{ cc}^{-1}$.

$$0 \text{ wts} = \frac{1}{33.0 \text{ cc}} \times 100 = 3.03 \times 10^{-2} \text{ cc}^{-1}$$

$$1 \text{ wt} = \frac{1}{29.4 \text{ cc}} \times 100 = 3.40 \times 10^{-2} \text{ cc}^{-1}$$

$$2 \text{ wts} = \frac{1}{26.5 \text{ cc}} \times 100 = 3.77 \times 10^{-2} \text{ cc}^{-1}$$

$$3 \text{ wts} = \frac{1}{24.0 \text{ cc}} \times 100 = 4.17 \times 10^{-2} \text{ cc}^{-1}$$

$$4 \text{ wts} = \frac{1}{21.7 \text{ cc}} \times 100 = 4.61 \times 10^{-2} \text{ cc}^{-1}$$

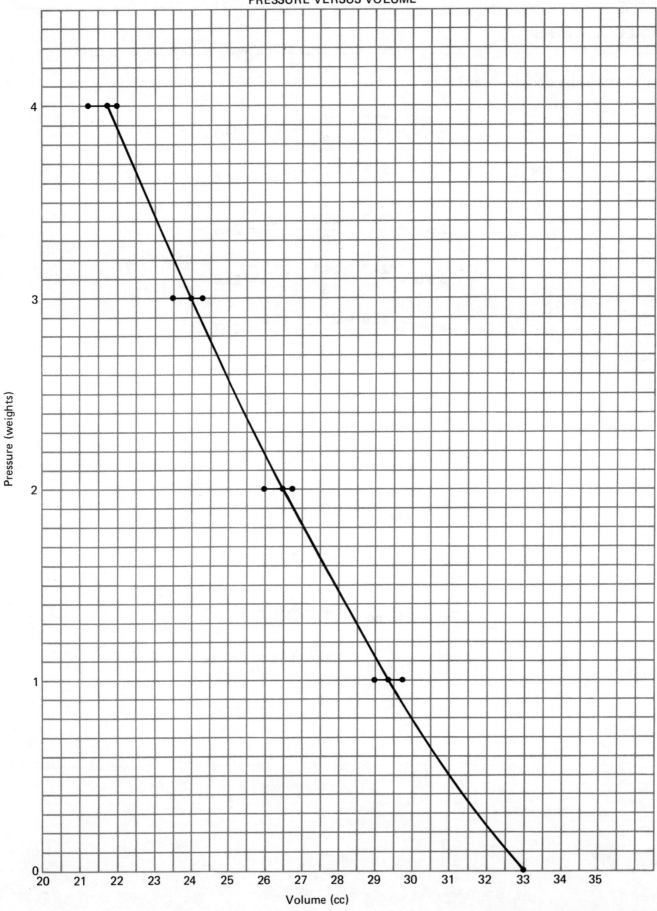

Exercises and Experiments in Modern Chemistry
Holt, Rinehart and Winston, Publishers

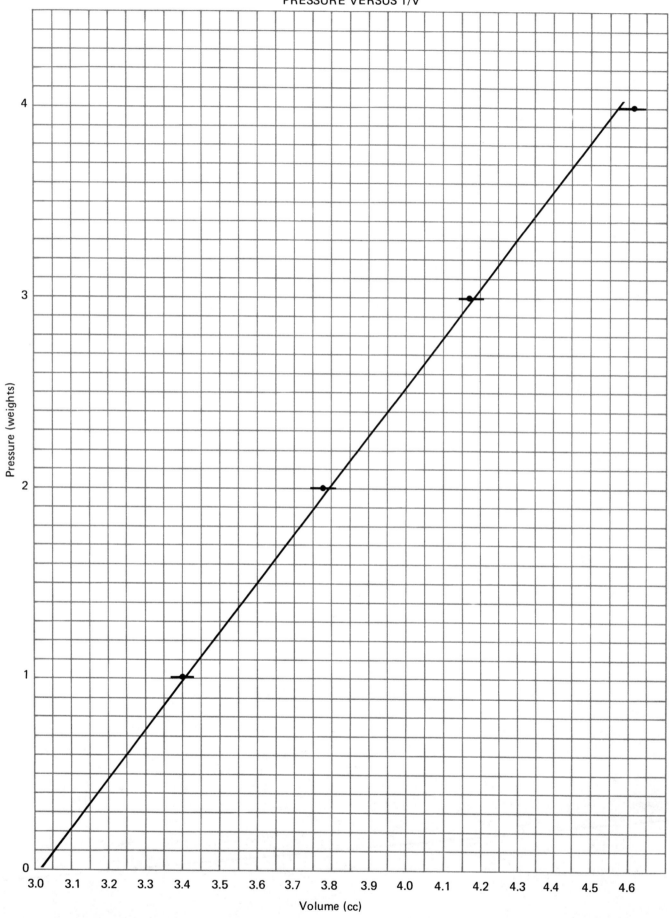

PRESSURE VERSUS 1/V

Pressure (weights)

Volume (cc)

QUESTIONS

1. Plot a full-page graph of pressure versus volume. Since the number of weights added to the piston is directly proportional to the pressure applied to the gas, we can use the number of weights to represent the changes in pressure. Plot the number of weights on the vertical axis and the adjusted volume on the horizontal axis. Draw the smoothest curve that goes through most of the points. Does your graph indicate that a change in volume is directly proportional to a change in pressure? Explain.

   No. The graph is not a straight line. Furthermore, as the pressure increases, the volume

   decreases.

2. Plot a full-page graph of pressure versus 1/volume. Place pressure on the vertical axis and 1/volume on the horizontal axis. Draw the best line that goes through the majority of the points. What do you conclude about the mathematical relationship between the pressure applied to a gas and its corresponding volume?

   The plot of p vs $1/V$ is approximately a straight line (within experimental uncertainty).

   Therefore, p must be proportional to $1/V$.

Exercises and Experiments in Modern Chemistry
Holt, Rinehart and Winston, Publishers

Comparing the Masses of Equal Volumes of Gases

EXPERIMENT
10

According to Avogadro's principle, equal volumes of gases measured at the same temperature and pressure contain equal numbers of molecules. This profound statement will allow you to determine the relative masses of individual molecules of gases. In this experiment you will find the masses of equal volumes of carbon dioxide and oxygen. Both gases will be measured at the same temperature and pressure. Although the number of molecules in the two samples of gas is unknown, Avogadro's principle states that the number in each is the same. Therefore, the ratio of the masses of the carbon dioxide to the oxygen sample must be in the same ratio as one molecule of carbon dioxide to one molecule of oxygen. Review Chapter 11, Section 11.2, for additional information.

OBJECTIVE

After completing this experiment you should be able to determine the mass ratio of two different gases measured at the same temperature, pressure, and volume.

APPARATUS

plastic bag, approximately 1 liter
rubber stopper, one-hole No. 6
rubber band
medicine dropper
balance, centigram

glass bottle, approximately 2 liters
rubber tubing, 50 cm
pinch clamp
pneumatic trough

MATERIALS

oxygen gas

carbon dioxide gas

SAFETY

Begin this experiment by taking the necessary safety precautions. Wear safety goggles, apron, and gloves. Read all safety cautions in your procedures and discuss them with your teacher. Conduct this experiment by using good safety techniques. See pages 114 and 115.

Recording Your Results

Where instructed to in the procedures, record your results in the data table.

PROCEDURES

1. **Apparent mass of carbon dioxide.** Inspect the plastic bag for any water drops or small holes. If the bag is wet, thoroughly dry it. If there are any holes, obtain another bag. Gather the open end of

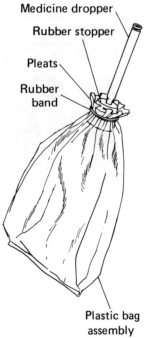

Medicine dropper

Rubber stopper

Pleats

Rubber band

Plastic bag assembly

Figure 10-1

Figure 10-2

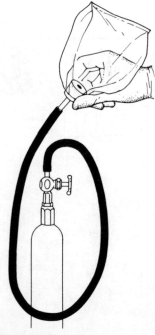

Figure 10-3

the plastic bag in small pleats around the wide end of the rubber stopper. Secure the bag tightly with a rubber band. Then insert the tapered end of the medicine dropper through the hole of the stopper. See Figure 10-1.

 CAUTION
Gloves should be worn and a layer of cloth wrapped around the medicine dropper before inserting it into the stopper. See page 114 and observe the precautions for inserting glass tubing. Remember to aim the medicine dropper away from the palm of the hand that holds the stopper.

Check to see if there are leaks in the bag. If so, see your instructor.

Press all the air out of the bag by rolling it up tightly. Then place the rubber cap on the medicine dropper. See Figure 10-2. Weigh the bag assembly to the nearest 0.01 g and record.

2. Your instructor will indicate where you will have your bag filled with carbon dioxide. Hold the bag by the rubber stopper. See Figure 10-3. When the bag is filled, do not replace the rubber cap until the pressure of the carbon dioxide in the bag has equalized with the outside atmospheric pressure. Why?
The pressure of the gas in the bag becomes equal with atmospheric pressure, and this enables us to have the same volume of gas each time we fill up the bag.

When the pressure inside the bag has stabilized, cap the medicine dropper. Remember: Handle the bag assembly by the rubber stopper only. Weigh the bag and carbon dioxide gas to the nearest 0.01 g and record.

3. **Apparent mass of oxygen.** Squeeze out all of the carbon dioxide gas from the bag. Your instructor will indicate where you will have your bag filled with oxygen. Fill the bag with oxygen gas, and again allow the pressure inside the bag to stabilize. Then cap the medicine dropper. Weigh the bag assembly and oxygen gas to the nearest 0.01 g and record.

4. **Measuring the volume of the bag.** Empty the bag and refill it with air. Your instructor will tell you how to fill the bag with air. Again allow the pressure inside the bag to equalize with the atmospheric pressure. Do not cap the medicine dropper.

Obtain a rubber tubing and fasten a pinch clamp about 5 cm from the end of the tubing. Secure this end of the tubing to the bag assembly at the medicine dropper.

Exercises and Experiments in Modern Chemistry
Holt, Rinehart and Winston, Publishers

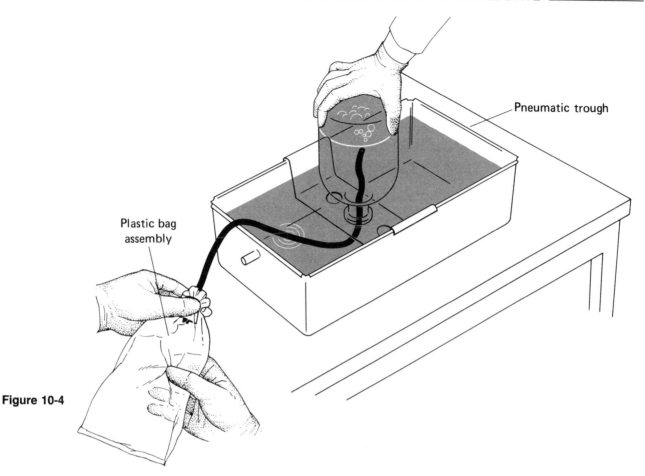

Pneumatic trough

Plastic bag
assembly

Figure 10-4

CAUTION
Gloves should be worn when inserting the medicine
dropper into the hose. See page 114 and observe the
precautions for inserting glass tubing.

5. Completely fill a 2-liter bottle with tapwater. Also fill the pneumatic
   trough with tapwater to the overflow spout. Position the overflow
   spout over a drain. Place your hand over the mouth of the bottle,
   invert it, and place the neck in the trough. Remove your hand from
   the bottle while under water, and allow the inverted bottle to rest on
   the shelf. Your lab partner will have to keep the bottle from tipping
   over. Insert the open end of the rubber tubing all the way into the
   bottle. See Figure 10-4.

6. Hold the bag above the level of the water. Remove the pinch clamp.
   Place one hand tightly around the rubber stopper. This will ensure a
   good seal where the bag is pleated. Now very gently squeeze the air
   out of the bag. As the bag deflates, crumple or roll the bag until all
   the air has been evacuated. Immediately squeeze off the rubber tubing
   and pull it out of the bottle.

7. Place your hand over the opening of the bottle that rests in water.
   Invert the bottle and place on the lab desk. Use a large graduated
   cylinder to determine the volume of water required to refill the bottle.
   Record this volume to the nearest mL as the volume of your bag.

   Record the room temperature (°C) and room pressure (mm Hg).

8. Clean, dry, and arrange all equipment in an orderly fashion for the next experiment. Ask your teacher how to dispose of the plastic bags.

DATA AND CALCULATIONS TABLES

DATA

Mass of empty bag	**27.30**	g
Mass of bag and carbon dioxide	**28.04**	g
Mass of bag and oxygen	**27.40**	g
Volume of bag	**1230**	mL
Room temperature	**26.0**	°C
Room pressure	**758**	mm

CALCULATIONS

Apparent mass of carbon dioxide	**0.73**	g
Mass of air displaced	**1.44**	g
Actual mass of carbon dioxide	**2.17**	g
Apparent mass of oxygen	**0.10**	g
Actual mass of oxygen	**1.54**	g
Ratio of actual mass of CO_2 to actual mass of O_2	$\dfrac{2.17 \text{ g}}{1.54 \text{ g}} = 1.41$	$\dfrac{\text{g } CO_2}{\text{g } O_2}$
Formula weight of carbon dioxide	**45.1**	g

CALCULATIONS

Show your computations in the spaces provided below. Place your answers in the calculations table.

1. Calculate the apparent mass of carbon dioxide. The apparent mass is simply the difference between the mass of the bag assembly when filled with carbon dioxide and when empty.

Mass of bag and CO_2 − mass of empty bag = apparent mass CO_2

28.04 g − 27.31 g = 0.73 g

2. Calculate the actual mass of carbon dioxide. When we weigh an object in a fluid such as air, the fluid buoys up the object. The density of air at 20°C and 760 mm Hg is 1.2 g/L. A 1-liter object that is weighed in air will appear to have a mass of 1.2 grams less than if it were measured in a vacuum. For solids, this is not a significant value. One liter of aluminum, for example, has a mass of 2700 g. A liter of gas, however, is not much different than that of air. To find the actual mass of a gas, therefore, the mass of air it displaces must be added to its apparent mass. If the volume of gas is exactly one liter, than 1.2 grams

Exercises and Experiments in Modern Chemistry
Holt, Rinehart and Winston, Publishers

must be added to the apparent mass. What mass must be added if the volume of the gas is 2 liters? Use the table on page 170 to find the density of air at the pressure and temperature you performed the experiment, for you will need this first when calculating the mass of air displaced. Then calculate the actual mass of CO_2.

$$\text{Mass of air displaced} = \text{density of air} \times \text{volume of bag}$$

$$= 1.17 \text{ g/L} \times 1230 \text{ mL} \times \frac{1 \text{ L}}{1000 \text{ mL}}$$

$$= 1.44 \text{ g}$$

$$\text{Actual mass of } CO_2 = \text{mass of air displaced} + \text{apparent mass of } CO_2$$

$$= 1.44 \text{ g} + 0.73 \text{ g}$$
$$= 2.17 \text{ g}$$

3. Calculate the apparent mass of oxygen gas.

$$\text{Apparent mass of oxygen} = \text{mass of oxygen and bag} - \text{mass of empty bag}$$

$$= 27.40 \text{ g} - 27.30 \text{ g}$$
$$= 0.10 \text{ g}$$

4. Calculate the actual mass of oxygen gas.

$$\text{Actual mass of oxygen} = \text{mass of air displaced} + \text{apparent mass of oxygen}$$

$$= 1.44 \text{ g} + 0.10 \text{ g}$$
$$= 1.54 \text{ g}$$

5. Determine the ratio of the actual mass of carbon dioxide to the actual mass of oxygen.

$$\frac{\text{actual mass } CO_2}{\text{actual mass } O_2} = \frac{2.17 \text{ g}}{1.54 \text{ g}} = 1.41$$

6. Assuming the formula weight of oxygen gas is 32.0 g, what is the formula weight of carbon dioxide according to your ratio in #5?

$$\text{Formula weight of carbon dioxide} = \text{formula weight } O_2 \times \text{ratio of } CO_2 \text{ to } O_2$$

$$= 32.0 \text{ g} \times 1.41 \text{ g}$$
$$= 45.1 \text{ g}$$

DENSITY OF AIR (g/L)

Pressure (mm Hg)	15 °C	20 °C	25 °C	30 °C
690	1.11	1.09	1.08	1.06
700	1.13	1.11	1.09	1.07
710	1.14	1.12	1.10	1.09
720	1.16	1.14	1.12	1.10
730	1.18	1.16	1.14	1.12
740	1.19	1.17	1.15	1.13
750	1.21	1.19	1.17	1.15
760	1.23	1.20	1.18	1.16
770	1.24	1.22	1.20	1.18

QUESTIONS

1. What assumption are you making when you determine the formula weight of carbon dioxide?
   The mass ratio of the gas samples equals the mass ratio of the individual molecules.

2. Why is it necessary to know the pressure and temperature when determining the density of air?
   The volume of air varies inversely with pressure and directly with temperature.

Exercises and Experiments in Modern Chemistry
Holt, Rinehart and Winston, Publishers

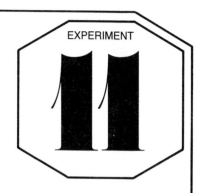

Molar Volume of a Gas

When magnesium metal reacts with hydrochloric acid, hydrogen gas is produced. The volume of this gas can be measured by using an eudiometer. Knowing the number of moles of magnesium used, we can calculate the volume of hydrogen produced per mole of magnesium consumed. The balanced equation for this reaction allows us to determine the volume that one mole of gas occupies at a specified temperature and pressure. Review Sections 10.5–10.12, 10.14, 11.5, 11.6, 11.10, and 11.11 in your textbook for additional information.

OBJECTIVE

After completing this experiment, you should be able to determine the molar volume of a gas.

APPARATUS

battery jar, 1 qt	ring stand	beakers, 250 mL, 50 mL
buret clamp	thermometer	centimeter rule
eudiometer, 50 mL	rubber stopper (one-hole, #00)	

MATERIALS

magnesium ribbon, untarnished	thread	hydrochloric acid, 6 *M*

SAFETY

Begin this experiment by taking the necessary safety precautions. Wear safety goggles, apron, and gloves. Read all safety cautions in your procedures and discuss them with your teacher. Conduct this experiment by using good safety techniques. See pages 118 and 106.

Recording Your Data

After completing each step of the procedures, record your results in the data table.

PROCEDURES

1. Half fill a battery jar with water. If possible, use water that has adjusted to room temperature. Obtain a piece of magnesium ribbon from your instructor. Measure the length of magnesium ribbon to the nearest 0.1 cm. (Note: If your piece of ribbon exceeds 4.5 cm, then return it for a smaller one.) Record the length of the ribbon in the data table. Also record the mass of one meter of this ribbon. You can obtain this mass from your teacher.

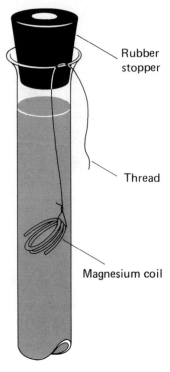

Figure 11-1

2. Roll the length of magnesium ribbon of known mass into a loose coil. Tie it with one end of a piece of thread, approximately 25 cm in length, in such a manner that all the loops of the coil are tied together.

3. This next procedure requires the use of 6 *M* hydrochloric acid. You may want to practice procedures 3 to 6 by using water in place of the acid. When you have mastered the technique using water, proceed to use the acid.

 CAUTION
Hydrochloric acid is caustic and corrosive. Avoid contact with skin and eyes. Avoid breathing vapor. Make certain that you are wearing safety goggles, apron, and gloves when working with the acid. If any acid should splash on you, immediately flush the area with water and then report the incident to your teacher. If you should spill any on the counter top or floor, ask your teacher for the appropriate spill package to be used in the clean-up.

Carefully pour approximately 10 mL of 6 *M* hydrochloric acid into a 50-mL beaker. Then pour the 10 mL of 6 *M* hydrochloric acid into the gas measuring tube or eudiometer.

4. Obtain a 250-mL beaker of water. While holding the eudiometer in a slightly tipped position, very slowly pour water from the beaker into the eudiometer, being careful to layer the water over the acid so that they do not mix. Add enough water to fill the eudiometer completely.

5. Lower the magnesium coil into the water in the eudiometer tube to a depth of about 5 cm. Insert the rubber stopper into the open end of the eudiometer to hold the thread in position. See Figure 11-1. The stopper should displace some water from the tube. This ensures that no air is left inside the tube.

6. Cover the hole of the stopper with your finger, and invert the eudiometer in the battery jar. Clamp the eudiometer tube into position on the ring stand, as shown in Figure 11-2. The acid flows down the tube (why?) and reacts with the magnesium. Is the acid now more concentrated or dilute? Describe your observations?
The acid is denser than water. The acid is being diluted.

Gas bubbles begin to form and rise to the top of the

liquid. The magnesium ribbon starts to disappear.

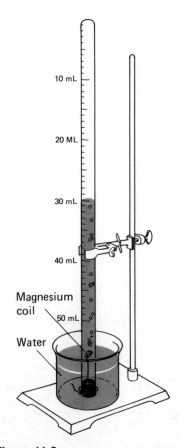

Figure 11-2

7. When the magnesium has disappeared entirely and the reaction has stopped, adjust the eudiometer tube until the liquid levels inside

Exercises and Experiments in Modern Chemistry
Holt, Rinehart and Winston, Publishers

and outside are the same. Add water to the battery jar if
necessary, using water at room temperature. If the battery jar is not
tall enough, carefully transfer the eudiometer tube and its contents to
a 1000-mL graduated cylinder or other tall vessel that has been filled
with water. Read as accurately as possible the volume of hydrogen
liberated. Take the temperature of the water in the battery jar and
assume this to be the temperature of the hydrogen gas collected. Why
is this a reasonable assumption?

The water is at room temperature, therefore the gas is at

room temperature. (They are both at thermal equilibrium.)

_____

_____

8. Obtain the vapor pressure of the water at observed temperature from
the table, Pressure of Water Vapor, in the textbook. Take a barometer
reading from the laboratory barometer. Record these data in the data
table.

DATA AND CALCULATIONS TABLES

DATA

Length of Mg used	4.2	cm
Mass per meter of Mg	0.981	g/m
Volume of H_2 collected (at laboratory conditions)	42.6	mL
Temperature of H_2 collected	20.0	°C
Barometer reading	755	mm
Vapor pressure of water at observed temperature .	17.5	mm

CALCULATIONS

Mass of Mg used	0.041	g
Moles of Mg consumed	0.0017	mol
Pressure of H_2 collected	738	mm
Volume of dry H_2 at SP	41.6	mL
Volume of dry H_2 at STP	38.8	mL
Volume of dry H_2 per mole Mg	23,000	mL/mol
Volume of 1 mole H_2 at STP	23,000	mL/mol

CALCULATIONS

Show your computations in the spaces provided below. Place your answers in the calculations table.

1. Determine the mass of your magnesium ribbon.

$$\text{Mass Mg} = 4.2 \text{ cm} \times \frac{1.0 \text{ m}}{100 \text{ cm}} \times 0.981 \frac{g}{m} = 0.041 \text{ g}$$

2. Calculate the number of moles of magnesium consumed.

$$\text{Moles Mg} = 0.041 \text{ g} \times \frac{1 \text{ mol Mg}}{24.3 \text{ g}} = 0.0017 \text{ mol}$$

3. Since the hydrogen was collected over water, two gases were actually present: hydrogen and water vapor. Calculate the partial pressure of the hydrogen gas collected. (Hint: The total atmospheric pressure equals the sum of the two partial pressures.)

$$\text{Pressure H}_2 = 755 \text{ mm} - 17.5 \text{ mm} = 738 \text{ mm}$$

4. Calculate the volume of dry hydrogen gas at standard atmospheric pressure. (Hint: How does the volume of a gas vary with a change in pressure?)

$$\text{Volume H}_2 = 42.6 \text{ mL} \times \frac{738 \text{ mm}}{755 \text{ mm}} = 41.6 \text{ mL}$$

5. Calculate the volume of dry hydrogen gas at standard temperature.

$$\text{Volume H}_2 = 41.6 \text{ mL} \times \frac{273°K}{293°K} = 38.8 \text{ mL}$$

6. Calculate the volume of dry hydrogen gas that would be produced by one mole of magnesium at standard temperature and pressure.

$$\text{Volume H}_2/\text{mole Mg} = \frac{38.8 \text{ mL}}{0.0017 \text{ mol Mg}} = 23,000 \text{ mL/mol}$$

7. Write a balanced equation for magnesium reacting with HCl. From the balanced reaction determine the volume that one mole of hydrogen gas occupies at standard temperature and pressure.

$$\text{Mg} + 2\text{HCl} \rightarrow \text{MgCl}_2 + \text{H}_{2(g)} \qquad \text{One-to-one mole ratio of Mg to H}_2$$

Therefore, molar volume of H_2 = 23,000 mL/mol at STP.

QUESTION

Why is it necessary to make a water-vapor pressure correction of the barometer reading in this experiment?
A gas collected over water has a pressure that is the sum of the partial pressure of the

dry gas and the partial pressure of the water vapor present.

Exercises and Experiments in Modern Chemistry
Holt, Rinehart and Winston, Publishers

Heat of Crystallization

In Experiment 3 you found that the temperature of a pure substance remained constant during a phase change. For example, as liquid acetamide froze, the temperature remained constant. When freezing, the molecules of acetamide in the liquid phase lost potential energy as they took up a crystalline structure. This loss in potential energy resulted in the release of heat as the liquid froze.

In this experiment you will determine the amount of heat released in calories for each gram of liquid sodium thiosulfate pentahydrate that crystallizes. In the liquid phase, substances like sodium thiosulfate tend to undercool; that is, they will cool below their normal freezing temperature without crystallizing. However, the addition of a seed crystal will cause the undercooled liquid to rapidly crystallize and release a large amount of heat. Review Chapter 12, Sections 12.11 and 12.13, for further information.

OBJECTIVES

After completing this experiment you should be able to determine the amount of heat released when a liquid crystallizes.

APPARATUS

Pyrex test tube, 25 x 100 mm
ring stand and ring
burner and tubing
wire gauze, ceramic-centered

test tube clamp
balance, centigram
sparker
2 beakers, 400 mL

styrofoam cup, 8 oz.
2 thermometers, 0.1°C
graduated cylinder, 100 mL

MATERIAL

sodium thiosulfate pentahydrate

SAFETY

Begin this experiment by taking the necessary safety precautions. Wear safety goggles, apron, and gloves. Read all safety cautions in your procedures and discuss them with your teacher. Conduct this experiment by using good safety techniques. See pages 105 and 112.

Recording Your Results

Record your results in the data table that follows the procedures.

Exercises and Experiments in Modern Chemistry
Holt, Rinehart and Winston, Publishers

PROCEDURES

1. Prepare a boiling-water bath using a 400-mL beaker.

CAUTION
Before you light the burner, check to see that long hair and loose clothing have been confined.

2. Weigh out approximately 15 g of sodium thiosulfate pentahydrate to the nearest 0.1 g. Record.

3. Place the sodium thiosulfate and the thermometer in a 25 x 100-mm Pyrex test tube. Clamp the test tube to the ring stand and lower it into the boiling-water bath. Allow the solid to melt. Continue heating until the temperature of the liquid sodium thiosulfate is approximately 75°C. Remove the test tube and contents from the boiling-water bath and place in a room-temperature water bath (use a 400-mL beaker). **Do not stir the liquid.**

4. Prepare a cold-water bath in a styrofoam cup with 75 mL of water cooled to between 10 and 15°C. Record the volume of the cold water to the nearest 0.1 mL in the data table. Determine the temperature of the cold-water bath in the styrofoam cup to the nearest 0.1°C and record in the data table.

5. When the liquid sodium thiosulfate drops below 35°C, remove the test tube from the room-temperature bath and then immediately put the test tube with the liquid sodium thiosulfate in the cold-water bath. Drop a seed crystal into the test tube. Record to the nearest 0.1°C the highest temperature reached by the cold-water bath.

6. Melt the solid sodium thiosulfate in the hot-water bath, and dispose of the liquid as directed by your instructor. Check to see that the gas valve is completely turned off. Wash your hands thoroughly before leaving the lab.

DATA AND CALCULATIONS TABLES

DATA TABLE

Mass of sodium thiosulfate	**15.0**	g
Volume of cold-water bath	**75.0**	mL
Initial temperature of cold-water bath	**13.5**	°C
Final temperature of cold-water bath	**23.5**	°C

Exercises and Experiments in Modern Chemistry
Holt, Rinehart and Winston, Publishers

CALCULATIONS TABLE

$\triangle t$ for cold-water bath	**10.0**	°C
Heat absorbed by the cold-water bath	**750**	cal
Heat released per gram of sodium thiosulfate	**50.0**	cal/g
Percentage (relative) error	**4.6**	%

CALCULATIONS

Show your computations in the spaces provided below. Place your answers in the calculations table.

1. Determine the change in temperature, $\triangle t$, of the cold-water bath.

$$\triangle t = 23.5°C - 13.5°C = 10.0°C$$

2. Calculate the heat in calories absorbed by the cold-water bath.

$$\textbf{Heat absorbed} = \textbf{M} \cdot \triangle t = \textbf{75.0 g} \cdot \textbf{10.0°C} = \textbf{750 cal}$$

3. Calculate the calories of heat released per gram of sodium thiosulfate.

$$\textbf{Heat released/gram} = \frac{\textbf{750 cal}}{\textbf{15.0 g}} = \textbf{50.0 cal/g}$$

4. The accepted value for the heat of crystallization of sodium thiosulfate is 47.8 cal/g. Calculate your percentage (relative) error.

$$\textbf{\% error} = \frac{\textbf{50.0 cal/g} - \textbf{47.8 cal/g}}{\textbf{47.8 cal/g}} \times \textbf{100\%} = \textbf{4.6\%}$$

CORRELATING YOUR FACTS

Review Chapter 12, Sections 12.11 and 12.13, and correlate what you have read in the textbook with what you have learned by performing this experiment.

Changes of Phase Involving Solids

a. solid + energy → liquid
b. liquid → solid + energy
c. solid + energy → vapor
d. solid + energy ⇆ liquid
e. solid + energy ⇆ vapor
f. vapor → solid + energy

Study the above word equations that portray the changes of phase involving solids. Which of the above word equations best represents the changes of phase taking place in 1 to 7 below? Place your answer in the space to the left of the phrase or terms.

1. _____ a _____   1. ice melting at 0°C

2. _____ b _____   2. ice freezing at 0°C

3. _____ d _____   3. a mixture of ice and water whose relative amounts remain unchanged

4. _____ c _____   4. a particle escaping from a solid and becoming a vapor particle

5. _____ e _____   5. solids like camphor and naphthalene (moth crystals) with high equilibrium vapor pressures

6. _____ f _____   6. snowing

7. _____ c _____   7. dry ice

Exercises and Experiments in Modern Chemistry
Holt, Rinehart and Winston, Publishers

EXPERIMENT

Solubility and Rate of Solution

The three factors that hasten the solution process of a solid in water will be studied in this experiment. You will observe the effect of temperature changes on the quantity of solid that can be dissolved in a given amount of water. You will also observe that some solids dissolve in water with the absorption of heat while others dissolve with the evolution of heat. This indicates that the heat of solution of a particular substance plays a role in the effect of temperature changes on the solubility of the substance. Solutes with positive heats of solution become more soluble as the temperature of their solution is raised. The effect of temperature on saturated solutions of solutes having negative heats of solution is the reverse. Review Chapter 13, Sections 13.5, 13.7, 13.8, 13.9, and 13.10, for additional information.

OBJECTIVES

After completing this experiment, you should be able to describe some of the factors affecting the solubility and the rate of solution of a solid in water. You should also be able to describe the relationship between the heat of solution of a substance and the effect of temperature on its solubility.

APPARATUS

balance, centigram
Erlenmeyer flask, 250 mL
burner and tubing
mortar and pestle

porcelain spatula
3 stoppers, No. 2
thermometer
sparker

3 Pyrex test tubes, 25 x 100 mm
plastic teaspoon
graduated cylinder, 100 mL

MATERIALS

sodium thiosulfate pentahydrate

sodium hydroxide (pellets)

SAFETY

Begin this experiment by taking the necessary safety precautions. Wear safety goggles, apron, and gloves. Read all safety cautions in your procedures and discuss them with your teacher. Conduct this experiment by using good safety techniques. See pages 107 and 115.

Recording Your Results

After completing each of the procedures, record your observations in the spaces provided.

PROCEDURES

1. Put approximately 3 mL of water in each of two test tubes.

2. Add one half of a teaspoon of sodium thiosulfate pentahydrate to one of the test tubes. Stopper the test tube and shake vigorously. Note whether heat is absorbed or evolved when the solute dissolves.

   Observations: **The test tube feels very cold. Heat is absorbed.**

3. Using a porcelain spatula, transfer 4 or 5 pellets of sodium hydroxide to the second test tube.

 CAUTION
Sodium hydroxide is a powerful caustic hydroxide. Be certain to wear safety goggles, apron, and gloves. Do not handle the pellets or permit any of the solution to touch your skin. If any should spill on you, immmediately flush the area with water and then notify your teacher.

Stopper the test tube and shake until the pellets have dissolved. Note whether heat is absorbed or evolved when the solute dissolves.

   Observations: **The test tube feels warm. Heat is evolved.**

 CAUTION
After procedure 3, immediately dispose of the sodium hydroxide solution in the test tube under the direction and supervision of your teacher. The sodium hydroxide solution may be flushed down the sink while diluting it with plenty of water.

4. Weigh out four 1.0-g portions of sodium thiosulfate pentahydrate on weighing papers. Put approximately 100 mL of water in an Erlenmeyer flask.

   For steps 5–8 determine the time needed to completely dissolve 1.0-g portions of sodium thiosulfate pentahydrate under the conditions specified.

5. Place 1.0 g of sodium thiosulfate pentahydrate in the flask. Do not stir.

   Time: **6 minutes**

6. Place 1.0 g in the same flask and continuously swirl.
   Time: **55 seconds**

Exercises and Experiments in Modern Chemistry
Holt, Rinehart and Winston, Publishers

7. Crush 1.0 g of sodium thiosulfate pentahydrate with a mortar and pestle. **See page 107 on how to use a mortar and pestle safely.** Return the crushed crystals to the weighing paper, and then transfer to the flask. Swirl continuously.

   Time: **25 seconds** _____

8. Heat the flask and solution to approximately 50°C. Add the last 1.0 g of sodium thiosulfate pentahydrate and swirl continuously.

   Time: **19 seconds at 57°C** _____

9. Place a heaping teaspoon of sodium thiosulfate pentahydrate in a test tube with approximately 3 mL of water. Stopper and shake well. Do all the crystals dissolve?

   Observations: **Not all the crystals dissolved. (Some students may find that all the crystals dissolve.)**

   _____

10. If all the crystals did dissolve, add another teaspoon of crystals. Is the solution saturated?

    Observations: **The solution is saturated; some of the crystals will not dissolve.**

    _____

    _____

11. Remove the stopper from the test tube and heat the solution in the test tube very gently. **See page 106 for the correct technique of safely heating a solution in a test tube.** When the liquid is near the boiling point, remove from the flame and observe the solution. What can you conclude about the solubility of sodium thiosulfate pentahydrate when the temperature is increased?

    Observations: **The undissolved crystals go into solution. An increase in temperature increases the solubility.**

    _____

    _____

    _____

12. Clean all apparatus at the end of this experiment. Wash your hands thoroughly before leaving the laboratory.

QUESTIONS

1. Explain why pulverizing a solid solute increases the rate of solution.
   Since solution action occurs only on the surface of the solid, grinding a solid to a

   powder increases total surface area and hence the rate of solution.

2. Why does stirring increase the rate at which most solids dissolve?
   Stirring or shaking brings fresh portions of the solvent in contact with undissolved

   solute.

3. Why does increasing the temperature, other conditions being kept constant, increase the rate of solution of sodium thiosulfate pentahydrate?
   The molecular activity of the solvent increases and the solubility of $Na_2S_2O_3 \cdot 5H_2O$

   is increased since the dissolving process is endothermic ($Na_2S_2O_3 \cdot 5H_2O$ has a positive

   heat of solution).

4. The heat of solution of lithium carbonate is -3.06 kcal/mole solute in 200 moles of H_2O. What effect would you expect increased temperature to have on the concentration of Li_2CO_3 in its saturated solution? Explain.
   It would decrease the concentration of the saturated solution, since the heat of solution

   is negative.

Exercises and Experiments in Modern Chemistry
Holt, Rinehart and Winston, Publishers

Freezing-Point Depression of a Solvent

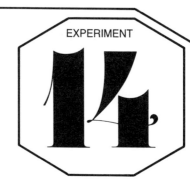

EXPERIMENT

14

When a solute is added to a pure solvent, the freezing point of the resulting solution is lowered. The freezing-point depressions of solvents are represented by the symbol $\triangle T_f$ and are expressed in °C. For example, if the freezing point of a solvent were lowered from 58.5°C to 57.3°C, $\triangle T_f$ would be 1.2°C. The freezing-point depression for a 1-molal solution is called the *molal freezing-point constant*, K_f. The relationship between K_f and T_f is simply

$$K_f = \frac{T_f}{m},$$

where

$$m = \text{molality} = \frac{\text{moles of solute}}{\text{kg solvent}}$$

For the purposes of this experiment, a more useful expression for the molal freezing-point constant is

$$K_f = \frac{\triangle T_f \cdot \text{kg solvent}}{\text{moles solute}}$$

In this experiment you will first determine the freezing temperature of acetamide. You will then add sugar and determine the new freezing temperature of the resultant solution. From your data you will calculate $\triangle T_f$ and K_f. Review Chapter 13, Section 13.12, for additional information.

OBJECTIVE

After completing this experiment, you will be able to determine the molal freezing-point constant of a pure solvent.

APPARATUS

Pyrex test tube, 25 x 100 mm
burner and tubing
sparker
balance, centigram

beaker, 600 mL
test tube clamp
ring stand

iron ring
thermometer, −10 to 110°C
wire gauze, ceramic-centered

MATERIALS

acetamide   See safety warning on next page.   sugar, granulated fine

SAFETY

Begin this experiment by taking the necessary safety precautions. Wear safety goggles, apron, and gloves. Read all safety cautions in your procedures and discuss them with your teacher. Conduct this experiment by using good safety techniques. See pages 112 and 115.

WARNING: Due to recent research on the toxicity of acetamide, this experiment at the discretion of the teacher should be performed as **a teacher demonstration only.** See Teacher Notes, pages T-19 and T-24, and consult a recent *NIOSH Registry of Toxic Effects of Chemical Substances*.

PROCEDURES

Note: If you previously completed Experiment 3 and have the freezing temperature data for pure acetamide, you may omit steps 1–3 of the procedures.

1. Place a 600-mL beaker three-fourths full of water on a ring stand and heat the water to boiling.

 CAUTION
Before lighting the burner, check to see that long hair and loose clothing have been confined. Remember to handle the heated apparatus with great care.

While the water is heating, measure out 10.00 g of acetamide. Record to the nearest 0.01 g.

2. Place the acetamide and a thermometer in a clean, dry, 25 × 100-mm Pyrex test tube. When the water boils, reduce the burner to a low flame. Clamp the test tube in the hot-water bath as shown in Figure 14-1. When the temperature of the acetamide reaches 90°C, remove the test tube from the boiling-water bath, and secure opposite the bath. See Figure 14-2.

3. Immediately begin to read the temperature of the cooling liquid acetamide at 30-second intervals. Record the temperatures to the nearest 0.1°C. Continuously stir the liquid acetamide with the thermometer. If crystals form on the sides of the test tube above the liquid, use the thermometer to scrape the crystals gently down into the liquid.

 CAUTION
If your mercury thermometer should ever break, notify your teacher, who will clean up the spill.

If the temperature of the liquid drops to 70°C without freezing, place a few seed crystals of acetamide into the liquid. Continue to take readings for about 3 minutes after freezing begins.

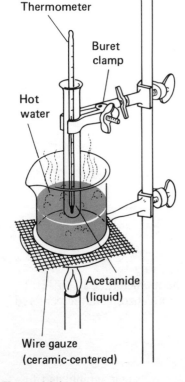

Thermometer

Buret clamp

Hot water

Acetamide (liquid)

Wire gauze (ceramic-centered)

Figure 14-1

Exercises and Experiments in Modern Chemistry
Holt, Rinehart and Winston, Publishers

4. Weigh out 1.75 g of sugar. Add this solute to the acetamide in the
   test tube. Reheat the mixture in the boiling-water bath. Stir
   continuously until all of the solute has dissolved. Remove from the
   boiling-water bath and secure the test tube as in Figure 14-2. Repeat
   procedure 3.

5. Repeat procedure 4 for an additional 1.75 g of sugar.

6. At the end of this experiment, check to see that the gas valve is
   completely shut off. Ask your instructor how to dispose of the
   acetamide. Wash your hands thoroughly before leaving the laboratory.

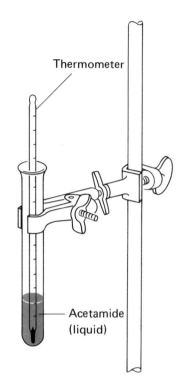

Figure 14-2

DATA AND CALCULATIONS TABLES

DATA TABLE

Time (s)	Temperature (°C)		
	Acetamide (10.00 g)	Acetamide + 1.75 g sugar	Acetamide + 3.50 g sugar
0	90.0	90.0	93.0
30	85.0	85.0	85.0
60	81.0	80.0	82.0
90	80.0	78.0	79.0
120	80.0	75.0	75.0
150	80.0	76.3	72.5
180	80.0	76.3	72.5
210	80.0	75.8	72.3
240	80.0	75.5	72.0
270		75.0	71.2
300		74.5	70.5
330			

CALCULATIONS TABLE

	Freezing Temperature (°C)	$\triangle T_f$ (°C)	Moles of Solute (mol)	K_f $\dfrac{°C\text{-kg solvent}}{\text{moles solute}}$
Acetamide (pure)	80.0			
Acetamide + 1.75 g sugar	76.3	3.7	0.00512	7.2
Acetamide + 3.50 g sugar	72.5	7.5	0.0102	7.4

Average K_f __7.3__ $\dfrac{°C\text{-kg}}{mol}$

CALCULATIONS

Show your computations in the space provided below. Place your answers in the calculations table.

1. Plot a full-page graph of your data. Put all three sets of data on the same graph. Place temperature on the vertical axis and time on the horizontal axis. Start the temperature units at 50°C. **See sample graph.**

2. From the graph, determine the freezing temperatures of pure acetamide, acetamide + 1.75 g of sugar, and acetamide + 3.50 g of sugar. Record in the calculations table.

Freezing temperatures: 10.00 g acetamide   80.0°C
    + 1.75 g sugar   76.3°C
    + 3.50 g sugar   72.5°C

3. Calculate $\triangle T_f$ for the addition of 1.75 g of sugar and the $\triangle T_f$ for the addition of 3.50 g of sugar. Record.

$$\triangle T_f \text{ for 1.75 g sugar} = 80.0°C - 76.3°C = 3.7°C$$
$$\triangle T_f \text{ for 3.50 g sugar} = 80.0°C - 72.5°C = 7.5°C$$

4. Calculate the moles of solute in 1.75 g and 3.50 g of sugar. Record.

$$\text{moles of sugar} = 1.75 \text{ g} \times \frac{1 \text{ mole}}{342 \text{ g}} = 0.00512 \text{ mol}$$

$$\text{moles of sugar} = 3.50 \text{ g} \times \frac{1 \text{ mole}}{342 \text{ g}} = 0.0102 \text{ mol}$$

Exercises and Experiments in Modern Chemistry
Holt, Rinehart and Winston, Publishers

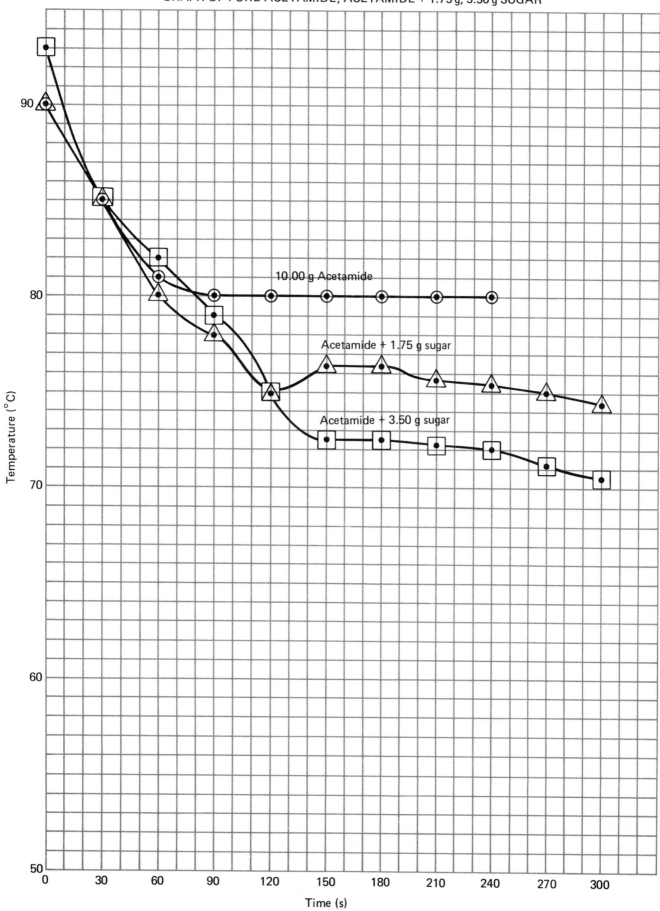

GRAPH OF PURE ACETAMIDE, ACETAMIDE + 1.75 g, 3.50 g SUGAR

10.00 g Acetamide

Acetamide + 1.75 g sugar

Acetamide + 3.50 g sugar

Temperature (°C)

Time (s)

5. Calculate the K_f for the addition of 1.75 g of sugar and the K_f for the addition of 3.50 g of sugar. Record.

$$K_f = \frac{\triangle T_f \cdot \textbf{kg acetamide}}{\textbf{moles of sugar}} = \frac{3.7°C \times 10.00 \text{ g} \times 0.0010 \text{ kg/g}}{0.00512 \text{ mol}} = 7.2 \frac{°C - \text{kg}}{\text{mol}}$$

$$K_f = \frac{7.5°C \times 10.00 \text{ g} \times 0.0010 \text{ kg/g}}{0.0102 \text{ mol}} = 7.4 \frac{°C - \text{kg}}{\text{mol}}$$

6. Calculate the average K_f for acetamide. Record.

$$\textbf{Average } K_f = \frac{7.4 + 7.2}{2} \quad \frac{°C - \text{kg}}{\text{mol}} = 7.3 \frac{°C - \text{kg}}{\text{mol}}$$

QUESTIONS

1. What happened to the $\triangle T_f$ of the acetamide (solvent) when the number of grams of sugar was doubled? What happened to K_f?

$\triangle T_f$ **was approximately doubled. K_f remained constant within experimental uncertainty.**

2. What would happen to $\triangle T_f$ and K_f if 1.75 g of camphor ($C_{10}H_{16}O$) were added instead of sugar?

1.75 g camphor = 1.75 g $\times \dfrac{\text{1 mole camphor}}{\text{152 g camphor}}$ = 0.0115 mol. There are over twice the

number of moles in 1.75 g of camphor than there are in 1.75 g of sugar. Since $\triangle T_f$

varies with the number of particles present, $\triangle T_f$ would double. K_f would remain constant,

since $\triangle T_f$ is divided by the moles of solute.

3. The temperature of a pure substance remains constant during solidification. Is the same true for a mixture? Justify your answer from the graph you plotted.

The temperature does *not* remain constant during the solidification of a mixture.

According to the graph, there is a gradual drop of about 0.5 °C for each 30 seconds.

ADDITIONAL ACTIVITY

Repeat the above procedures using a different solute. Consult your instructor for possible substances.

Exercises and Experiments in Modern Chemistry
Holt, Rinehart and Winston, Publishers

Reacting Ionic Species in Aqueous Solution

Ionic solids dissolve in water forming positive *cations* and negative *anions.* If two solutions containing dissolved ionic solids are mixed together, new combinations of cations and anions are possible. Sometimes the new combination of ions is not soluble in water and a precipitate (solid) forms. For example, silver nitrate in solution breaks up into Ag^+ and NO_3^- ions, while KCl in solution breaks up into K^+ and Cl^- ions. If the two solutions are mixed, the positive Ag^+ ions combine with the negative Cl^- ions to form an insoluble AgCl precipitate. The overall reaction is

$$Ag^+_{(aq)} + NO_3^-_{(aq)} + K^+_{(aq)} + Cl^-_{(aq)} \rightarrow AgCl_{(s)} + K^+_{(aq)} + NO_3^-_{(aq)} \qquad (1)$$

Since the K^+ and NO_3^- ions did not form a precipitate, they are called spectator ions. The *net ionic* equation for the reaction is written with the spectator ions omitted:

$$Ag^+_{(aq)} + Cl^-_{(aq)} \rightarrow AgCl_{(s)} \qquad (2)$$

In this experiment you will mix 6 different ionic solutions, two at a time, and observe which combinations form precipitates. You will also determine which pairs of ions form the precipitates and write the appropriate net ionic equations for the reactions. Review Chapter 14, Section 14.5, for additional information.

OBJECTIVE

After completing this experiment, you should be able to devise a method to determine which pair of ions form a precipitate and write the appropriate net ionic equation for the reaction.

APPARATUS

plastic sheet

MATERIALS

0.1 M Ba(NO$_3$)$_2$	0.1 M NaNO$_3$	0.1 M Na$_2$CrO$_4$
0.1 M Na$_2$SO$_4$	0.1 M BaCl$_2$	0.1 M NaCl

SAFETY

Begin this experiment by taking the necessary safety precautions. Wear safety goggles, apron, and gloves. Conduct this experiment by using good safety techniques. See page 103.

Recording Your Results

Use the data table provided at the end of the procedures. For each possible combination, indicate **PPT** if a precipitate formed and **clear** if no precipitate formed.

PROCEDURES

1. Place a drop or two of one of the solutions on the plastic sheet. Add a drop or two of a second solution. **Do not allow the tip of the dropper to touch the drops on the plastic sheet.** Record your result.

2. Choose a clean spot and repeat the above procedure for another pair of solutions. Repeat for all possible combinations listed in the data table.

3. At the end of this experiment follow your teacher's directions for the cleaning of all apparatus and the disposal of chemicals. Remember to wash your hands thoroughly before leaving the laboratory.

DATA TABLE

	Na^+ Cl^-	Na^+ NO_3^-	Na^+ CrO_4^{--}	Na^+ SO_4^{--}	Ba^{++} Cl^-
Ba^{++} NO_3^-	clear	clear	PPT	PPT	clear
Ba^{++} Cl^-	clear	clear	PPT	PPT	
Na^+ SO_4^{--}	clear	clear	clear		
Na^+ CrO_4^{--}	clear	clear			
Na^+ NO_3^-	clear				

QUESTIONS

1. When a precipitate formed, a new combination of ions must have occurred. For example, suppose a precipitate forms when $CaCl_2$ is mixed with Na_2SO_4. The possible combinations that could have formed the precipitate are $CaSO_4$ and NaCl. Write the possible formulas for each precipitate that you observed.

NaNO₃ and BaCrO₄

NaNO₃ and BaSO₄

NaCl and BaCrO₄

NaCl and BaSO₄

Exercises and Experiments in Modern Chemistry
Holt, Rinehart and Winston, Publishers

2. For each pair of possible precipitates listed in question #1, attempt to eliminate one of them using your data table. For example, of the two possible combinations stated in question #1, NaCl could be eliminated, since it is also one of the original clear solutions. In a similar manner, list all the new combinations that can be eliminated as possible precipitates.

NaCl and NaNO$_3$ were both original clear solutions and, therefore, can be eliminated.

3. Write a balanced equation for each precipitate formed. Use reaction (1) in the introductory section as a guide.

$Ba^{++} + 2NO_3^- + 2Na^+ + CrO_4^{--} \rightarrow BaCrO_{4(s)} + 2Na^+ + 2NO_3^-$

$Ba^{++} + 2NO_3^- + 2Na^+ + SO_4^{--} \rightarrow BaSO_{4(s)} + 2Na^+ + 2NO_3^-$

$Ba^{++} + 2Cl^- + 2Na^+ + CrO_4^{--} \rightarrow BaCrO_{4(s)} + 2Na^+ + 2Cl^-$

$Ba^{++} + 2Cl^- + 2Na^+ + SO_4^{--} \rightarrow BaSO_{4(s)} + 2Na^+ + 2Cl^-$

Write a net ionic equation for each reaction in which a precipitate formed. Use reaction (2) in the introductory section as a guide.

$Ba^{++} + CrO_4^{--} \rightarrow BaCrO_{4(s)}$

$Ba^{++} + SO_4^{--} \rightarrow BaSO_{4(s)}$

CORRELATING YOUR FACTS

Review Chapter 14, Section 14.5, and correlate what you have read in the textbook with what you have learned by performing this experiment.

Study the following information that was obtained from a chart entitled Solubilities of Compounds. The solubilities were given in moles of anhydrous compound that can be dissolved in 1 liter of water at the indicated temperature.

Compound	Formula	20 °C
silver nitrate	$AgNO_3$	13
silver chloride	$AgCl$	1×10^{-5}
sodium nitrate	$NaNO_3$	10.3
sodium chloride	$NaCl$	6.2

According to the chart, $NaNO_3$, $NaCl$, and $AgNO_3$ are very soluble ionic compounds. Their aqueous solutions contain hydrated ions that can be present in very high concentrations at room temperature.

1. Suppose that at room temperature we mix fairly concentrated solutions of NaCl and $AgNO_3$. In our single solution environment, what four ionic species are present?

$Na^+_{(aq)}$, $Cl^-_{(aq)}$, $Ag^+_{(aq)}$, $NO_3^-_{(aq)}$

2. Upon mixing the concentrated solutions of NaCl and $AgNO_3$, what compound is likely to precipitate out of solution and why?

The concentrations of the Ag^+ and Cl^- ions in solution

greatly exceed the solubility of AgCl, which is only

1×10^{-5} moles/liter of water at 20 °C. Excess Ag^+ and

Cl^- ions will separate from the solution as a precipitate

of solid AgCl.

3. Write the empirical equation for the precipitation reaction that takes place in #2 above.

$NaCl + AgNO_3 \rightarrow NaNO_3 + AgCl_{(s)}$

4. As is shown in the solubility chart, the salts NaCl, $AgNO_3$, and $NaNO_3$ are all very soluble in water. Only their aqueous ions are present in the solution environment. A more useful representation for the reaction that takes place in #3 would be to write the ionic equation. Write the ionic equation.

$Na^+_{(aq)} + Cl^-_{(aq)} + Ag^+_{(aq)} + NO_3^-_{(aq)} \rightarrow Na^+_{(aq)} + NO_3^-_{(aq)} +$

$Ag^+Cl^-_{(s)}$

5. The ionic equation in #4 shows clearly that the $Na^+_{(aq)}$ and $NO_3^-_{(aq)}$ ions take no part in the action. What is the name given to ions that take no part in a chemical reaction?

They are called spectator ions.

6. Suppose we retain only the reacting species in our chemical equation. The chemical action that takes place is then shown most simply by the net ionic equation. Write the net ionic equation for the reaction of NaCl with $AgNO_3$.

$Ag^+_{(aq)} + Cl^-_{(aq)} \rightarrow Ag^+Cl^-_{(s)}$

Exercises and Experiments in Modern Chemistry
Holt, Rinehart and Winston, Publishers

Hydronium Ion Concentration, pH

EXPERIMENT

16

The concentration of hydronium ion is usually represented by the expression $[H_3O^+]$, which means the hydronium ion concentration in moles (gram-ions) per liter of solution. A one molar (1.0-*M*) solution of hydronium ions contains 1 mole, 19 g, of hydronium ion per liter of solution.

Pure water is slightly ionized and contains 0.0000001 moles of hydronium ion per liter. Its hydronium ion concentration, $[H_3O^+]$, is therefore represented as 1.0×10^{-7} *M* or 10^{-7} *M*. Since pure water is neutral, its hydroxide ion concentration is also 1.0×10^{-7} *M* or 10^{-7} *M*. In any water solution, the product of the hydronium and hydroxide ion concentrations is known as the ion-product of water and is equal to 1.0×10^{-14}. This equilibrium is represented by the equation

$$H_2O + H_2O \rightleftarrows H_3O^+ + OH^-$$

For neutral water (25 °C),

$$K_w = [H_3O^+] \times [OH^-] = 1 \times 10^{-14}$$
$$= (1 \times 10^{-7})(1 \times 10^{-7}) = 1 \times 10^{-14}$$

The pH of a solution is defined as the common logarithm of the reciprocal of the hydronium ion concentration. For neutral water,

$$pH = \log \frac{1}{0.0000001} = \log \frac{1}{10^{-7}}$$

Therefore, pH $= \log 10^7$, and pH $= 7$. If the hydronium ion concentration of a solution is greater than that of pure water ($[H_3O^+] > 1 \times 10^{-7}$ *M*), the pH of the solution will be numerically less than 7 and the solution considered acidic. Thus for a solution that is acidic such as 0.000001-*M* (1×10^{-6}-*M*) HCl that is completely ionized, the hydronium ion concentration is greater than water (1×10^{-6} *M* $> 1 \times 10^{-7}$ *M*) and the pH is 6 (numerically less than 7). For acidic solutions, therefore, the hydronium ion concentration is greater than 10^{-7} *M* and the pH is *smaller* than 7. For acidic solutions, the smaller the pH, the larger the hydronium ion concentration.

If the solution is basic, its hydronium ion concentration is less than 10^{-7} *M* and its pH is *larger* than 7. For a 1×10^{-6}-*M* solution of NaOH (completely dissociated), the hydroxide ion concentration is 1×10^{-6}. Its hydronium ion concentration therefore is 1×10^{-8} ($[H_3O^+] = 10^{-8}$) and its pH is 8. For basic solutions, the larger the pH the smaller the hydronium ion concentration. Review Chapter 16, Sections 16.6 to 16.8, for further information.

OBJECTIVE
After completing this experiment, you should be able to determine the pH of various solutions and to describe the effect of dilution on the pH of acids and a metallic hydroxide.

APPARATUS
beaker, 250 mL
12 test tubes, small

glass plate
stirring rod

graduated cylinders, 10 mL, 50 mL
sheet of white paper

MATERIALS
pH papers, wide and narrow range
0.10 M ammonia water
0.10 M hydrochloric acid
0.050 M sodium carbonate

0.10 M sodium hydrogen carbonate
0.10 M acetic acid
0.10 M ammonium acetate

0.033 M phosphoric acid
0.10 M sodium chlrodie
0.10 M sodium hydroxide

SAFETY

Begin this experiment by taking the necessary safety precautions. Wear safety goggles, apron, and gloves. Read all safety cautions in your procedures and discuss them with your teacher. Conduct this experiment by using good safety techniques. See pages 100 and 103.

Recording Your Results
After completing each of the procedures, record your observations in the spaces provided for your data in the data tables.

PROCEDURES

1. Test for the pH of each of the solutions by dipping a stirring rod into each of the solutions and applying first to the wide-range pH papers and, if necessary, to the narrow-range paper. See Figure 16-1 for the correct technique. Complete Data Table I.

 CAUTION
Whenever you handle acids or bases, wear safety goggles, apron, and gloves. Avoid contact with skin and eyes. Avoid breathing vapors. If any should spill on you, immediately flush the area with water and then notify your teacher.

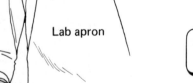

Safety goggles

Lab apron

Stirring rod with drop of solution to be tested

Glass plate

Indicator test strips

Sheet of white paper

Figure 16-1

2. Dilute 5.0 mL of 0.10 M HCl to $5\overline{0}$ mL. Save 5 mL of the diluted solution in a properly labeled test tube and use another 5.0 mL for the next dilution to $5\overline{0}$ mL. Repeat the dilution process 2 more times. When completed, you should have 0.10 M, 0.010 M, 0.0010 M, and 0.00010 M solutions of HCl. Repeat the entire process for 0.10 M NaOH and 0.10 M acetic acid. Test each concentration with pH paper and record your results in Data Table II.

Exercises and Experiments in Modern Chemistry
Holt, Rinehart and Winston, Publishers

3. Clean all apparatus at the end of this experiment. Remember to wash
   your hands before leaving the laboratory.

DATA AND CALCULATIONS TABLES

DATA TABLE I

0.1-M Solutions	Numerical pH
HCl	1
$HC_2H_3O_2$	3
H_3PO_4	1.5
NaOH	13
NH_3	11
NaCl	7
Na_2CO_3	11$^+$
$NaHCO_3$	8$^+$
$NH_4C_2H_3O_2$	7

CALCULATIONS TABLE I

← Decreasing Acid Strength →   Increasing Base Strength →

HCl
H_3PO_4
$HC_2H_3O_2$
$NH_4C_2H_3O_2$
NaCl
$NaHCO_3$
NH_3
Na_2CO_3
NaOH

DATA TABLE II

CALCULATIONS TABLE II

Concentration (M)	Observed pH				Calculated pH	
	HCl	NaOH	$HC_2H_3O_2$		HCl	NaOH
0.10		**Student**			1	13
0.010		**answers**			2	12
0.0010					3	11
0.00010					4	10

CALCULATIONS

1. Order the solutions in procedure 1 according to decreasing acid strength (strongest acid first). Record in Calculations Table I.
2. Calculate the pH values for the given concentrations of procedure 2. Record in Calculations Table II.

QUESTIONS

1. Which of the substances among those having a definite acidic reaction is (a) the strongest acid, (b) the weakest acid?

   (a) __**HCl is the strongest acid.**_____

   (b) __**$HC_2H_3O_2$ is the weakest acid.**_____

2. What effect does dilution have on the pH of (a) an acid, (b) a base?

   (a) __**The pH of an acid is increased.**_____

   (b) __**The pH of a base is decreased.**_____

Exercises and Experiments in Modern Chemistry
Holt, Rinehart and Winston, Publishers

EXPERIMENT
17

Titration of an Acid and a Base

Titration is a process by which the concentration of a solution is determined by its reaction with a standard solution, the concentration of which is precisely known. The process consists of the gradual addition of the standard solution to a measured quantity of the solution of unknown concentration until the same number of gram-equivalent weights (equivalents) of each solute has been used. The point in the titration at which equal equivalents are present is known as the equivalence point. An indicator is used to detect the equivalence point in the process.

An indicator that undergoes a color change in the pH region of the equivalence point of the reactants should be selected. In this experiment, the equivalence point will be reached at a pH of about 7. Litmus is a suitable indicator. Where the precision is not too exacting, little difference will be noticed if phenolphthalein is chosen instead of litmus. Phenolphthalein is a somewhat more suitable indicator for beginning students.

The concentration of solutions in titration is commonly expressed in *normality*. The advantage of normality over molarity (formality) or molality is that equal volumes of solutions of the same normality are always chemically equivalent. If solution No. 1 has a higher normality than solution No. 2, a smaller volume of No. 1 will be required to reach an equivalence point with a given volume of No. 2. *That is, the relative volumes are inversely proportional to the normalities of the solutions when equal equivalents of both have reacted:*

$$\frac{N_1}{N_2} = \frac{V_2}{V_1}$$

The normality of the standard solution and the volumes of both solutions are known when the equivalence point of the titration is reached. Therefore, the normality of the solution of unknown normality can be found:

$$N_2 = \frac{N_1 V_1}{V_2}$$

Neutralization is the reaction between hydronium ions and hydroxide ions to form water. In a broader sense, acid-base neutralization is the reaction that occurs when equivalent quantities of an acid and a base are mixed. Review Chapter 16, Sections 16.2, 16.5, 16.10, 16.11, 16.13, and 16.14 for further information.

OBJECTIVE

After completing this experiment, you should be able to standardize the concentration, expressed in normality, of a basic solution.

APPARATUS
two beakers, 150 mL
wash bottle
two burets

double buret clamp
Erlenmeyer flask

ring stand
beaker, 125 mL (for discards)

MATERIALS
solution of hydrochloric acid, 0.5 N
solution of sodium hydroxide

phenolphthalein indicator

SAFETY

Begin this experiment by taking the necessary safety precautions. Wear safety goggles, apron, and gloves. Read all safety cautions in your procedures and discuss them with your teacher. Conduct this experiment by using good safety techniques. See pages 118 and 119.

Recording Your Results
Where instructed to in the procedures, record your data in the data table.

PROCEDURES

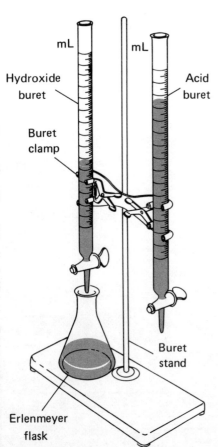

Figure 17-1

1. Set up apparatus as shown in Figure 17-1. Take approximately 100 mL each of hydrochloric acid and sodium hydroxide separately in clean, dry, labeled 150-mL beakers.

CAUTION
Whenever you handle acids or bases, wear safety goggles, apron, and gloves. Avoid contact with skin and eyes. Avoid breathing vapors. If any acid or base should spill on you, immediately flush the area with water and then notify your teacher.

Pour a 10-mL portion of sodium hydroxide solution directly from the beaker into one buret. Rinse the walls of the buret thoroughly with this solution, allow it to drain through the stopcock and into a beaker, and then discard it. Rinse the buret two more times in similar fashion, using a new 10-mL portion of sodium hydroxide each time. Discard all rinsings. Then fill the buret with sodium hydroxide solution above the zero mark. Withdraw enough solution to remove the air from the jet tip and bring the liquid level into the graduated region of the buret. In a similar fashion, rinse and fill the acid buret.

2. Record the initial reading of each buret, estimating to the nearest 0.01 mL, in the data table. Then draw off about 15 mL of the hydroxide into an Erlenmeyer flask and add approximately 25 mL of distilled water to give volume to the solution. Add one or two drops of phenolphthalein solution as an indicator. Now run in the acid solution slowly, stopping occasionally to mix, using a swirling motion. See Figure 17-2. Wash down the inside surface of the flask frequently with a little distilled water, using your wash bottle. Why may distilled

Exercises and Experiments in Modern Chemistry
Holt, Rinehart and Winston, Publishers

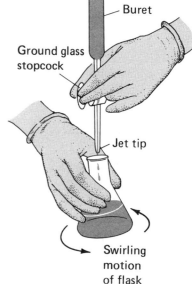

- Buret
- Ground glass stopcock
- Jet tip
- Swirling motion of flask

Figure 17-2

water be added without disturbing the titration procedure?
The number of equivalents of base is not changed by
the addition of distilled water to the flask.

_____

_____

_____

3. When the pink color of the solution begins to disappear at the point of contact with the acid, add the acid drop by drop, swirling the flask gently after each addition, until the last drop added causes the color to disappear. A sheet of white paper under the flask makes it easier to detect the color change. Now add the basic solution dropwise just to return the color. Go back and forth over the end point several times until one drop of the basic solution just brings out a faint pink color. Wash down the inside surface of the flask and make dropwise additions if necessary to re-establish the faint pink equivalence point color. Read the burets, estimating to the nearest 0.01 mL, and record in the data table.

Repeat the titration for a second and third trial.

4. Clean and rinse all apparatus at the end of this experiment. Discard all excess solutions by pouring them down the drain with plenty of water. Remember to wash your hands before leaving the laboratory.

DATA AND CALCULATIONS TABLES

	DATA				CALCULATIONS		
	Buret Readings (mL)				HCl	NaOH	
	HCl		NaOH		Volume (mL)	Volume (mL)	Normality (N)
TRIAL	initial	final	initial	final			
1	0.70	10.90	5.08	13.58	10.20	8.50	0.600
2	10.90	20.80	13.58	21.80	9.90	8.22	0.602
3	20.80	28.81	21.80	28.33	8.01	6.53	0.613
	Normality of HCl _____0.500_____ N				Average Normality of NaOH _____0.605_____ N		

CALCULATIONS

Show your computations in the spaces provided below. Place your answers in the calculations table.

1. Calculate the volumes of acid used in the three trials. Record in the calculations table.

Trial #1	**Volume HCl = 10.90 mL − 0.70 mL = 10.20 mL**
Trial #2	**Volume HCl = 20.80 mL − 10.90 mL = 9.90 mL**
Trial #3	**Volume HCl = 28.81 mL − 20.80 mL = 8.01 mL**

2. Calculate the volumes of base used in the three trials. Record.

Trial #1	**Volume NaOH = 13.58 mL − 5.08 mL = 8.50 mL**
Trial #2	**Volume NaOH = 21.80 mL − 13.58 mL = 8.22 mL**
Trial #3	**Volume NaOH = 28.33 mL − 21.80 mL = 6.53 mL**

3. Calculate the normality of the basic solution for each trial, using the equation given in the Introduction. Record.

Trial #1 $\text{Normality NaOH} = \dfrac{\text{Normality Acid} \times \text{Volume Acid}}{\text{Volume Base}}$

$$= \frac{0.500\ N \times 10.20\ \text{mL}}{8.50\ \text{mL}} = 0.600\ N$$

Trial #2 $\text{Normality NaOH} = \dfrac{0.500\ N \times 9.90\ \text{mL}}{8.22\ \text{mL}} = 0.602\ N$

Trial #3 $\text{Normality NaOH} = \dfrac{0.500\ N \times 8.01\ \text{mL}}{6.53\ \text{mL}} = 0.613\ N$

4. Calculate the average normality of the base. Record.

$$\text{Average Normality} = \frac{0.600\ N + 0.602\ N + 0.613\ N}{3} = 0.605\ N$$

Exercises and Experiments in Modern Chemistry
Holt, Rinehart and Winston, Publishers

Percentage of Acetic Acid in Vinegar

EXPERIMENT

18

The quantity of acid in a sample of vinegar may be found by titrating the sample against a standard basic solution. Most commercial vinegars have a mass percentage of between 4.0% and 5.5% acetic acid. By determining the volume of sodium hydroxide solution of known normality necessary to neutralize a measured quantity of the vinegar, the normality of the vinegar can be calculated. Review Chapter 16, Sections 16.2, 16.5, 16.10, 16.11, 16.13, and 16.14, for further information.

OBJECTIVE

After completing this experiment, you should be able to determine the acidity of a vinegar sample of unknown acidity using the titration technique.

APPARATUS

two beakers, 150 mL
double buret clamp
two burets

beaker, 125 mL (for discards)
Erlenmeyer flask

ring stand
wash bottle

MATERIALS

white vinegar

phenolphthalein indicator

standardized solution of NaOH

SAFETY

Begin this experiment by taking the necessary safety precautions. Wear safety goggles, apron, and gloves. Read all safety cautions in your procedures and discuss them with your teacher. Conduct this experiment by using good safety techniques. See pages 118 to 120.

Recording Your Results
Where instructed to in the procedures, record your data in the data table.

PROCEDURES

1. Transfer approximately 100 mL each of vinegar and sodium hydroxide solutions to separate clean, dry, labeled 150-mL beakers.

   CAUTION
   Whenever you handle acids or bases, wear safety goggles, apron, and gloves. Avoid contact with skin and eyes. Avoid breathing vapors. If any acid or base should spill on you, immediately flush the area with water and then notify your teacher.

Pour directly from the beaker into one buret a 10-mL portion of the vinegar. Rinse the walls of the buret thoroughly with the vinegar, allow it to drain through the stopcock, and discard it. Rinse the buret two more times in a similar fashion, using a new 10-mL portion of vinegar each time. Discard all rinsings. Then fill the buret with vinegar above the zero mark. Withdraw enough solution to remove the air from the jet tip and bring the liquid level into the graduated region of the buret. In similar fashion, rinse and fill the other buret with sodium hydroxide solution. Record the initial readings of both burets, estimating to the nearest 0.01 mL.

2. Withdraw about 15 mL of the vinegar into an Erlenmeyer flask. Add 50 mL of distilled water to the flask to add volume, thus making it easier to determine the color change when the equivalence point is reached. Add one or two drops of phenolphthalein solution to serve as an indicator. Then titrate the vinegar with the standard solution of sodium hydroxide, swirling and washing down the flask frequently. Add the hydroxide solution, drop by drop near the end of the operation, until the last drop (after swirling) just turns the solution a pink color. Now add successive quantities of both solutions drop by drop, going back and forth over the equivalence point, until it is clearly established. This is indicated by the slightest suggestion of pink coloration in the flask. The equivalence point is most satisfactorily determined with the flask resting on a sheet of white paper and with a beaker of distilled water alongside for comparison purposes. Record the final buret readings of both solutions, estimating to the nearest 0.01 mL.

3. Discard the liquid in the flask, rinse thoroughly with distilled water, and run a second titration, proceeding as before. A third titration should also be made. Chemists like to have three consistent determinations before they feel confident that their titrations are reliable.

DATA AND CALCULATIONS TABLES

DATA

| | Buret Readings (mL) | | | |
| | NaOH | | Vinegar | |
TRIAL	initial	final	initial	final
1	1.38	11.57	0.55	9.21
2	11.57	23.69	9.21	19.43
3	23.69	32.33	19.43	26.67
Normality of NaOH		0.605	N	

Exercises and Experiments in Modern Chemistry
Holt, Rinehart and Winston, Publishers

CALCULATIONS (Method I)

TRIAL	1	2	3
VOLUME NaOH (mL)	10.19	12.12	8.64
VOLUME Vinegar (mL)	8.66	10.22	7.24
NORMALITY Vinegar (N)	0.712	0.717	0.722

Average normality of vinegar .... **0.717** N

G-eq. weight of $HC_2H_3O_2$ .... **60.0** g

Mass of acetic acid per L of vinegar .... **43.0** g/L

% mass of acetic acid in vinegar .... **4.30** %

CALCULATIONS (Method II)

Molarity of NaOH   0.605   M

TRIAL	1	2	3
VOLUME NaOH (mL)	10.19	12.12	8.64
VOLUME Vinegar (mL)	8.66	10.22	7.24
MOLES NaOH (mol)	0.00617	0.00733	0.00523
MOLES $HC_2H_3O_2$ (mol)	0.00617	0.00733	0.00523
MOLARITY $HC_2H_3O_2$ (M)	0.712	0.717	0.722

Average molarity of $HC_2H_3O_2$ .... **0.717** M

Mass of 1 mole of $HC_2H_3O_2$ .... **60.0** g/mol

Mass of $HC_2H_3O_2$ in 1 L of vinegar .... **43.0** g/L

% mass of acetic acid in vinegar .... **4.30** %

Exercises and Experiments in Modern Chemistry
Holt, Rinehart and Winston, Publishers

CALCULATIONS

Note: You may choose either Method I or Method II to perform the necessary calculations.

Method I: Calculations based on normality

1. Calculate the volumes of vinegar and NaOH used for each of the three trials. Record in the calculations table for Method I.

VOLUME NaOH:	#1	11.57 mL − 1.38 mL = 10.19 mL
	#2	23.69 mL − 11.57 mL = 12.12 mL
	#3	32.33 mL − 23.69 mL = 8.64 mL
VOLUME Vinegar:	#1	9.21 mL − 0.55 mL = 8.66 mL
	#2	19.43 mL − 9.21 mL = 10.22 mL
	#3	26.67 mL − 19.43 mL = 7.24 mL

2. Use the equation in the introduction for Experiment 17 to calculate the normality of the vinegar for each trial. Record.

#1
$$N_{vinegar} = \frac{N_{NaOH} \cdot V_{NaOH}}{V_{vinegar}} = \frac{0.605\ N \cdot 10.19\ mL}{8.66\ mL} = 0.712\ N$$

#2
$$= \frac{0.605\ N \cdot 12.12\ mL}{10.22\ mL} = 0.717\ N$$

#3
$$= \frac{0.605\ N \cdot 8.64\ mL}{7.24\ mL} = 0.722\ N$$

3. Calculate the average normality of vinegar. Record.

$$\textbf{Average normality} = \frac{0.712\ N + 0.717\ N + 0.722\ N}{3} = 0.717\ N$$

4. Acetic acid, $HC_2H_3O_2$, is a *monoprotic* acid. Calculate the g-eq. wt. of acetic acid. Record.

$$H = 1.00\ g \times 4 = 4.00\ g$$

$$C = 12.0\ g \times 2 = 24.0\ g$$

$$O = 16.0\ g \times 2 = \underline{32.0\ g}$$
$$60.0\ g$$

5. By definition,

$$\textbf{normality} = \frac{\textbf{number of equivalents of solute}}{\textbf{1 liter of solution}}$$

Exercises and Experiments in Modern Chemistry
Holt, Rinehart and Winston, Publishers

A 0.500 N solution, for example, has 0.500 equivalents of solute in one liter of solution. The mass of acetic acid per liter of vinegar is

$$\frac{\text{mass } HC_2H_3O_2}{\text{1 liter vinegar}} = \frac{\text{number of equivalents } HC_2H_3O_2 \cdot \text{g-eq. wt. } HC_2H_3O_2}{\text{1 liter vinegar}}$$

A 0.500 N solution of vinegar would contain

$$\frac{\text{0.500 equivalents } HC_2H_3O_2}{\text{1 liter vinegar}} \cdot \frac{\text{60.0 g}}{\text{equivalent}} = \frac{\text{30.0 g } HC_2H_3O_2}{\text{1 L vinegar}}$$

Using the average value of normality for your sample of vinegar, calculate the mass of acetic acid in one liter of vinegar. Record.

$$\text{mass } HC_2H_3O_2 = \frac{\text{0.717 equivalents}}{\text{1 L vinegar}} \cdot \frac{\text{60.0 g}}{\text{equivalent}} = \frac{\text{43.0 g}}{\text{L vinegar}}$$

6. If we assume the density of vinegar is very close to 1.00 g/mL, then the mass of 1.00 L of vinegar is $10\overline{0}0$ g. The percent, by mass, of acetic acid can be expressed as

$$\% \, HC_2H_3O_2 = \frac{\text{mass } HC_2H_3O_2}{10\overline{0}0 \text{ g vinegar}} \cdot 100\%$$

Calculate the percentage mass of acetic acid in your vinegar sample. Record.

$$\% \, HC_2H_3O_2 = \frac{\text{43.0 g } HC_2H_3O_2}{10\overline{0}0 \text{ g vinegar}} \cdot 100\% = 4.30\%$$

Method II: Calculations based on molarity

7. Calculate the volumes of vinegar and NaOH used for each of the three trials. Record in the calculations table for Method II.

VOLUME NaOH:	#1	11.57 mL − 1.38 mL = 10.19 mL
	#2	23.69 mL − 11.57 mL = 12.12 mL
	#3	32.33 mL − 23.69 mL = 8.64 mL
VOLUME Vinegar:	#1	9.21 mL − 0.55 mL = 8.66 mL
	#2	19.43 mL − 9.21 mL = 10.22 mL
	#3	26.67 mL − 19.43 mL = 7.24 mL

Exercises and Experiments in Modern Chemistry
Holt, Rinehart and Winston, Publishers

8. Since NaOH produces a single hydroxide ion per molecule, the numerical values for normality and molarity are the same. Record the molarity of the NaOH you standardized in Experiment 17.

$$\text{molarity NaOH} = 0.605 \ M$$

9. By definition

$$\text{molarity} = \frac{\text{moles solute}}{1 \text{ L solution}}$$

and

$$\text{moles solute} = \text{molarity} \cdot \text{liters solution}$$

Determine the moles of NaOH used in each of the three trials. Record.

MOLES NaOH:	#1	$0.605 \ M \cdot 0.01019 \ L = 0.00617 \ mol$
	#2	$0.605 \ M \cdot 0.01212 \ L = 0.00733 \ mol$
	#3	$0.605 \ M \cdot 0.00864 \ L = 0.00523 \ mol$

10. The balanced equation for the reaction between vinegar and sodium hydroxide is

$$HC_2H_3O_2 + NaOH \rightarrow H_2O + NaC_2H_3O_2$$

The balanced equation tells us that exactly one mole of NaOH reacts with one mole of $HC_2H_3O_2$. At the equivalence point, therefore, the moles of the acid are equal to the moles of the base. Record the moles of acid for each trial in the calculations table for Method II.

11. Given the moles of acid and volumes of acid for each trial, calculate the molarities of the three trials. Record.

$$\text{molarity of vinegar} = \frac{\text{moles vinegar}}{\text{volume vinegar}}$$

#1 $\dfrac{0.00617 \text{ mol}}{0.00866 \text{ L}} = 0.712 \ M$ 　　　 #2 $\dfrac{0.00733 \text{ mol}}{0.01022 \text{ L}} = 0.717 \ M$

#3 $\dfrac{0.00523 \text{ mol}}{0.00724 \text{ L}} = 0.722 \ M$

12. Calculate the average molarity of the acid. Record.

$$\text{Average molarity of vinegar} = \frac{0.712 \ M + 0.717 \ M + 0.722 \ M}{3} = 0.717 \ M$$

Exercises and Experiments in Modern Chemistry
Holt, Rinehart and Winston, Publishers

13. Calculate the mass of one mole of $HC_2H_3O_2$. Record.

$$H = 1.00 \text{ g} \times 4 = 4.00 \text{ g}$$
$$C = 12.0 \text{ g} \times 2 = 24.0 \text{ g}$$
$$O = 16.0 \text{ g} \times 2 = \underline{32.0 \text{ g}}$$
$$60.0 \text{ g}$$

14. A 0.500 M solution of $HC_2H_3O_2$ contains 0.500 moles of solute in one liter of solution. The mass of $HC_2H_3O_2$ in 1 L of a 0.500 M vinegar solution would be

$$\frac{\text{mass } HC_2H_3O_2}{1 \text{ L vinegar}} = \frac{0.500 \text{ moles } HC_2H_3O_2}{1 \text{ L vinegar}} \cdot \frac{60.0 \text{ g } HC_2H_3O_2}{1 \text{ mole } HC_2H_3O_2} = \frac{30.0 \text{ g } HC_2H_3O_2}{1 \text{ L vinegar}}$$

Use the average molarity for your vinegar sample to determine the mass of $HC_2H_3O_2$ in one L of vinegar. Record.

$$\frac{\text{mass } HC_2H_3O_2}{1 \text{ L vinegar}} = \frac{0.717 \text{ mol } HC_2H_3O_2}{1 \text{ L vinegar}} \cdot \frac{60.0 \text{ g } HC_2H_3O_2}{1 \text{ mole } HC_2H_3O_2} = \frac{43.0 \text{ g } HC_2H_3O_2}{1 \text{ L vinegar}}$$

15. If we assume the density of vinegar is very close to 1.00 g/mL, then the mass of 1.00 L of vinegar is 1000 g. The percent, by mass, of acetic acid can be expressed as

$$\% \ HC_2H_3O_2 = \frac{\text{mass } HC_2H_3O_2}{1000 \text{ g vinegar}} \cdot 100\%$$

Calculate the percentage mass of acetic acid in your vinegar sample. Record.

$$\% \ HC_2H_3O_2 = \frac{43.0 \text{ g } HC_2H_3O_2}{1000 \text{ g vinegar}} \cdot 100\% = 4.30\%$$

Correlating Your Facts

Review Chapter 16, Sections 16.1 to 16.5, and correlate what you have read with what you have learned by performing this experiment.

Complete the following table:

METHODS OF EXPRESSING CONCENTRATION OF SOLUTIONS

Name	Symbol	Solute Unit	Solvent Unit	Dimensions
molality	*m*	mole	kilogram solvent	**mole solute** / **kg solvent**
molarity	*M*	**mole**	liter solution	mole solute / liter solution
normality	*N*	equivalent	**liter solution**	**equiv solute** / **liter solution**

QUESTIONS

Answer the following questions after completing the above table.

1. Which of the above methods express the concentrations of solutions in a ratio of solute to solution?
   Molarity and normality both express the ratio of solute to solution, but in different ways.

2. Which of the above methods expresses the concentrations of solutions in a ratio of solute to solvent?
   Molality expresses the ratio of solute to solvent.

3. Discuss one important way in which solutions of known molality have proved useful to chemists in studying the effects of solutes on solvents.
   Chemists use solutions of known molalities for studying the effects of solutes on the freezing and boiling points of solvents. These studies in turn provide chemists with one way of determining the molecular weights of soluble substances.

Exercises and Experiments in Modern Chemistry
Holt, Rinehart and Winston, Publishers

Carbon

EXPERIMENT

19

Carbon exhibits allotropy, the existence of an element in two or more forms in the same physical state. Its two crystalline allotropic forms are diamond and graphite. Black residues obtained by heating substances that contain combined carbon are sometimes called amorphous carbon. Examples of amorphous carbon include charcoal, coke, bone black, and lampblack. Carbon atoms form covalent bonds with other elements and link with each other in different ways to produce the diamond and graphite structures. The diamond structure is the result of sp^3 hybridization while the resonant graphite structure probably involves a different type of hybridization known as sp^2. The amorphous forms are produced by a variety of procedures, including destructive distillation and incomplete combustion. Carbon is an important reducing agent. The uses of its different varieties are related to particular properties, including combustibility and adsorption. Review Chapter 17, Sections 17.2 to 17.12 and 17.14, for additional information.

OBJECTIVE

After completing this experiment, you should be able to prepare and demonstrate the behavior of some of the allotropic forms of carbon and explain these forms in terms of crystalline structure.

APPARATUS

balance
burner and tubing
sparker
1 Erlenmeyer flask, 125 mL
pipestem triangle
1 graduated cylinder, 50 mL
iron ring

1 Pyrex test tube, 13 × 100 mm
6 Pyrex test tubes, 25 × 100 mm
test tube holder
molecular model kit (Sargent)
1 rubber stopper, solid No. 4
5 rubber stoppers, solid No. 2

1 beaker, 250 mL
buret clamp
crucible and cover
funnel
forceps
ring stand

MATERIALS

sugar, white granular
filter paper
dark-brown sugar solution
activated charcoal, norit A
(for decolorizing)

3.0 M HCl
1.0 M NaOH
3.0 M HNO₃

charcoal wood splinters
wooden splints
limewater

SAFETY

Begin this experiment by taking the necessary safety precautions. Wear safety goggles, apron, and gloves. Read all safety cautions in your procedures and discuss them with your teacher. Conduct this experiment by using good safety techniques. See pages 105 to 107.

Recording Your Results

After completing each of the procedures, record your results in the spaces provided below.

Figure 19-1

PROCEDURE

1. Each student team is to use two molecular model sets, each of which contains 20 black carbon spheres. Using the short stick connectors, construct a model of the diamond. See Figure 19-1. Start the construction of the model of graphite by constructing two hexagons, using only the short connectors. Recall that the distances between the centers of adjacent carbon atoms in a layer of graphite are identical, 1.42 Å. Using Figure 19-2 as a model, connect the two hexagons, using the longer stick connectors to represent the distance between centers in adjacent layers (3.35 Å). Use the remaining carbon spheres to build up each layer. Two carbons in the existent hexagons (those first constructed) are to be common to the newly constructed hexagons. Use long connectors, as needed, between the rest of the constructed layers. To how many carbons is each carbon bonded in the hexagon layer of graphite? What is the nature of the bonding between layers in graphite?

   Observations: **Each carbon is bonded to 3 carbons in the hexagon layer. The layers are held together by weak dispersion interaction forces.**

   _____

   _____

   _____

   _____

CAUTION
Before lighting the burner in procedures 2, 3, and 4, check to see that long hair and loose clothing have been confined.

2. Ignite a wood splint in the burner flame. Note how it burns.

   Then break several splints and place the pieces in the bottom of a Pyrex test tube, clamped so its mouth is slightly downward. Place a piece of paper on the table under the mouth of this test tube and heat the contents strongly (until no more volatile matter is released).

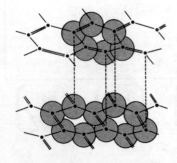

Figure 19-2

CAUTION
Do not breathe the vapor or get any of the liquid on your hands.

Exercises and Experiments in Modern Chemistry
Holt, Rinehart and Winston, Publishers

Remove the residue from the test tube carefully. Describe its appearance.

Observations: **Water forms on the paper. The residue is charcoal black.**

_____

Using forceps, ignite one piece of the residue in the burner and observe how it burns.

Observations: **Student observation**

_____

Pour one inch of limewater into a small test tube. Ignite another piece of the solid residue (hold with forceps) and insert the ignited end in the test tube, holding it above the limewater. Remove the ignited piece. Immediately stopper and shake the test tube. If nothing happens to the limewater, repeat with another ignited piece. What happens to the limewater? What does this indicate about the nature of the residue?

Observations: **Limewater turns cloudy, indicating the presence of CO_2 gas.**

_____

3. Conduct an experiment to show that sugar may be decomposed into carbon and water vapor. Place 2 g of sugar in a porcelain crucible and cover it. Set the crucible and contents in a pipestem triangle and heat.

Observations: **Student observations**

_____

4. Hold a test tube horizontally with its closed end in the yellow burner flame. What form of carbon is produced?

Observations: **Carbon black is deposited on the test tube.**

_____

Change to the standard blue flame and hold the test tube so that the deposit is in the hottest part of the flame.

Observations: **The deposit is removed by the oxidizing blue flame.**

CAUTION
Be careful when handling the acids and bases in procedure 5. Avoid contact with skin and eyes. Avoid breathing vapors. If any of these chemicals should spill on you, immediately flush the area with water and then notify your teacher.

5. Conduct experiments to determine the activity and solubility of wood charcoal splinters in dilute hydrochloric acid, dilute nitric acid, water, and sodium hydroxide solution. Using four separate test tubes, place charcoal splints into 5 mL of each of the solutions. Stopper the test tubes and shake the contents. Describe your results. Discard the liquids into the sink, but be sure that any pieces of charcoal that remain are placed in the waste jar and not in the sink.

Observations: **There was no evidence of reactions taking place in any of the solutions.**

6. Pour 50 mL of dark-brown sugar solution into a 125-mL Erlenmeyer flask. Add to it 1 g of powdered activated charcoal and stopper the flask. Shake the mixture vigorously for a minute. Filter. Pour the filtrate through the funnel a second time, and even a third time if necessary to remove the color from the sugar solution. Finally, compare the color of the filtrate with that of the original brown-sugar solution.

Observations: **Solution turns clear.**

7. At the end of this experiment clean all apparatus. Ask your teacher how to discard all waste materials. Thoroughly wash your hands before leaving the laboratory and check to see that the gas valve is completely shut off.

QUESTIONS

1. How active an element is carbon at room temperature?
Carbon is inactive at room temperature.

2. Of what use is charcoal in water purification processes?
To remove objectionable color and odors from the water.

3. What is adsorption? Why are certain forms of charcoal good adsorbing agents?
Adsorption is the concentration of a gas, liquid, or solid on the surface of a liquid or solid with which it is in contact. Charcoal has tremendous surface particles of colloidal dimensions. Charcoal may be activated by treating it with steam.

Exercises and Experiments in Modern Chemistry
Holt, Rinehart and Winston, Publishers

Heat of Combustion ✓

+ 2 labs models

+ saponification

The heat of reaction released by the complete combustion of 1 mole of a substance is the *heat of combustion* of the substance. In this experiment you will determine the heat of combustion of a candle.

The unit of heat is the *calorie*. The *calorie* is defined as the quantity of heat required to raise the temperature of 1 gram of water through 1 Celsius degree. In this experiment a burning candle will heat a can of water. Measuring the temperature change and volume of the water will allow us to calculate the heat released by the candle. The heat, in calories, is simply equal to the product of the mass of the water and its change in temperature. (The mass of the water is the same as its volume, since 1 milliliter of water has a mass of 1 gram.)

We can calculate the heat released per gram of candle wax, if the mass of wax burned is determined. Knowing the molecular formula of the candle wax, we can calculate its *heat of combustion* for one mole. Review text Sections 1.16, 20.2, and 20.5 for additional information.

OBJECTIVE

After completing this experiment, you should be able to determine the heat of combustion of a candle.

APPARATUS

tin can, 10 oz, open at one end	stirring rod	graduated cylinder, 100 mL
tin can lid	iron ring	thermometer
tin can, 46 oz, open at both ends	ring stand	crucible tongs

MATERIALS

candle	ice cubes	matches

SAFETY

Begin this experiment by taking the necessary safety precautions. Wear safety goggles, apron, and gloves. Read all safety cautions in your procedures and discuss them with your teacher. Conduct this experiment by using good safety techniques. See pages 101 and 102.

Recording Your Data

Where instructed to in the procedures, record your results in the data table.

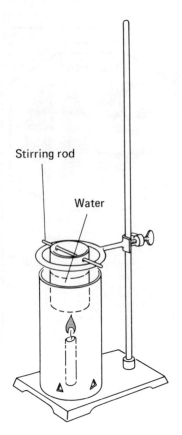

Stirring rod

Water

Figure 20-1

PROCEDURES

1. Attach the candle to a tin can lid or similar base by melting a few drops of candle wax on the lid. Using the small tin can, insert the glass stirring rod through the two small holes. Support the can by the stirring rod on the iron ring and ring stand. Refer to Figure 20-1. Adjust the can so the bottom is approximately 5 cm above the top of the wick. You will want the flame of the candle to just barely miss touching the bottom of the can. (You may wish to light the candle momentarily to see if you have the correct height.) Remove the can and stirring rod from the iron ring.

2. Weigh the candle and lid to the nearest 0.01 g and record. Replace the candle and lid on the ring stand. Place the large can over the candle. Make sure the air vents are at the bottom.

3. Fill the small can about two-thirds full with tap water. Cool the water with ice until the temperature drops 15 to 20 degrees below room temperature. Remove any ice that remains. Read and record the temperature of the water to the nearest 0.1°C.

4. Before lighting the candle in this next procedure observe the following safety guidelines.

CAUTION
Before lighting the candle, check to see that loose clothing and long hair have been confined. Remember to throw the matches away in a waste container designated by your teacher.

Using crucible tongs to hold the match, light the candle. Immediately position the can of ice water on the iron ring. While the candle heats the water, stir gently with the thermometer.

CAUTION
If your mercury thermometer should ever break, immediately notify your teacher, who will clean up the spill.

When the temperature is approximately the same number of degrees above room temperature as it was below, blow out the candle. Continue to stir the water and watch the thermometer until the maximum temperature is reached. Record this temperature to the nearest 0.1°C.

5. Weigh the candle and lid again to the nearest 0.01 g. Make sure you have caught all the drippings.

Use a graduated cylinder to measure the total volume of water in the can. Record to the nearest mL.

Exercises and Experiments in Modern Chemistry
Holt, Rinehart and Winston, Publishers

DATA AND CALCULATIONS TABLES

DATA

Mass of candle and base before burning	**52.90**	g
Lowest temperature of water	**12.0**	°C
Highest temperature of water	**32.0**	°C
Mass of candle and base after burning	**51.94**	g
Volume of water heated	**338**	mL

CALCULATIONS

Change in temperature of water	**20.0**	°C
Mass of water heated	**338**	g
Heat absorbed by can of water	**6760**	cal
Mass of candle wax burned	**0.96**	g
Heat required to burn 1 gram of candle wax	**7100**	cal/g
Heat of combustion of candle wax	**3600**	$\dfrac{\text{kcal}}{\text{mol}}$

CALCULATIONS
Show your computations in the spaces provided below. Place your answers in the calculations table.

1. Calculate the change in temperature of the water.

$$32.0°C - 12.0°C = 20.0°C$$

2. Determine the mass of water heated.

$$\text{mass of water} = \text{volume of water} \times \text{density of water}$$

$$338 \text{ mL} \times 1.00 \text{ g/mL} = 338 \text{ g}$$

3. Calculate the amount of heat absorbed by the can of water.

$$\text{mass of water} \times \text{temperature change of water} = \text{heat absorbed by water (in calories)}$$

$$338 \text{ g} \times 20.0°C = 6760 \text{ cal}$$

₄. Calculate the mass of candle wax burned.

$$52.90 \text{ g} - 51.94 \text{ g} = 0.96 \text{ g}$$

5. Calculate the heat required to burn one gram of candle wax.

$$\frac{\text{mass of water} \times \text{temperature change}}{\text{mass of candle wax burned}} = \frac{338 \text{ g} \times 20.0 \text{ °C}}{0.96 \text{ g}} = \frac{6760 \text{ cal}}{0.96 \text{ g}} = 7100 \text{ cal/g}$$

6. Your candle was probably made of a mixture of waxes, mostly paraffin waxes. Paraffin waxes are hydrocarbons with high molecular masses. Assume the molecular formula of your candle is $C_{36}H_{74}$. Calculate the heat of combustion of your candle in kcal/mol.

$$\text{cal/g} \times \text{mass of one mole of } C_{36}H_{74} = 7100 \text{ cal/g} \times 506 \text{ g/mol} \times \frac{1 \text{ kcal}}{1000 \text{ cal}} = 3600 \text{ kcal/mol}$$

QUESTIONS

1. What was the purpose of cooling the water below room temperature, and then allowing the water to heat to the same amount above room temperature?

   Purpose was to minimize heat loss to the environment. When the water was below room

   temperature, heat was absorbed from the air. A similar amount of heat was released to the

   air when heated above room temperature.

2. Was all the heat released by the candle absorbed by the water? If not, where was some of the heat absorbed?

   Not all of the heat was absorbed by the water. The can and also the surrounding air

   absorbed a small portion of the heat.

Exercises and Experiments in Modern Chemistry
Holt, Rinehart and Winston, Publishers

Heats of Reaction

During any chemical reaction, a certain amount of chemical binding energy is changed into thermal energy, or vice versa. This energy change can be measured as heat released or absorbed during the reaction. The quantity of heat released or absorbed during a chemical reaction is called the *heat of reaction.* Heat of reaction is measured in kcal per mole. If the change in heat, $\triangle H$, is exothermic, its numerical value has a *negative* sign. If the change in heat is endothermic, then $\triangle H$ is *positive.*

Heats of reaction can be classified according to the type of chemical reaction. For example, in Experiment 20 the *heat of combustion* of a candle is determined. Other types include the *heat of formation,* the *heat of solution,* and the *heat of neutralization.*

In this experiment you will determine the *heat of solution* for sodium hydroxide and the *heat of neutralization* for HCl and NaOH. The *heat of solution* is the difference between the heat content of a solution and the heat contents of its components. The balanced reaction for solid NaOH dissolving in water is

$$\text{NaOH}_{(s)} + \text{H}_2\text{O} \rightarrow \text{Na}^+ + \text{OH}^- + \text{H}_2\text{O} + \triangle H_1 \tag{1}$$

The *heat of neutralization* is the heat liberated, when one mole of water is formed by the reaction between one mole of hydronium ions and one mole of hydroxide ions. The balanced reaction is

$$\text{Na}^+ + \text{OH}^- + \text{H}_3\text{O}^+ + \text{Cl}^- \rightarrow 2\text{H}_2\text{O} + \text{Na}^+ + \text{Cl}^- + \triangle H_2 \tag{2}$$

Heats of reaction can be added together to form another heat of reaction. You will determine the heat of reaction for a third reaction in which solid NaOH is dissolved in HCl. The balanced reaction is

$$\text{NaOH}_{(s)} + \text{H}_3\text{O}^+ + \text{Cl}^- \rightarrow 2\text{H}_2\text{O} + \text{Na}^+ + \text{Cl}^- + \triangle H_3 \tag{3}$$

You will show that $\triangle H_1 + \triangle H_2$ is equivalent to $\triangle H_3$. Review text sections 13.10, 14.5, 20.2, 20.3, and 20.5 for additional information.

OBJECTIVES

After completing this experiment, you should be able to determine the heats of solution and neutralization. You will also be able to demonstrate that heats of reaction can be additive.

APPARATUS

styrofoam cup
balance, centigram
graduated cylinder, 100 mL

stirring rod
thermometer, -10 to 110 °C

porcelain spatula
watch glass

NaOH pellets   2 *M* NaOH solution   1 *M* HCl solution
2 *M* HCl solution

SAFETY

Begin this experiment by taking the necessary safety precautions. Wear safety goggles, apron, and gloves. Read all safety cautions in your procedures and discuss them with your teacher. Conduct this experiment by using good safety techniques. See pages 106 and 115.

Recording Your Results
Where instructed to in the procedures, record your results in the data table provided.

PROCEDURES

Reaction 1   Pour $10\overline{0}$ mL of distilled water into a styrofoam cup. Record the volume to the nearest mL and the temperature of the water to the nearest 0.1°C. Use a porcelain spatula to obtain *approximately* 4 grams of sodium hydroxide pellets.

CAUTION
Sodium hydroxide is caustic and corrosive. Avoid contact with skin and eyes. Avoid breathing vapors. If any of the pellets or base should spill on you, immediately flush the area with water and then notify your teacher.

Place the pellets on a watch glass. Weigh and record the mass of the pellets to the nearest 0.01 g. *Immediately* place the pellets in the styrofoam cup and gently stir the solution. Record the highest temperature to the nearest 0.1°C. Discard the solution as directed by your instructor.

Reaction 2   The following safety guidelines should be observed throughout this experiment.

CAUTION
Sodium hydroxide and hydrochloric acid are caustic and corrosive substances. Avoid contact with skin and eyes. Avoid breathing vapors. If any should spill on you, immediately flush the area with water and then notify your teacher. Work cautiously when using these substances throughout this experiment.

Place $5\overline{0}$ mL of 2.0 *M* HCl in the styrofoam cup. Record the volume to the nearest mL and the temperature to the nearest 0.1°C. Obtain $5\overline{0}$ mL of a 2 *M* NaOH solution. Record the volume to the nearest mL and the temperature to the nearest 0.1°C. Pour the NaOH solution into the styrofoam cup. Stir the mixture gently.

Exercises and Experiments in Modern Chemistry
Holt, Rinehart and Winston, Publishers

Record the highest temperature reached to the nearest 0.1°C. Discard the solution as directed by your instructor.

Reaction 3   Pour 10$\overline{0}$ mL of a 1.0 *M* HCl solution into the styrofoam cup. Record the volume to the nearest mL and the temperature to the nearest 0.1°C. Use a porcelain spatula to obtain *approximately* 4 grams of sodium hydroxide pellets. Weigh the pellets on a watch glass and record the mass of the pellets to the nearest 0.01 g. *Immediately* place the pellets in the HCl solution. Gently stir the mixture. Record the highest temperature reached to the nearest 0.1°C. Discard the solution as directed by your instructor.

At the end of this experiment clean all apparatus and thoroughly wash your hands before leaving the laboratory.

DATA AND CALCULATIONS TABLES

DATA

Reaction 1

Mass NaOH (g)	Volume H$_2$O (mL)	Temperature (°C)	
		initial	final
4.00	100	21.5	31.5

Reaction 2

	Molarity (*M*)	Volume (mL)	Temperature (initial) (°C)
HCl	2.0	50	22.0
NaOH	2.0	50	22.0
		Highest Temperature **34.0** °C	

Reaction 3

Mass NaOH (g)	Volume 1.0 *M* HCl (mL)	Temperature (°C)	
		initial	final
4.00	100	22.0	44.0

CALCULATIONS

Reaction	Δt (°C)	Heat Released (cal)	Moles NaOH (mol)	ΔH per Mole NaOH (kcal/mol)
1	10.0	$10\overline{0}0$	0.100	10.0
2	12.0	$12\overline{0}0$	0.10	12
3	22.0	$22\overline{0}0$	0.100	22.0

$\Delta H_1 + \Delta H_2$ ___**22**___ (kcal/mol)

Percentage Discrepancy ___**0**___ %

CALCULATIONS

Show your computations in the spaces provided below. Place your answers in the calculations table.

1. Calculate the change in temperature, Δt, for each reaction. Record.

$$\Delta t_1 = 31.5°C - 21.5°C = 10.0°C$$

$$\Delta t_2 = 34.0°C - 22.0°C = 12.0°C$$

$$\Delta t_3 = 44.0°C - 22.0°C = 22.0°C$$

2. Using the volumes of liquid and Δt values, calculate the heat released for each reaction. Record.

(1) Heat released $= m_1 \cdot \Delta t_1 = 100$ g $\cdot$ 10.0°C $= 10\overline{0}0$ cal

(2) Heat released $= m_2 \cdot \Delta t_2 = 100$ g $\cdot$ 12.0°C $= 12\overline{0}0$ cal

(3) Heat released $= m_3 \cdot \Delta t_3 = 100$ g $\cdot$ 22.0°C $= 22\overline{0}0$ cal

3. Calculate the moles of NaOH used in each of the reactions. For reactions 1 and 3, determine the moles using the recorded masses of NaOH and the mass of one mole of NaOH. For Reaction 2, determine the moles using the volume and the molarity of the NaOH solution. Record.

(1) moles NaOH $= 4.00$ g $\times \dfrac{1 \text{ mole}}{40.0 \text{ g}} = 0.100$ mole

(2) moles NaOH $= 2.0 \dfrac{\text{mol}}{\text{L}} \times 0.050$ L $= 0.10$ mole

(3) moles NaOH $= 4.00$ g $\times \dfrac{1 \text{ mole}}{40.0 \text{ g}} = 0.100$ mole

Exercises and Experiments in Modern Chemistry
Holt, Rinehart and Winston, Publishers

4. Calculate the heat released per mole of NaOH ($\triangle H$) for each reaction. Record.

$$\triangle H_1 = \frac{10\overline{0}0 \text{ cal} \times 0.001 \text{ kcal/cal}}{0.100 \text{ mol}} = 10.0 \frac{\text{kcal}}{\text{mol}}$$

$$\triangle H_2 = \frac{12\overline{0}0 \text{ cal} \times 0.001 \text{ kcal/cal}}{0.10 \text{ mol}} = 12 \frac{\text{kcal}}{\text{mol}}$$

$$\triangle H_3 = \frac{22\overline{0}0 \text{ cal} \times 0.001 \text{ kcal/cal}}{0.100 \text{ mol}} = 22.0 \frac{\text{kcal}}{\text{mol}}$$

5. The equations for the three reactions are given in the introduction to this experiment. Rewrite each of these reactions as net ionic equations.

(1) $NaOH_{(s)} + H_2O \rightarrow Na^+ + OH^- + H_2O + 10.0 \text{ kcal/mol}$

(2) $Na^+ + OH^- + H_3O^+ + Cl^- \rightarrow 2H_2O + Na^+ + Cl^- + 12 \text{ kcal/mol}$

(3) $NaOH_{(s)} + H_3O^+ + Cl^- \rightarrow 2H_2O + Na^+ + Cl^- + 22.0 \text{ kcal/mol}$

6. Show that net ionic equation (1) plus net ionic equation (2) is equivalent to net ionic equation (3).

(1) $NaOH_{(s)} \rightarrow Na^+ + OH^- + 10.0 \text{ kcal/mol}$

(2) $OH^- + H_3O^+ \rightarrow 2H_2O + 12 \text{ kcal/mol}$
$\overline{NaOH_{(s)} + H_3O^+ \rightarrow 2H_2O + Na^+ + 22 \text{ kcal/mol}}$

(3) $NaOH_{(s)} + H_3O^+ \rightarrow 2H_2O + Na^+ + 22 \text{ kcal/mol}$

7. Find the sum of $\triangle H_1$ and $\triangle H_2$.

$$\triangle H_1 + \triangle H_2 = 10.0 \text{ kcal/mole} + 12 \text{ kcal/mole} = 22 \text{ kcal/mole}$$

8. Calculate the percent discrepancy between $\triangle H_1 + \triangle H_2$ and $\triangle H_3$.

$$\% \text{ discrepancy} = \frac{(\triangle H_1 + \triangle H_2) - \triangle H_3}{\frac{(\triangle H_1 + \triangle H_2) + \triangle H_3}{2}} \times 100\%$$

$$= \frac{22 - 22 \text{ kcal/mol}}{\frac{(22 + 22 \text{ kcal/mol})}{2}} \times 100\% = 0.0\%$$

Exercises and Experiments in Modern Chemistry
Holt, Rinehart and Winston, Publishers

Rate of a Chemical Reaction

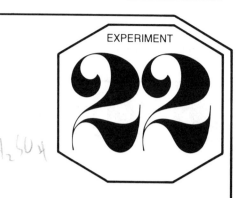

EXPERIMENT

22

H₂SO₄

The rate of a chemical reaction is affected by changes in the concentration of reactants, changes in temperature, and the addition of catalysts. Review Chapter 20, Section 20.12.

Sodium Sulfite

The reaction you will be investigating involves two solutions. Solution A is a mixture of KI (a source of I^- ions) and $Na_2S_2O_3$ (a source of $S_2O_3^{--}$ ions). This solution also contains a small amount of starch. Solution B contains $(NH_4)_2S_2O_8$ (a source of $S_2O_8^{--}$ ions).

The overall reaction you will be timing is

$$2I^- + S_2O_8^{--} \rightarrow I_2 + 2SO_4^{--} \text{ (slow)}$$ (1)

solution solution
A B

In order to determine when the reaction has reached equilibrium, you will measure how long it takes to produce a certain amount of iodine, I_2. To measure the time to produce the I_2, another reaction is utilized:

$$I_2 + 2S_2O_3^{--} \rightarrow 2I^- + S_4O_6^{--} \text{ (fast)}$$ (2)

solution
A

As the I_2 is formed in reaction 1, the $S_2O_3^{--}$ immediately breaks up the I_2 into I^- ions. When all the $S_2O_3^{--}$ is consumed, then the I_2 can remain in solution and reacts with the starch, producing a deep-blue color. The blue color denotes that the reaction is complete.

In Part I of the experiment you will vary the concentration of solution B, the $S_2O_8^{--}$ ions, and time how long it takes the solution to turn blue. In Part II you will vary the temperature, and in Part III you will add a catalyst.

OBJECTIVE

After completing this experiment, you should be able to determine the effect of concentration, temperature, and catalyst on the rate of a chemical reaction.

APPARATUS

2 graduated cylinders, 25 mL	sparker	ring stand
1 beaker, 100 mL	stirring rod	iron ring
burner and tubing	clock	thermometer
2 Pyrex test tubes, 18 × 150 mm	1 beaker, 600 mL	wire gauze, ceramic-centered

MATERIALS

solution A*   ice   0.01 M CuSO$_4$
solution B*   distilled water

*Refer to the teacher notes for the preparation of these solutions.

SAFETY

Begin this experiment by taking the necessary safety precautions. Wear safety goggles, apron, and gloves. Read all safety cautions in your procedures and discuss them with your teacher. Conduct this experiment by using good safety techniques. See pages 97 and 98.

Recording Your Data

Record your observations in the data table provided at the end of the procedures.

PROCEDURES

Part I: Concentration effect

1. Measure out 20 mL of solution A in one of the graduated cylinders. Label this graduated cylinder "A." Measure out 20 mL of solution B in the other graduated cylinder and label it "B."

2. Your partner will have to time the reaction while you mix the solutions. On signal, quickly pour the two solutions together in the 100-mL beaker. Continuously stir the mixture with a stirring rod. Time how long it takes the clear mixture to turn a deep-blue color. Record the time in your data table. Also record the temperature of the mixture.

3. Repeat steps 1 and 2 until you can obtain the same results within ± 2 seconds.

4. Measure out another 20 mL of Solution A. Measure out 15 mL of Solution B plus 5 mL of distilled water. Repeat step 2.

5. Measure out another 20 mL of Solution A. Measure out 10 mL of Solution B plus 10 mL of distilled water. Repeat step 2.

Part II: Temperature effect

6. In this part of the experiment you will obtain readings for 3 different temperatures: room temperature, approximately 10°C below room temperature, and 10°C above room temperature. You already have the data for room temperature from the results of step 2 (20 mL A + 20 mL B). Record that time and temperature under Part II, room temperature, in your data table.

7. Fill a 600-mL beaker about 2/3 full with tapwater. Add several ice cubes and cool the water bath to approximately 10°C below room

temperature. Measure out 20 mL of solution A and pour into a 18 × 150 mm test tube. Measure out 20 mL of solution B and pour into a second test tube. Immerse the test tubes in the cold water bath. Record the temperature of solution A. Assume this is also the temperature of solution B. **Do not add any ice to either test tube!**

8. Now repeat step 2. Pour the solutions directly from the test tubes into the beaker.

9. Warm the water bath to approximately 10°C above room temperature.

CAUTION
Before you light the burner, check to see that long hair and loose clothing have been confined.

Measure out 20 mL of solutions A and B in separate test tubes and immerse them in the warm water bath. Record the temperature of solution A. Assume this is also the temperature of solution B.

10. Now repeat step 2.

Part III: Catalyst effect

11. Measure out 20 mL of solutions A and B in their respective graduated cylinders. Add exactly 5 drops of 0.01 *M* $CuSO_4$ to the beaker. Repeat step 2.

DATA TABLE

	Volume (mL)		Temperature (°C)	Time (s)
	Solution A	Solution B		
Part I	20 mL	20 mL	22.2	29
	20 mL	15 mL	22.2	42
	20 mL	10 mL	22.2	71
Part II	20 mL	20 mL	12.0	58
	20 mL	20 mL	22.2	29
	20 mL	20 mL	32.2	18
Part III	20 mL	20 mL	22.2	19

QUESTIONS

1. According to your results in Part I, what is the effect of decreasing the volume of solution B ($S_2O_8^{--}$ ions) on the reaction rate?

   As the volume of $S_2O_8^{--}$ solution decreases, the reaction rate slows (the time increases).

   Half the volume approximately doubles the time for completion.

2. Express, in terms of a ratio, the change in reaction rate due to a 10°C change in temperature. For example, if the time at 10°C was 80 s and the time at 20°C was 20 s, the ratio change would be 80 s/20 s = 4/1.

   At 12°C, time = 58 s; At 22 °C, time = 29 s; 58 s/29 s = 2/1 ratio. A 10°C, change doubles

   the reaction rate.

3. What effect did the addition of 5 drops of 0.01 M $CuSO_4$ have on the reaction rate?

   Reaction rate was faster. Rate changed from 29 s to 19 s.

Exercises and Experiments in Modern Chemistry
Holt, Rinehart and Winston, Publishers

Equilibrium

EXPERIMENT
23

Chemical reactions in which a product is essentially un-ionized, is given off as a gas, or is precipitated, may be thought of as running to completion and are commonly referred to as *end reactions*. Many of the reactions you have studied are of importance because they run to completion, yielding products that are easily recovered. Many other reactions, however, do not run to completion. The products, if formed at all, do not leave the fields of action, but remain in contact and react to re-form the original reactants. Under suitable conditions, both reactions may proceed at the same speed. An equilibrium is thus established. Both the forward and the reverse actions continue with no net change in the quantities of either reactants or products.

An equilibrium exists in a saturated solution between undissolved particles and particles in solution. An ionic equilibrium may be established between un-ionized molecules of a molecular solute and the ions of the solution, or between undissociated ions of an ionic solute and the ions in solution. An equilibrium is affected by both concentration and temperature. By the principle of Le Chatelier, we know that a system in equilibrium tends to shift so as to relieve the stress placed upon it by a change in concentration or temperature. Review Chapter 21, Sections 21.1 to 21.6, for additional information.

OBJECTIVE
After completing this experiment, you should be able to describe the effect of concentration on various equilibria and apply Le Chatelier's principle.

APPARATUS
Erlenmeyer flask, 125 mL   stirring rod   beaker, 250 mL
balance, centigram   8 test tubes, 13 × 100 mm   graduated cylinder, 125 mL

MATERIALS
CH_3COONa (crystals of sodium acetate)   1 M HCl
NH_4SCN (crystals of ammonium thiocyanate)   0.15% acetic acid
KCl (crystals of potassium chloride)   0.1 M K_2CrO_4
$Fe(NO_3)_3$ (crystals of ferric nitrate)   1 M NaOH
Na_2HPO_4 (crystals of sodium phosphate)   1 M KSCN
methyl red indicator solution   0.1 M $K_2Cr_2O_7$
                                                             1 M $FeCl_3$

SAFETY

Begin this experiment by taking the necessary safety precautions. Wear safety goggles, apron, and gloves. During the procedures of this experiment, you are required to handle various chemicals. Do not touch the chemicals with your hands. Carefully check the labels on the reagent bottles and containers before removing any of their contents. Never use more of a chemical than directed. Conduct this experiment by using good safety techniques. See pages 103 and 106.

Recording Your Results

After completing each of the procedures, record your observations in the spaces provided below.

PROCEDURES

Part I: Common-ion effect

1. Put approximately 25 mL of a 0.15% acetic acid solution in a 125-mL Erlenmeyer flask. Add a few drops of methyl red indicator and swirl until completely mixed.

   Observations: **A violet-red color appears.**

2. Add 1 g of sodium acetate (CH_3COONa) to the flask and swirl the mixture.

   Observations: **An orange to yellow color appears.**

Part II: Le Chatelier's principle

3. Put approximately 1 mL of 0.1 M K_2CrO_4 in a 13 × 100 mm test tube. In another test tube, put approximately 1 mL of 0.1 M $K_2Cr_2O_7$. Record the color of each solution.

   Observations: **CrO_4^{--} is yellow. $Cr_2O_7^{--}$ is orange.**

4. Add a drop of 1 M NaOH to each test tube. Continue to add drops alternately to each solution until a definite color change occurs in one of the solutions. Save these solutions.

   Observations: **$Cr_2O_7^{--}$ turns yellow. CrO_4^{--} remains yellow.**

Exercises and Experiments in Modern Chemistry
Holt, Rinehart and Winston, Publishers

5. Repeat steps 3 and 4 with fresh solutions of K_2CrO_4 and $K_2Cr_2O_7$, but this time use 1 M HCl in place of 1 M NaOH.

   Observations: **CrO_4^{--} turns orange. CrO_7^{--} remains orange.**

6. Add 1 M HCl, a drop at a time, to each of the solutions in step 4.

   Observations: **The color changes back to orange for both solutions.**

7. Add 1 M NaOH, a drop at a time, to each of the solutions in step 5.

   Observations: **The color changes back to yellow for both solutions.**

Part III: Complex-ion equilibrium

8. Mix approximately 1 mL each of $FeCl_3$ and KSCN solutions in a 250-mL beaker.

   Observations: **A deep-red color appears.**

9. Now dilute with approximately 100 mL of water to give a color of light red to orange-yellow. Half-fill 4 test tubes with the diluted solution. To test tube 1, add 0.5 g of $Fe(NO_3)_3$. To test tube 2, add 0.5 g of NH_4SCN. To test tube 3, add 0.5 g of KCl. To test tube 4, add 0.5 g of Na_2HPO_4.

   Observations:

   1. **Color darkens (deep-red).**
   2. **Color darkens (deep-red).**
   3. **No change.**
   4. **Solution turns clear.**

10. Clean all apparatus at the end of this experiment. Ask your teacher how to dispose of all waste materials. Thoroughly wash your hands before leaving the laboratory.

QUESTIONS

Part I: Common-ion effect

1. Methyl red indicator has a pH range from 4.2 (red-violet color) to 6.2 (yellow color). Explain the color change that occurred in Part I of the procedure, when solid sodium acetate (CH_3COONa) was added to the acetic acid solution.

   When sodium acetate dissolved into solution, the acetate ions reacted with the H^+ ions

   and lowered the H^+ ion concentration.

Part II: Le Chatelier's principle

2. (a) What is the color of the CrO_4^{--} ion? (b) What is the color of the $Cr_2O_7^{--}$ ion?

   (a) **Yellow**

   (b) **Orange**

3. (a) When NaOH was added to the $Cr_2O_7^{--}$ ion, what ion was produced? (b) The unbalanced equation for this reaction is $Cr_2O_7^{--} + OH^- \rightleftarrows CrO_4^{--} + H_2O$. Write a balanced equation for this reaction. (c) Use Le Chatelier's principle to explain the role of OH^- ions in the $CrO_4^{--} \rightleftarrows Cr_2O_7^{--}$ reaction.

   (a) **CrO_4^{--} ion.**

   (b) **$Cr_2O_7^{--} + 2OH^- \rightleftarrows 2\,CrO_4^{--} + H_2O$.**

   (c) **When OH^- is added, the $Cr_2O_7^{--}$ reacted with the OH^-, thereby relieving the stress of the addition of OH^-.**

4. (a) When HCl was added to the CrO_4^{--} ion, what ion was produced? (b) Write a balanced equation for the reaction between the CrO_4^{--} ion and the H^+ ion forming the $Cr_2O_7^{--}$ ion and water. (c) Using Le Chatelier's principle, explain the role of H^+ ions in the $CrO_4^{--} \rightleftarrows Cr_2O_7^{--}$ reaction.

   (a) **$Cr_2O_7^{--}$**

   (b) **$2CrO_4^{--} + 2H^+ \rightleftarrows Cr_2O_7^{--} + H_2O$.**

   (c) **When H^+ was added, the CrO_4^{--} reacted with the H^+, thereby relieving the stress of the addition of H^+.**

Part III: Complex-ion equilibrium

5. The Fe^{+++} ion and the CNS^- ion form the complex $FeCNS^{++}$ ion, which shows a deep-red color. Write the balanced reaction for the formation of $FeCNS^{++}$ ion.

   $Fe^{+++} + SCN^- \rightleftarrows FeSCN^{++}$.

6. (a) What is the effect on the equilibrium conditions, when additional Fe^{+++} ions are added (test tube 1)?
   (b) What is the effect on the equilibrium conditions, when additional SCN^- ions are added (test tube 2)?
   (c) What is the effect on the equilibrium conditions, when solid KCl is added (test tube 3)?

   (a) **Equilibrium shifts to more $FeSCN^{++}$ (product).**

   (b) **Equilibrium shifts to more $FeSCN^{++}$ (product).**

   (c) **No effect.**

7. What was the effect on the equilibrium conditions, when solid Na_2HPO_4 was added?
   Equilibrium shifts to more reactants.

Exercises and Experiments in Modern Chemistry
Holt, Rinehart and Winston, Publishers

The Solubility Product Constant of Sodium Chloride

At equilibrium, a saturated solution contains the maximum amount of solute possible at a given temperature. This solute usually exists in equilibrium with an undissolved excess of the solute.

For slightly soluble salts, we have the equilibrium of a solid salt with its ions in solution. Since the concentration of a pure substance in the solid (or liquid) phase remains constant, the equilibrium constant expression may be expressed in a simplified form, called the *solubility product law.* The solubility product law states that in a saturated solution of a slightly soluble salt, the product of molar concentrations of its ions in its saturated solution is a constant, the *solubility product constant K_{sp}.* For a salt composed of an ion with a plus one charge and an ion with a charge of negative one:

$$AB(s) \rightleftarrows A^+_{(aq)} + B^-_{(aq)}$$

$$K_{sp} = [A^+][B^-]$$

If the salt is composed of ions with a charge greater than one, the expression of the solubility product law must reflect the greater molar concentration of certain ions. In a salt such as A_2B_3, the solubility-product constant is the product of the molar concentrations of its ions in a saturated solution, each ion raised to the power of its corresponding subscript:

$$A_2B_{3(s)} \rightleftarrows 2A^{+++}_{(aq)} + 3B^{--}_{(aq)}$$

$$K_{sp} = [A^{+++}]^2 [B^{--}]^3$$

Although sodium chloride is not considered to be sparingly soluble, its solubility is such that a K_{sp} for it may be experimentally determined by fairly simple procedures. You will also investigate how the addition of either of its ions to its saturated solution may or may not result in the formation of a precipitate. Review Chapter 21, Sections 21.12 and 21.13, for additional information.

OBJECTIVE

After completing this experiment, you should be able to determine the solubility product constant of a solute and demonstrate precipitation by addition of a common ion to a saturated solution.

APPARATUS

2 beakers, 150 mL	iron ring	evaporating dish
burner and tubing	tongs	graduated cylinder, 50 mL, 10 mL
sparker	stirring rod	2 test tubes, 25 × 100 mL
ring stand	centigram balance	wire gauze, ceramic-centered

MATERIALS

sodium hydroxide pellets	sodium chloride	2 *M* NaOH

SAFETY

Begin this experiment by taking the necessary safety precautions. Wear safety goggles, apron, and gloves. Read all safety cautions in your procedures and discuss them with your teacher. Conduct this experiment by using good safety techniques. See pages 104 and 111.

Recording Your Data
Where instructed to in the procedures, record your results in the data table and in the spaces provided.

PROCEDURES

1. Prepare a saturated solution of sodium chloride by adding 10 g of the salt to 25 mL of water in a beaker. Stir constantly until there is an excess of the solid in the bottom of the beaker. Decant the saturated solution according to the procedure shown in Figure S-3 on page 104.

2. Determine the mass of the evaporating dish to the nearest 0.01 g and record. Measure approximately 10 mL of the salt solution in a graduated cylinder. Record the volume to the nearest 0.1 mL. Pour this sample of the saturated salt solution into the evaporating dish. Using the ring stand assembly in Figure S-5 on page 105, place the evaporating dish (without a watch glass cover) on the wire gauze and evaporate the solution to dryness.

   CAUTION
   Before lighting the burner, check to see that long hair and loose clothing have been confined.

   To prevent spattering, place the ring assembly several centimeters above the flame and reduce to a very low flame when the solution reaches dryness. Remove the hot evaporating dish with tongs. Place it on the base of the ring stand and permit it to cool. Then determine the mass of the evaporating dish and solid residue to the nearest 0.01 g and record.

3. **Addition of common ions to a saturated solution of salt.**
   (a) To 5 mL of the saturated sodium chloride solution in a test tube, add two pellets of solid sodium hydroxide.

Exercises and Experiments in Modern Chemistry
Holt, Rinehart and Winston, Publishers

CAUTION
Sodium hydroxide is a caustic and corrosive substance.
Do not allow any of the pellets or solution to come in
contact with your skin or eyes. Avoid breathing the
vapors. If any of the base should spill on you, immediately
flush the area with water and then notify your teacher.

Stir carefully to dissolve as much of the sodium hydroxide as
possible. Record your observations.
A white precipitate forms.

_____

(b) To 5 mL of the saturated sodium chloride solution in a test tube,
add 5 mL of 2 M NaOH solution. Stir carefully. Record your
observations.
The solution remains clear.

_____

4. At the end of this experiment follow the directions of your teacher for
the proper disposal of all waste materials. Clean all apparatus and
wash your hands thoroughly before leaving the laboratory.

DATA AND CALCULATIONS TABLES

DATA

Mass of empty evaporating dish	**41.36**	g
Volume of saturated NaCl solution	**10.0**	mL
Mass of evaporating dish and NaCl	**44.50**	g

CALCULATIONS

Mass of NaCl	**3.14**	g
Moles of NaCl	**0.0537**	mol
Molarity of NaCl solution	**5.37**	M
Concentration of [Na$^+$]	**5.37**	M
Concentration of [Cl$^-$]	**5.37**	M
K_{sp} for NaCl	**28.8**	

CALCULATIONS

Show your computations in the spaces provided below. Place your answers in the calculations table.

1. Determine the mass of dry NaCl residue. Record.

$$\text{mass NaCl} = 44.50\ g - 41.36\ g = 3.14\ g$$

2. Calculate the moles of dry NaCl. Record.

$$\text{moles NaCl} = 3.14\ g \times \frac{1\ \text{mole}}{58.5\ g} = 0.0537\ mol$$

3. Calculate the concentration of the original 10 mL of NaCl solution before drying. Record.

$$\text{molarity NaCl} = \frac{0.0537\ mol}{10.0\ mL} \times \frac{1000\ mL}{L} = 5.37\ M$$

4. Write (a) the equilibrium equation for the saturated salt solution and (b) the solubility product constant expression for the system.

(a) $$\text{NaCl}_{(s)} \rightleftarrows \text{Na}^{+}_{(aq)} + \text{Cl}^{-}_{(aq)}$$

(b) $$K_{sp} = [\text{Na}^{+}]\,[\text{Cl}^{-}]$$

5. Determine the concentrations of Na^{+} and Cl^{-} ions. Record.

$$[\text{NaCl}] = [\text{Na}^{+}] = [\text{Cl}^{-}] = 5.37\ M$$

1 to 1 to 1 mole ratio

6. Calculate the K_{sp} for sodium chloride. Record.

$$K_{sp} = [\text{Na}^{+}]\,[\text{Cl}^{-}] = [5.37]\,[5.37] = 28.8$$

QUESTIONS

1. Explain your observations for procedure 3a.
   The addition of Na^{+} ions exceeds the solubility of the NaCl solution and NaCl precipitates.

2. Explain any differences in observations between procedures 3a and 3b.
   The addition of 2 M NaOH did not produce a precipitate because the concentration of Na^{+} ions (2 M) was less than the K_{sp} value for NaCl.

Exercises and Experiments in Modern Chemistry
Holt, Rinehart and Winston, Publishers

Oxidation-Reduction Reactions

Substances that lose electrons during chemical action are said to be oxidized. Those that gain electrons are said to be reduced. If one reactant gains electrons, another must lose an equal number. Thus, oxidation and reduction actions must occur simultaneously and to a comparable degree.

The stronger the tendency of an oxidizing agent to gain electrons, the greater is its strength. The weaker the tendency for a reducing agent to hold electrons, the greater is its strength as a reducing agent. Thus, the silver ion, Ag^+, has a strong tendency to acquire an electron to form the silver atom, Ag. The Ag^+ ion is a strong oxidizing agent. Review Chapter 22, Sections 22.1, 22.2, and 22.4 for additional information.

OBJECTIVE
After completing this experiment, you should be able to describe some typical oxidation-reduction reactions and to determine the relative strengths of some oxidizing and reducing agents.

APPARATUS
centigram balance   forceps   7 test tubes, 18 × 150 mm
medicine dropper

MATERIALS
copper strip, 1 × 5 cm   0.1 M silver nitrate   0.1 M copper(II) nitrate
zinc strip, 1 × 5 cm   0.1 M tin(II) chloride   0.1 M zinc nitrate
iron(II) sulfate   lead strip, 1 × 5 cm   0.1 M iron(III) chloride
sulfuric acid, 6 M   silver strip, 1 × 5 cm   sandpaper
0.1 M lead(II) nitrate   potassium permanganate

SAFETY

Begin this experiment by taking the necessary safety precautions. Wear safety goggles, apron, and gloves. During the procedures of this experiment, you are required to handle various chemicals. Do not touch the chemicals with your hands. Carefully check the labels on the reagent bottles and containers before removing any of their contents. Never use more of a chemical than directed. Conduct this experiment by using good safety techniques. See pages 103 and 106.

Recording Your Results
After completing each step of the procedures, record your observations in the spaces provided.

PROCEDURES

1. Add 5 mL of silver nitrate solution to a test tube and insert a strip of sandpapered copper. To 5 mL of copper(II) nitrate solution in a second test tube, add a strip of silver foil. After a few minutes, examine both pieces of metal.

   Observations: **Crystals of Ag form on the Cu strip. There is no evidence of a reaction between Ag and Cu(NO₃)₂ solution.**

2. Place a strip of sandpapered zinc in 5 mL of copper(II) nitrate solution. Insert a strip of shiny copper in 5 mL of zinc nitrate solution. After a few minutes, examine both pieces of metal.

   Observations: **Cu deposits on the Zn strip. There is no evidence of a reaction between Cu and Zn(NO₃)₂.**

3. Test a strip of brightened lead in 5 mL of zinc nitrate solution and a second strip in 5 mL of copper(II) nitrate solution. Similarly test zinc and copper in separate solutions of lead(II) nitrate. After a few minutes, examine both pieces of metal.

   Observations: **Pb replaces Cu. Zn replaces Pb. There is no reaction of Cu in Pb(NO₃)₂ or Pb in Zn(NO₃)₂.**

4. Note the color of a 5-mL solution of iron(III) chloride solution. Add tin(II) chloride solution, dropwise near the end, until the color of the iron(III) chloride has disappeared. Describe the color change.

   Observations: **The color changes from yellow-brown to practically colorless (pale green).**

 CAUTION
In procedure 5, sulfuric acid is caustic and corrosive. Avoid contact with skin and eyes. Avoid breathing vapors. If any of the acid should spill on you, immediately flush the area with water and then notify your teacher. Remember that safety goggles, apron, and gloves should be worn at all times during an experiment.

Exercises and Experiments in Modern Chemistry
Holt, Rinehart and Winston, Publishers

5. Using forceps, place 1 or 2 crystals of potassium permanganate in 10 mL of water and dissolve. Note the intensity of the color. Dissolve 2 or 3 crystals of iron(II) sulfate in 5 mL of water. Acidify with 4 or 5 drops of 6 M sulfuric acid. Then add the potassium permanganate solution to the solution containing the Fe^{++} ions, a very little at a time (mix) and finally dropwise, until the color remains.

Observations: **The almost colorless (pale green) solution of Fe^{++} changes to the yellow-brown of Fe^{+++}. At the end-point the solution turns back to purple.**

_____

_____

6. At the end of this experiment, ask your teacher how to dispose of all waste materials. Clean all apparatus and wash your hands thoroughly before leaving the laboratory.

QUESTIONS

1. Which metal was oxidized by the other ~~three~~ 2 ions?
   zinc
   _____

2. Which metal was oxidized by ~~two~~ 1 other ions?
   lead
   _____

3. Which metal was oxidized by only one other ion?
   copper
   _____

4. Which metal was not oxidized by any of the ions?
   silver
   _____

5. *Table 22-3* Arrange the four metals in order of their relative strengths as reducing agents, placing the strongest first. Write each metal as a half reaction: $M \rightarrow M^+ + e^-$.
   $Zn \rightarrow Zn^{++} + 2e^-$
   _____
   $Pb \rightarrow Pb^{++} + 2e^-$
   _____
   $Cu \rightarrow Cu^{++} + 2e^-$
   _____
   $Ag \rightarrow Ag^+ + e^-$
   _____

6. Arrange the four metallic ions in order of their relative strengths as oxidizing agents, placing the weakest first.

$Zn^{++} < Pb^{++} < Cu^{++} < Ag^+$

7. Since copper oxidized in the presence of silver ions, the net ionic reaction would be

step¹

$$Cu + 2Ag^+ \rightarrow Cu^{++} + 2Ag.$$

Write net ionic reactions for (a) copper and zinc, (b) lead and zinc, (c) copper and lead. (Hint: determine which metal is oxidized and which ion is reduced from your answers to questions 5 and 6.)

work a)

(a) **$Zn + Cu^{++} \rightarrow Zn^{++} + Cu$** $Zn + Cu^{++}(NO_3)_2^- \rightarrow Cu + Zn^{++}(NO_3)_2^-$

(b) **$Zn + Pb^{++} \rightarrow Zn^{++} + Pb$**

(c) **$Pb + Cu^{++} \rightarrow Pb^{++} + Cu$**

start here

8. In procedure 4, the Fe^{+++} ion was reduced to the Fe^{++} ion. (a) What was the reducing agent? (b) What change did the ion undergo? (c) Write the net ionic equation for the overall reaction: $2FeCl_3 + SnCl_2 \rightarrow 2FeCl_2 + SnCl_4$.

$2Fe^{+++} + 2e^- \rightarrow 2Fe^{++}$

$Sn^{++} \rightarrow Sn^{++++} + 2e^-$

work on board

(a) **Sn^{++} ion**

(b) **Sn^{++} oxidized to Sn^{++++}**

(c) **$2Fe^{+++} + Sn^{++} \rightarrow 2Fe^{++} + Sn^{++++}$**

9. The permanganate ion, MnO_4^-, which is purple in color, is a strong oxidizing agent. The manganese(II) ion, Mn^{++}, is practically colorless. (a) What occurred during the addition of the permanganate to the Fe^{++} ions? (b) What was oxidized? (c) What was reduced? (d) What changes in oxidation number occurred?

(a) **The almost colorless (pale green) solution of Fe^{++} changes to the yellow-brown of Fe^{+++}.**

(b) **The Fe^{++} is oxidized to Fe^{+++}.**

(c) **MnO_4^- is reduced to Mn^{++}.**

(d) **Mn changed from +7 to +2. Fe changed from +3 to +2.**   *+2 to +3*

Exercises and Experiments in Modern Chemistry
Holt, Rinehart and Winston, Publishers

Relative Solubilities of the Group II Metals

EXPERIMENT
26

The elements of the second column in the periodic table are called the *alkaline earth metals.* They form oxides (or peroxides) and hydroxides with properties generally similar to those of the alkali metals. Their hydroxides, carbonates, chromates, oxalates, and sulfates vary in solubility.

In this experiment you will test the solubilities of the above mentioned anions with each of the alkaline earth metallic ions and then, using qualitative analysis, determine which metal ions are present in an unknown solution. Review Chapter 25, Sections 25.1, 25.8, 25.10, 25.12 and 25.13, for additional information.

OBJECTIVE

After completing this experiment, you should be able to identify one or more alkaline earth metals in solution by qualitative analysis. You should also be able to devise a scheme to separate a mixture of three alkaline earth metallic ions.

MATERIALS

0.2 M $(NH_4)_2C_2O_4$	6 M $NH_{3(aq)}$	0.2 M $Mg(NO_3)_2$
2 M $(NH_4)_2CO_3$ with $NH_{3(aq)}$	0.5 M K_2CrO_4	double unknown
1 M $(NH_4)_2SO_4$	0.1 M $Ba(NO_3)_2$	single unknown
0.1 M $Ca(NO_3)_2$	0.1 M $Sr(NO_3)_2$	plastic sheet

SAFETY

Begin this experiment by taking the necessary safety precautions. Wear safety goggles, apron, and gloves. During the procedures of this experiment, you are required to handle various chemicals. Do not touch the chemicals with your hands. Carefully check the labels on the reagent bottles and containers before removing any of their contents. Never use more of a chemical than directed. Conduct this experiment by using good safety techniques. See page 103.

Recording Your Results

After completing each of the procedures, record your results in the data table provided at the end of the procedures.

PROCEDURES

1. Make a full page copy of the data table. Place a plastic sheet over the data sheet. Place drops for each reagent (negative ion) in the appropriate boxes. Add a drop of each of the solutions (alkaline earth ions) so that all of these positive ions have been tested for solubility

with all of the negative reagent ions. **Do not allow the dropper to touch the drops!** If a precipitate occurs, record its color. If there is no reaction, write "NR."

2. Study your results very carefully and then obtain a single unknown. This unknown contains one of the alkaline ions. Test the unknown ion with each of the negative reagent ions. Record your results and the identity of the unknown in the data table.

3. Obtain a double unknown. This unknown contains two alkaline earth ions. Test the unknown with each of the negative reagent ions. Your results will be some combination of your original observations in procedure 1. Record your observations and the identity of the unknown.

4. At the end of this experiment, ask your teacher how to dispose of all waste materials. Clean all apparatus and thoroughly wash your hands before leaving the laboratory.

DATA TABLE

Alkaline Earth Metals	Reagents				
	SO_4^{--}	$C_2O_4^{--}$	$NH_{3(aq)}$	CrO_4^{--}	CO_3^{--}
Mg^{++}	NR	NR	slight white PPT	NR	NR
Ca^{++}	NR	white PPT	NR	NR	white PPT
Sr^{++}	white PPT	white PPT	NR	NR	white PPT
Ba^{++}	white PPT	white PPT	NR	yellow PPT	white PPT
Single unknown					
Double unknown					

Single unknown

Double unknown

Exercises and Experiments in Modern Chemistry
Holt, Rinehart and Winston, Publishers

QUESTIONS

1. Which alkaline earth ion is the least soluble with the five reagents used in this experiment?
   Ba^{++}

2. Which alkaline earth ion is the most soluble with the five reagents used in this experiment?
   Mg^{++}

3. What can you conclude about the relative solubilities of the alkaline earth ions with the reagents in this experiment and their position in the periodic table?
   Magnesium, highest in the periodic table, is the most soluble, while barium, lowest in the

   table, is the least soluble. Solubility decreases as one moves down the column.

4. How could you analytically separate a solution containing a mixture of 0.1 M Mg^{++}, Sr^{++}, and Ba^{++} ions?
   Add $NH_{3(aq)}$. The Mg^{++} ion would precipitate. Decant the liquid containing the Sr^{++} and

   Ba^{++} ions. Add K_2CrO_4. $BaCrO_4$ would precipitate. Decant the liquid containing the Sr^{++}

   ions.

Correlating Your Facts
Review Chapter 24, Section 24.1, and Chapter 25, Section 25.1, and correlate what you have read in the textbook with what you have learned by performing this experiment.

Study the table on page 242. Read the following statements and indicate whether they are true or false. Place your answer in the space provided next to the statement.

1. Ionization energy decreases steadily as atomic radius increases.   _____**True**_____ 1.

2. The alkaline earth metals have higher ionization energies than the alkali metals.   _____**True**_____ 2.

3. The alkali metals have smaller atomic radii than the alkaline earth metals.   _____**False**_____ 3.

4. The Group II metals have higher densities than the Group I metals.   _____**True**_____ 4.

5. The Group II metals have higher melting points than the alkali metals.   _____**True**_____ 5.

6. ____**True**____   6. Beryllium is the least metallic of all the elements in Groups I and II.

7. ____**True**____   7. Cesium is the most metallic of all the elements in Groups I and II.

8. ____**False**____   8. Atomic radius, and metallic character, decrease as we move down Groups I and II.

9. ____**True**____   9. Judging from the table on the properties of these two groups of metals, ionization energy increases as we move across the periodic table.

10. ____**True**____   10. Compounds of the metals in Group II tend to be less soluble in water than those of the Group I metals.

PROPERTIES OF GROUP I AND GROUP II ELEMENTS

Element	Atomic Number	Melting Point °C	Boiling Point °C	Density (g/cm³)	Ionization Energy (kcal/mol)	Atomic Radius Å
Group I						
lithium	3	179	1317	0.53	126	1.55
sodium	11	97.8	892	0.97	120	1.90
potassium	19	63.6	774	0.86	102	2.35
rubidium	37	38.8	701	1.53	98	2.48
cesium	55	28.7	685	1.87	90	2.67
Group II						
beryllium	4	1278	2970	1.85	216	1.12
magnesium	12	651	1107	1.74	178	1.60
calcium	20	842	1487	1.54	142	1.97
strontium	38	769	1384	2.60	133	2.15
barium	56	725	1140	3.50	122	2.22

Exercises and Experiments in Modern Chemistry
Holt, Rinehart and Winston, Publishers

EXPERIMENT

Oxidation States of Transition Elements

The transition elements exhibit variable oxidation states and strong color. In the first-row transition metals, several $4s$ and $3d$ electrons are available to be transferred to or shared with other substances. Thus several oxidation states become possible. The color of transition metals and their compounds is due to the $3d$ electrons in their structure. The compounds of chromium are all colored, the name of the element coming from the Greek word *chroma,* meaning color. Chromium occurs in oxidation states $+2$, $+3$, and $+6$.

The hydrated Fe^{++} ion appears to be pale green. The hydrated Fe^{+++} ion usually undergoes hydrolysis so that its solutions have a yellow-brown color. The changes in the oxidation states observed in this experiment illustrate the ease or difficulty with which the transition elements undergo changes in their oxidation states. Review Chapter 26, Sections 26.1 to 26.4 and Section 26.16, for additional information.

OBJECTIVE

After completing this experiment, you should be able to show that typical transition metals may exist in a variety of oxidation states, each with characteristic colors, and to show how these oxidation states may be changed in oxidation-reduction reactions.

APPARATUS

centigram balance
test tube clamp

rubber stopper, No. 2
burner and tubing

graduated cylinder, 25 mL
6 test tubes, 18 × 150 mm

MATERIALS

$FeSO_4$
$3\ M\ H_2SO_4$
$3\%\ H_2O_2$
$0.1\ M\ K_2CrO_4$

$6\ M$ NaOH
mossy zinc
$0.16\ M\ Cr_2(SO_4)_3$

$0.1\ M\ FeCl_3$
$0.1\ M\ K_2Cr_2O_7$
$0.1\ M\ SnCl_2$

SAFETY

Begin this experiment by taking the necessary safety precautions. Wear safety goggles, apron, and gloves. Read all safety cautions in your procedures and discuss them with your teacher. During the procedures of this experiment, you are required to handle various chemicals. Do not touch the chemicals with your hands. Carefully check the labels on the reagent bottles and containers before removing any of their contents. Never use more of a chemical than directed. Conduct this experiment by using good safety techniques. See pages 103 and 106.

Recording Your Results

After completing each of the procedures, record your results in the spaces provided below.

PROCEDURES

Part I: Chromium

1. Add 5 mL of 6 M NaOH to 5 mL of 0.16 M $Cr_2(SO_4)_3$ in a test tube.

   Observations: **A green precipitate of $Cr(OH)_3$ forms.**

2. Add an excess of 6 M NaOH to the above until solution occurs. Add 3% H_2O_2 drop by drop until a color change occurs.

   Observations: **The green color changes to the yellow color of CrO_4^{--} ion.**

3. Record the color of a 0.1 M K_2CrO_4 solution. To 5 mL of 0.1 M K_2CrO_4 in a test tube, add 3 M H_2SO_4 drop by drop until a definite color change occurs. Compare this color with 5 mL of 0.1 M $K_2Cr_2O_7$ solution.

   Observations: **0.1 M K_2CrO_4 is yellow. The solution turns to the orange color of $Cr_2O_7^{--}$ ions upon addition of H_2SO_4.**

4. Add 3% H_2O_2 drop by drop to the above 5 mL of 0.1 M $K_2Cr_2O_7$ solution until a definite color change occurs.

   Observations: **The orange solution turns to the green color of Cr^{+++} ions.**

5. To 5 mL of $Cr_2(SO_4)_3$ in a Pyrex test tube, add two pieces of mossy zinc. Heat *gently* until a color change occurs.

   ^{2} ~~5~~ $+\ 3\,\text{ml}/H_2O$

    CAUTION
   Before you light the burner, check to see that long hair and loose clothing have been confined.

   The product causing the color is $Cr(H_2O)_6^{++}$.

   Observations: **The color changes to bright blue of the hydrated $Cr(H_2O)_6^{++}$ ion.**

Exercises and Experiments in Modern Chemistry
Holt, Rinehart and Winston, Publishers

6. Decant the above solution into another test tube. Stopper the test tube and shake the solution with the air in the test tube until another color change occurs.

Observations: **The green color of Cr^{+++} appears.**

Part II: Iron

7. Make a solution of FeSO$_4$ by dissolving 0.5 g of FeSO$_4$ in 15 mL of cold water in a test tube. *Do not agitate the solution unnecessarily, and do not apply heat.*

Observations: **A pale-green to colorless solution occurs. (Fe^{++} ions.)**

8. Stopper the test tube and shake the solution thoroughly for two minutes. Let it stand in the test tube rack for a few minutes. Then shake it thoroughly again. Observe any change in appearance of the contents of the tube. Fe(OH)SO$_4$ is formed and is only sparingly soluble. Set the tube aside to see if a brown precipitate finally appears.

Observations: **A yellow-brown color of Fe^{+++} ions occurs. Eventually Fe(OH)SO$_4$ precipitates.**

9. To 5 mL of 0.1 M FeCl$_3$ in a test tube, add 0.1 M SnCl$_2$ drop by drop until the color has completely changed.

Observations: **Yellow-brown color of Fe^{+++} ions changed to the pale-green color of Fe^{++}.**

10. At the end of this experiment, ask your teacher how to dispose of all waste materials. Clean all apparatus and thoroughly wash your hands. Check to see that the gas valve is completely shut off before leaving the laboratory.

QUESTIONS

1. (a) In procedure 2, what color change occurred when H$_2$O$_2$ was added? (b) What new chromium ion must have been produced? (c) What change in oxidation state occurred? (d) Was chromium oxidized or reduced?

(a) **Green changed to yellow.**

(b) **CrO$_4$$^{--}$ was produced.**

(c) **+3 to +6.**

(d) **Chromium was oxidized.**

2. Complete the table to the right by filling in the oxidation states and colors after completing the procedures of this experiment.

	Procedure Number	Substance	Oxidation State	Color
Part I Cr	----	Cr	0	silvery
	5	$Cr(H_2O)_6^{++}$	*give them* +2	blue
	1	$Cr(OH)_3$	+3	green
	3	$K_2CrO_4^{--}$	+6	yellow
	3	$K_2Cr_2O_7^{--}$	+6	orange
Part II Fe	----	Fe	0	silvery
	7	$FeSO_4$	+2	pale green
	8	$Fe(OH)SO_4$	+3	yellow brown

3. (a) In procedure 4 what color change occurred when H_2O_2 was added? (b) What does this color indicate about the oxidation state of chromium? (c) Was chromium oxidized or reduced?

(a) **Orange turned green.**

(b) **Cr^{+++} was produced.**

(c) **Cr changed from $Cr_2O_7^{--}$ (+6) to Cr^{+++} (+3). Cr was reduced.**

4. (a) In procedure 6, what color change occurred when the solution was shaken in the presence of air? (b) What changes in oxidation state occurred to chromium? (c) What was the oxidizing agent?

(a) **Blue turned green.**

(b) **Cr changed from +2 to +3.**

(c) **Oxygen in the air was the oxidizing agent.**

5. In which oxidation state is iron more stable in air? Answer this question on the basis of your observations in procedure 8.

Iron is more stable in air as Fe^{+++}. Upon exposure to air, Fe^{++} oxidizes to Fe^{+++}.

6. What change in oxidation state occurred to the iron when $SnCl_2$ was added to $FeCl_3$?

A yellow-brown color of Fe^{+++} changed to the pale-green color of Fe^{++}. The oxidation state changed from +3 to +2.

Exercises and Experiments in Modern Chemistry
Holt, Rinehart and Winston, Publishers

EXPERIMENT
28

Aluminum and Its Compounds

Aluminum is a self-protective metal that rapidly becomes covered with an adherent impervious layer of aluminum oxide. Some acids react with aluminum readily, while other acids do not react at all. A strong hydroxide also reacts with aluminum, setting free hydrogen and forming an aluminate.

Aqueous solutions of most aluminum salts are acidic because of the hydrolysis of the hydrated aluminum ion, $Al(H_2O)_6^{+++}$, which may be regarded as a Brønsted acid according to the following reaction:

$$Al(H_2O)_6^{+++} + H_2O \rightleftharpoons Al(H_2O)_5(OH)^{++} + H_3O^+$$

Aluminum hydroxide is amphoteric. Review Chapter 27, Sections 27.2 and 27.4, and Chapter 15, Section 15.9, for additional information.

OBJECTIVE
After completing this experiment, you should be able to demonstrate some of the chemical properties of aluminum and its compounds.

APPARATUS
graduated cylinder, 10 mL   solid rubber stopper, No. 2   test tube rack
9 test tubes, 18 × 150 mm

MATERIALS
aluminum chips or granules $0.2\ M$ AlCl$_3$ $6\ M$ HNO$_3$
red and blue litmus papers $0.3\ M$ (NH$_4$)$_2$S $0.1\ M$ Al$_2$(SO$_4$)$_3$
$4\ M$ NH$_{3(aq)}$ $2.5\ M$ NaOH $0.3\ M$ Na$_2$CO$_3$
$6\ M$ H$_2$SO$_4$ $6\ M$ HCl

SAFETY

Begin this experiment by taking the necessary safety precautions. Wear safety goggles, apron, and gloves. Read all safety cautions in the experiment and discuss them with your teacher. During the procedures of this experiment, you are required to handle various chemicals. Do not touch the chemicals with your hands. Carefully check the labels on the reagent bottles and containers before removing any of their contents. Conduct this experiment by using good safety techniques. See pages 103 to 106.

Recording Your Results
After completing each procedure, record your observations in the appropriate spaces.

PROCEDURES

1. Test 5 mL of 0.2 M $AlCl_3$ with red and blue litmus papers. Repeat for 0.1 M $Al_2(SO_4)_3$.

   Observations: **Both salt solutions turn blue litmus to red.**

> **CAUTION**
> The acids and bases that you will be working with in procedures 2 through 5 are caustic and corrosive. Avoid contact with skin and eyes. Avoid breathing their vapors. Be certain to wear safety goggles, apron, and gloves. If any of these chemicals should spill on you, immediately flush the area with water and then notify your teacher.

2. Cover a few aluminum chips or granules with 6 M HCl in a test tube.

   Observations: **H_2 gas is produced. The aluminum reacts readily with HCl.**

   ---

3. Repeat procedure 2 using 6 M H_2SO_4, 6 M HNO_3, and 2.5 M NaOH.

   Observations: **Aluminum reacts readily with H_2SO_4 and NaOH, liberating H_2 gas. There is no apparent reaction of aluminum with HNO_3.**

   ---

4. To 5 mL of 0.2 M $AlCl_3$, add 1 mL of 4 M $NH_{3(aq)}$ in a test tube.

   Observations: **A white gelatinous precipitate of $Al(OH)_3$ is produced.**

   ---

5. Stopper the above test tube and shake to flocculate the precipitate. Allow the precipitate to settle, and pour off the supernatant liquid. See page 105 for the proper technique of decanting a liquid. Transfer one-half of the precipitate to a second test tube. To the precipitate in one test tube, add 1 mL of 2.5 M NaOH. To the other test tube, add 1 mL of 6 M HCl.

   Observations: **Precipitate dissolves in both HCl and NaOH. $Al(OH)_3$ is amphoteric.**

Exercises and Experiments in Modern Chemistry
Holt, Rinehart and Winston, Publishers

6. Add 1 mL of 0.3 M Na_2CO_3 to 5 mL of 0.1 M $Al_2(SO_4)_3$ in a test tube.

   Observations: **A white precipitate of Al(OH)₃ is formed.**

   (If Al₂(CO₃)₃ formed initially, it would be immediately

   hydrolyzed, causing Al(OH)₃ to form.)

   _____

   _____

   _____

7. Add 5 mL of 0.3 M $(NH_4)_2S$ to 5 mL of 0.1 M $Al_2(SO_4)_3$ in a test tube.

   Observations: **A white precipitate of Al(OH)₃ is formed.**

   (Al₂S₃ was not formed, since it is a salt of a weak acid and

   a weak hydroxide, therefore undergoing hydrolysis.)

   _____

   _____

   _____

   _____

8. Clean all apparatus at the end of this experiment. Ask your teacher how to dispose of all waste materials. Remember to wash your hands thoroughly before leaving the laboratory.

QUESTIONS

1. To what color did the litmus paper change when immersed in aluminum chloride and aluminum sulfate? Explain.

   Both salt solutions turn blue litmus to red because of the hydrolysis of the Al(H₂O)₆⁺³ ion.

   _____

2. Balance the following reactions.

   (a) $\underline{\textbf{2}}$ $Al_{(s)}$ + $\underline{\textbf{6}}$ $HCl \rightleftarrows \underline{\textbf{2}}$ $AlCl_3$ + $\underline{\textbf{3H}_{2(g)}}$

   (b) $\underline{\textbf{2}}$ $Al_{(s)}$ + $\underline{\textbf{2}}$ $NaOH$ + $\underline{\textbf{2}}$ $H_2O \rightleftarrows \underline{\textbf{2}}$ $NaAlO_2$ + $\underline{\textbf{3H}_{2(g)}}$

   (c) $Al_2(SO_4)_3$ + $\underline{\textbf{3}}$ Na_2CO_3 + $\underline{\textbf{6}}$ $H_2O \rightleftarrows \underline{\textbf{2}}$ $Al(OH)_{3(s)}$ + $\underline{\textbf{3Na}_2\textbf{SO}_4}$ + $\underline{\textbf{3}}$ H_2CO_3

(d)* $Al_2(SO_4)_3$ + **3** $(NH_4)_2S$ + **6** $H_2O \rightleftarrows$ **2Al(OH)$_{3(s)}$** + **3** $(NH_4)_2SO_4$ + **3** H_2S

*Hint: Did the precipitate in procedure 7 look identical to the precipitate in procedure 6?

Exercises and Experiments in Modern Chemistry
Holt, Rinehart and Winston, Publishers

EXPERIMENT

Halide Ions

The principal oxidation state of the halogens is -1. With the exception of fluorine, they may exist in other oxidation states. The specific tests that you will develop in this experiment involve the production of recognizable precipitates and complex ions. You will use your observations to determine the halide ion content of an unknown solution. Review Chapter 30, The Halogen Family, for additional information.

OBJECTIVE

After completing this experiment, you should be able to identify the halogen ions F^-, Cl^-, Br^-, and I^-.

APPARATUS

graduated cylinder, 10 mL	test tube rack	12 test tubes, 18 × 150 mm

MATERIALS

5% NaOCl (commercial bleach)	0.1 M NaF	0.2 M KBr
3% starch solution	4 M $NH_{3(aq)}$	0.1 M NaCl
0.5 M $Ca(NO_3)_2$	0.2 M $Na_2S_2O_3$	0.1 M $AgNO_3$
0.2 M KI		

SAFETY

Begin this experiment by taking the necessary safety precautions. Wear safety goggles, apron, and gloves. During the procedures of this experiment, you are required to handle various chemicals. Do not touch the chemicals with your hands. Carefully check the labels on the reagent bottles and containers before removing any of their contents. Never use more of a chemical than directed. Conduct this experiment by using good safety techniques. See pages 103 and 106.

Recording Your Results

After completing each procedure, record your observations in the appropriate spaces.

PROCEDURES

1. Place 5 mL of NaF, NaCl, KBr, and KI in separate test tubes. Add 1 mL of 0.5 M Ca(NO$_3$)$_2$ to each of the test tubes.

   Observations:

   F$^-$ **A white precipitate forms.**

   Cl$^-$ **Clear**

   Br$^-$ **Clear**

   I$^-$ **Clear**

2. Place 5 mL of NaF, NaCl, KBr, and KI in separate clean test tubes. Add 1 mL of 0.1 M AgNO$_3$ to each of the test tubes. Record the color of any precipitates formed. Indicate which, if any, did not form a precipitate.

   Observations:

   F$^-$ **Clear**

   Cl$^-$ **A white precipitate forms.**

   Br$^-$ **A pale-yellow precipitate forms.**

   I$^-$ **A yellow-tan precipitate forms.**

3. Pour half of each of the precipitates from procedure 2 into separate clean test tubes. To each of the first set of test tubes containing the precipitates, add 5 mL of 4 M NH$_{3(aq)}$.

   Observations:

   Cl$^-$ **The precipitate dissolves completely.**

   Br$^-$ **The precipitate only slightly dissolves.**

   I$^-$ **The precipitate does not dissolve.**

4. To the second set of test tubes containing the precipitates from procedure 2 add 5 mL of 0.2 M Na$_2$S$_2$O$_3$.

   Observations:

   Cl$^-$ **The precipitate dissolves completely.**

   Br$^-$ **The precipitate dissolves completely.**

   I$^-$ **The precipitate does not dissolve.**

Exercises and Experiments in Modern Chemistry
Holt, Rinehart and Winston, Publishers

5. Place 2 mL of NaF, NaCl, KBr, and KI in separate test tubes. Add 5 mL of 3% starch solution to each test tube. Add a drop or two of 5% NaOCl (commercial bleach).

   Observations:

   F⁻ **No change** _____

   Cl⁻ **No change** _____

   Br⁻ **No change** _____

   I⁻ **Turns blue** _____

6. Obtain an unknown solution containing a halide ion and repeat procedures 1–5.

   Observations:

   1. **Student answers** _____

   2. _____

   3. _____

   4. _____

   5. _____

7. Optional: Obtain an unknown solution containing a mixture of halide ions. Repeat procedures 1–5.

   Observations:

   1. **Student answers** _____

   2. _____

   3. _____

   4. _____

   5. _____

8. Clean all apparatus at the end of this experiment. Ask your teacher how to dispose of all waste materials. Remember to wash your hands thoroughly before leaving the laboratory.

QUESTIONS

1. Which procedure(s) confirm(s) the presence of (a) F⁻ ions? (b) Cl⁻ ions? (c) Br⁻ ions? (d) I⁻ ions?

   (a) **Procedure 1**

   (b) **Procedures 2 and 3**

   (c) **Procedures 2 and 4**

   (d) **Procedure 5**

2. Identify your unknown(s) and state the experimental evidence for your conclusions.

   Student answers

Exercises and Experiments in Modern Chemistry
Holt, Rinehart and Winston, Publishers

Radioactivity

The types of radiation emitted by radioactive materials include alpha particles, which are helium nuclei; beta particles, which are high speed electrons; and gamma rays, which are extremely high frequency photons. Alpha particles will discharge an electroscope, but their penetrating power is not great enough to affect a Geiger counter tube. A few centimeters of air will stop an alpha particle. Beta particles can be detected by a Geiger counter tube and can penetrate several centimeters of air. Several layers of paper or aluminum foil, however, can stop beta particles. Gamma rays, however, can penetrate through several centimeters of concrete.

The environment contains a small amount of natural radiation, which is detected by a Geiger counter. This is called background radiation and is primarily due to cosmic rays (from stars). A small amount of radiation may also come from the walls, dust particles, etc. Review Chapter 31, Sections 31.3 and 31.5, for additional information.

OBJECTIVE

After completing this experiment, you will be able to demonstrate the range and penetrability of beta particles.

APPARATUS

radioactivity demonstrator

MATERIALS

Thallium 204 (beta source)   aluminum foil   several index cards

SAFETY

Begin this experiment by taking the necessary safety precautions. Wear safety goggles, apron, and gloves. Read all safety cautions in your procedures and discuss them with your teacher. Conduct this experiment by using good safety techniques. See pages 101 to 103. Wash your hands thoroughly at the end of this experiment.

Recording Your Results

After completing each procedure, record your results in the data tables provided at the end of the procedures.

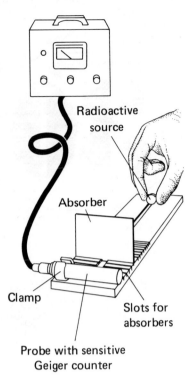

Radioactive
source

Absorber

Clamp

Slots for
absorbers

Probe with sensitive
Geiger counter

Figure 30-1

PROCEDURES

Part I: Background count

1. Carefully read the directions on the operation of your counter. Set the counter to zero. Do not have any radioactive sources within a meter of the Geiger counter tube. Turn on the counter for one minute and count the frequency of clicks. Record in Data Table I. Repeat for 2 more trials. The average of these trials will be your background count in counts per minute (cpm).

Part II: Range of beta particles in various media

2. Air: Place the beta source approximately 5 cm from the Geiger tube. See Figure 30-1 for the proper setup.

 CAUTION
You should never directly handle a radioactive source. Be certain you are wearing gloves when handling the beta source (Thallium 204).

Determine the count for 1 minute. Record in Data Table II. Move the source back another 5 cm and determine the count for 1 minute. Continue this procedure until you reach background or have completed 10 trials.

3. Paper: Place the beta source approximately 5 cm from the Geiger tube. Place a single index card in front of the beta source and determine the count for one minute. Record in Data Table III. Repeat this procedure with an additional index card. Keep the distance from the source to the Geiger tube constant. Continue adding index cards until background is reached or 10 trials have been completed.

4. Aluminum: Repeat procedure 3, but use sheets of aluminum foil in place of index cards.

5. Return the beta source to your teacher and wash your hands thoroughly at the end of this experiment.

DATA TABLES

DATA TABLE I

Background Count	
Trial	Counts/min
1	
2	
3	
Average	

Exercises and Experiments in Modern Chemistry
Holt, Rinehart and Winston, Publishers

DATA TABLE II

Air

Distance	Count	Distance	Count	Distance	Count

DATA TABLE III

Index Cards		Aluminum	
No. Sheets	Count	No. Sheets	Count
0		0	
1		1	
2		2	
3		3	
4		4	
5		5	
6		6	
7		7	
8		8	
9		9	
10		10	

QUESTIONS

1. On a separate piece of graph paper plot a graph of counts per minute versus distance between the beta source and the Geiger tube. Place the counts per minute on the vertical axis and the distance on the horizontal axis. Remember to subtract the background count from each of the readings.

Graph is an inverse relationship

2. On a separate piece of graph paper plot a graph of the number of index cards versus counts per minute. Place the counts per minute on the vertical axis.

Graph is an inverse relationship

3. On a separate piece of graph paper plot a graph for aluminum foil versus counts per minute. Place the counts per minute on the vertical axis.

Graph is an inverse relationship

4. According to the 3 graphs, which substance is the greatest absorber of beta particles?
The aluminum foil is the greatest absorber of beta particles.

Exercises and Experiments in Modern Chemistry
Holt, Rinehart and Winston, Publishers

Observing a Candle

Scientific theory is based upon observations. As a beginning chemistry student, your observational powers are probably not as refined as those of a scientist. In this experiment, you will be given the opportunity to develop these skills by making as many observations of a candle as you possibly can.

Observations are either *quantitative* or *qualitative*. *Quantitative* data specifies quantity, that is, how much or how many. For example, the candle is 5 cm tall is a *quantitative* observation. A *qualitative* observation simply describes a quality of an observation. For example, the candle is white and cylindrical in shape are *qualitative* observations.

Scientists must always make a clear distinction between an observation and an *interpretation*. An *interpretation* is a conclusion based upon observations. For example, the candle produces CO_2 and H_2O gases is an *interpretation*, since CO_2 and H_2O gases cannot be directly observed. Review Chapter 1, Section 4.1, for additional information.

OBJECTIVE

After completing this experiment, you should improve your observational techniques. You should be able to distinguish between qualitative and quantitative observations. You should also be able to distinguish between interpretations and observations.

MATERIALS

candle, with base   ruler   matches

SAFETY

Begin this experiment by taking the necessary safety precautions. Wear safety goggles, apron, and gloves. Before lighting the candle in this experiment, check to see that you and your partner have confined loose clothing and long hair. Conduct this experiment by using good safety techniques. See pages 101 and 102. At the end of this experiment, be certain to dispose of the matches in the proper waste container.

Recording Your Results

Record your observations in the data table provided at the end of the procedure.

PROCEDURE

Using the materials provided, record all the possible observations of burning a candle.

DATA TABLE—OBSERVATIONS

1 **Student answers**	10
2	11
3	12
4	13
5	14
6	15
7	16
8	17
9	18

Analyzing Your Data

Classify your observations according to whether they are quantitative or qualitative. Use the data analysis table provided. If you had any interpretations, list them separately.

DATA ANALYSIS TABLE — OBSERVATIONS

Quantitative	Qualitative
1 **Student answers**	1
2	2
3	3
4	4
5	5
6	6
7	7
8	8
9	9

INTERPRETATIONS

1 **Student answers**	4
2	5
3	6

Exercises and Experiments in Modern Chemistry
Holt, Rinehart and Winston, Publishers

Equilibrium Expression

EXPERIMENT

SE-2

Chemical equilibrium is a state of balance in which the rates of opposing reactions are exactly equal. When the reaction

$$Fe^{+++} \quad + \quad SCN^- \quad \rightleftarrows \quad FeSCN^{++} \qquad (1)$$

(light yellow)   **(colorless)**   **(blood red)**

reaches equilibrium, the rate at which $FeSCN^{++}$ is produced is exactly equal to the rate at which $FeSCN^{++}$ breaks up into Fe^{+++} and SCN^-. If additional Fe^{+++} ions were added, a new equilibrium condition would be created, since the concentrations of reactants and product would be changed. However, there exists a certain mathematical relationship between the concentrations of the products and the concentrations of reactants that yields a constant value for a given reaction at a specified temperature. This relationship between products and reactants is called the *equilibrium expression.* The *equilibrium constant* is the numerical value of the equilibrium expression.

In this experiment you will attempt to experimentally determine the equilibrium expression for reaction (1). You will vary the concentration of one of the reactants, Fe^{+++}, and then determine the concentrations of each species at equilibrium.

When additional Fe^{+++} is added to reaction (1), the color of the solution becomes a deeper red (indicating an increase in $FeSCN^{++}$ ions). The depth of the color change is in direct proportion to the concentration of $FeSCN^{++}$ at equilibrium. You will use a color photometer to determine the change in color, thereby allowing you to calculate the final concentrations of the product and reactants.

When the final concentrations are known, you will try these values in three different mathematical relationships:

$$\frac{[FeSCN^{++}]}{[Fe^{+++}] + [SCN^-]} \qquad (2)$$

$$\frac{[Fe^{+++}] \, [FeSCN^{++}]}{[SCN^-]} \qquad (3)$$

$$\frac{[FeSCN^{++}]}{[Fe^{+++}] \, [SCN^-]} \qquad (4)$$

The correct relationship will be the one that yields approximately the same numerical values regardless of the changes in equilibrium concentrations. Review Chapter 21, Sections 21.1 to 21.3, for additional information.

OBJECTIVE

After completing this experiment, you should be able to experimentally determine the equilibrium expression of a chemical reaction and state the expression in terms of the products and reactants.

APPARATUS

color photometer with test tubes
5 test tubes, 18 x 150 mm

test tube rack
graduated cylinder, 10 mL

stirring rod

MATERIALS

0.6 M HNO_3

0.200 M $Fe(NO_3)_3$*

0.00200 M KSCN*

*Refer to the teacher's edition for preparation of these solutions.

SAFETY

Begin this experiment by taking the necessary safety precautions. Wear safety goggles, apron, and gloves. Read all cautions in your procedures and discuss them with your teacher. Conduct this experiment by using good safety techniques. See pages 106.

Recording Your Results

Record the color photometer value of each test tube in the data table provided at the end of the procedures.

PROCEDURES

1. Carefully measure out 5.0 mL of 0.200 M $Fe(NO_3)_3$ in a 10 mL graduated cylinder. Pour this into a test tube labeled number 1.

CAUTION
Nitric acid is caustic and corrosive. Avoid contact with skin and eyes. If any of the chemicals in procedures 2 through 7 should spill on you, immediately flush the area with water and then notify your teacher.

2. Carefully measure out another 5.0 mL of 0.200 M $Fe(NO_3)_3$ in the 10 mL graduated cylinder. Add 5.0 mL of 0.6 M HNO_3. Mix well. Pour 5.0 mL of this mixture into a test tube labeled number 2.

3. Add 5.0 mL of 0.6 M HNO_3 to the remaining 5.0 mL of the mixture in the graduated cylinder. Mix well. Pour 5.0 mL of this mixture into another test tube labeled number 3.

4. Repeat procedure 3 until you have 6 test tubes labeled 1-6.

5. Discard the contents of test tube 2. (The first dilution is not great enough to provide a measurable difference in light absorption.)

Exercises and Experiments in Modern Chemistry
Holt, Rinehart and Winston, Publishers

6. Add 5.0 mL of 0.00200 M KSCN to test tubes 1, 3, 4, 5, and 6. Mix thoroughly.

7. Transfer the solutions in the 5 test tubes to the special test tubes designed to be used with the color photometer. Follow the instructions on the operation of the color photometer and obtain absorbance readings for test tubes 1, 3, 4, 5, and 6. Record your results in the data table.

8. Clean all apparatus at the end of this experiment. Ask your teacher how to dispose of all waste materials. Remember to wash your hands thoroughly before leaving the laboratory.

DATA AND CALCULATIONS TABLES

DATA

Test Tube Number	Absorbance Value
1	1.0
3	0.94
4	0.89
5	0.80
6	0.72

CALCULATIONS

Test Tube No.	Initial Concentration (M)		Absorbance	Equilibrium Concentration (M)		
	A	B	C	D	E	F
	$[Fe^{+++}]$	$[SCN^-]$		$[FeSCN^{++}]$	$[Fe^{+++}]$	$[SCN^-]$
1	0.100	0.00100	1.0	0.0010	0.099	0.0
3	0.0250	0.00100	0.94	0.00094	0.024	0.000060
4	0.0125	0.00100	0.89	0.00089	0.012	0.00011
5	0.00625	0.00100	0.80	0.00080	0.0055	0.00020
6	0.00312	0.00100	0.72	0.00072	0.0024	0.00028

	Value of K					RATIO: largest K
	1	3	4	5	6	smallest K
$\dfrac{FeSCN^{++}}{[Fe^{+++}] + [SCN^-]}$		0.039	0.076	0.14	0.27	6.9
$\dfrac{[Fe^{+++}][FeSCN^{++}]}{[SCN^-]}$		0.38	0.094	0.022	0.0062	61
$\dfrac{[FeSCN^{++}]}{[Fe^{+++}][SCN^-]}$		650	700	730	1100	1.6

CALCULATIONS

1. Calculate the initial concentrations (before reacting) of Fe^{+++} from the dilution factors used in procedures 1–5. For example, for test tube 2 you added 5 mL of 0.200 M $Fe(NO_3)_3$ to 5 mL of 0.6 M HNO_3. The dilution factor is

$$\frac{5\text{ mL } Fe(NO_3)_3}{5\text{ mL } Fe(NO_3)_3 + 5\text{ mL } HNO_3} \times 0.200\ M\ Fe(NO_3)_3 = 0.100\ M\ Fe(NO_3)_3.$$

Remember that each dilution with HNO_3 is followed by another dilution with 5 mL of KSCN. Record the values for all 5 test tubes in the calculations tables (column A).

Test tube 1: $\dfrac{5\text{ mL } Fe(NO_3)_3}{5\text{ mL } Fe(NO_3)_3 + 5\text{ mL KSCN}} \times 0.200\ M\ Fe(NO_3)_3 = 0.100\ M\ Fe(NO_3)_3$

3:
$$\frac{5\text{ mL } Fe^{+++}}{5\text{ mL } Fe^{+++} + 5\text{ mL } H^+} \times \frac{5\text{ mL } Fe^{+++}}{5\text{ mL } Fe^{+++} + 5\text{ mL } SCN^-} \times 0.100\ M\ Fe^{+++} = 0.0250\ M\ Fe^{+++}$$

4:
$$\frac{5\text{ mL } Fe^{+++}}{5\text{ mL } Fe^{+++} + 5\text{ mL } H^+} \times \frac{5\text{ mL } Fe^{+++}}{5\text{ mL } Fe^{+++} + 5\text{ mL } SCN^-} \times 0.050\ M\ Fe^{+++} = 0.0125\ M\ Fe^{+++}$$

5:
$$\frac{5\text{ mL } Fe^{+++}}{5\text{ mL } Fe^{+++} + 5\text{ mL } H^+} \times \frac{5\text{ mL } Fe^{+++}}{5\text{ mL } Fe^{+++} + 5\text{ mL } SCN^-} \times 0.025\ M\ Fe^{+++} = 0.00625\ M\ Fe^{+++}$$

6:
$$\frac{5\text{ mL } Fe^{+++}}{5\text{ mL } Fe^{+++} + 5\text{ mL } H^+} \times \frac{5\text{ mL } Fe^{+++}}{5\text{ mL } Fe^{+++} + 5\text{ mL } SCN^-} \times 0.0125\ M\ Fe^{+++} = 0.00312\ M\ Fe^{+++}$$

2. Calculate the initial concentrations of SCN^- for test tubes 1, 3, 4, 5, 6 (column B). Remember that each 5 mL of 0.00200 M KSCN was mixed with 5 mL of $Fe(NO_3)_3$.

$$\frac{5\text{ mL } SCN^-}{5\text{ mL } SCN^- + 5\text{ mL } Fe^{+++}} \times 0.00200\ M\ SCN^- = 0.00100\ M\ SCN^-\text{ for all test tubes}$$

Exercises and Experiments in Modern Chemistry
Holt, Rinehart and Winston, Publishers

NAME _____ CLASS _____ DATE _____

3. The absorbance values you measured on the color photometer must be adjusted so that the values are based on test tube 1 having a value of 1.0. The values of the other mixtures should all read less than 1. If your instrument was adjusted already in such a manner, then simply record these values in column C of your calculations table. If your instrument was not capable of adjusting test tube 1 to a reading of 1.0, then divide each of the values of test tubes 1, 3, 4, 5, and 6 by the value obtained for test tube 1. Record in column C.

Same as absorbance values. If the values had originally read 2.00, 1.88, 1.78, 1.60, 1.44, then divide all values by 2.

$$\frac{2.00}{2} = 1.00 \qquad \frac{1.88}{2} = 0.94 \qquad \text{etc.}$$

4. Calculate the equilibrium concentration of $FeSCN^{++}$. In test tube 1 the initial concentration of Fe^{+++} was $0.100\ M$ and the initial concentration of SCN^- was $0.001\ M$. Since the Fe^{+++} concentration is a thousandfold greater than SCN^-, we can assume that practically all the SCN^- ions are consumed. From the balanced equation, the mole ratio of $FeSCN^{++}$ to SCN^- is one-to-one. Therefore, the final concentration of $FeSCN^{++}$ in the first test tube must be $0.00100\ M$, the same as the initial SCN^- concentration. To calculate the $FeSCN^{++}$ concentration for the remaining test tubes, simply multiply the original concentration of SCN^- ($0.00100\ M$) by the adjusted absorbance values. We can use the absorbance values in this way, since depth of color is directly proportional to the concentration of $FeSCN^{++}$. Record your values in column D.

Test tube 3: $0.00100\ M \times 0.94 = 0.00094\ M$
4: $0.00100\ M \times 0.89 = 0.00089\ M$
5: $0.00100\ M \times 0.80 = 0.00080\ M$
6: $0.00100\ M \times 0.72 = 0.00072\ M$

5. Calculate the Fe^{+++} concentration at equilibrium for each test tube. The equilibrium concentration of Fe^{+++} is simply the initial Fe^{+++} concentration (column A) less the concentration of $FeSCN^{++}$ that formed (column D). Record your results in column E.

Test tube 1: $0.100\ M - 0.0010\ M = 0.099\ M$
3: $0.0250\ M - 0.00094\ M = 0.024\ M$
4: $0.0125\ M - 0.00089\ M = 0.012\ M$
5: $0.00625\ M - 0.00080\ M = 0.0055\ M$
6: $0.00312\ M - 0.00072\ M = 0.0024\ M$

Exercises and Experiments in Modern Chemistry
Holt, Rinehart and Winston, Publishers

6. Calculate the SCN⁻ concentration for each test tube at equilibrium. The final concentration of SCN⁻ is the difference between the initial concentration of SCN⁻ (column B) and the concentration of FeSCN⁺⁺ (column D). Record your results in column F.

$$
\begin{aligned}
\text{Test tube 1:} \quad & 0.00100\ M - 0.00100\ M = 0.0\ M \\
\text{3:} \quad & 0.00100\ M - 0.00094\ M = 0.000060\ M \\
\text{4:} \quad & 0.00100\ M - 0.00089\ M = 0.00011\ M \\
\text{5:} \quad & 0.00100\ M - 0.00080\ M = 0.00020\ M \\
\text{6:} \quad & 0.00100\ M - 0.00072\ M = 0.00028\ M
\end{aligned}
$$

7. Using the equilibrium concentration values of columns D, E, and F, determine the values of K for test tubes 3–6 for mathematical relationship (2) in the introductory section. Record all 4 values of K in the calculations table. Repeat for mathematical relationships (3) and (4) of the introductory section.

Test tube 3

$$\frac{[0.00094]}{[0.024] + [0.000060]}$$

Relationship (3)

$$\frac{[0.024]\,[0.00094]}{[0.000060]}$$

Relationship (4)

$$\frac{[0.00094]}{[0.024]\,[0.000060]}$$

Test tube 4

$$\frac{[0.00089]}{[0.012] + [0.00011]}$$

$$\frac{[0.012]\,[0.00089]}{[0.00011]}$$

$$\frac{[0.00089]}{[0.012]\,[0.00011]}$$

Test tube 5

$$\frac{[0.00080]}{[0.0055] + [0.00020]}$$

$$\frac{[0.0055]\,[0.00080]}{[0.00020]}$$

$$\frac{[0.00080]}{[0.0055]\,[0.00020]}$$

Test tube 6

$$\frac{[0.00072]}{[0.0024] + [0.00028]}$$

$$\frac{[0.0024]\,[0.00072]}{[0.00028]}$$

$$\frac{[0.00072]}{[0.0024]\,[0.00028]}$$

8. For ratio (2) determine the lowest and highest value of K. Then calculate the ratio of the highest to lowest value of K. Repeat for ratios (3) and (4). Record.

$$(2)\ \frac{0.27}{0.039} = 6.9 \qquad (3)\ \frac{0.38}{0.0062} = 61 \qquad (4)\ \frac{1100}{650} = 1.6$$

9. If there were no experimental errors, the ratio of the highest value over lowest value of K for one of the mathematical relationships (2), (3), or (4) would be one-to-one. It is unlikely that your results will yield such a ratio. Assuming that the relationship with the lowest ratio in question 8 is the correct equilibrium expression, express in words the mathematical relationship between reactants and products that yields a nearly constant value.

$$\frac{[FeSCN^{++}]}{[Fe^{+++}]\,[SCN^-]}$$ **yields the lowest ratio and is, therefore, most nearly constant.**

Expressed in words: the ratio of the product divided by the product of reactants is a constant value.

Exercises and Experiments in Modern Chemistry
Holt, Rinehart and Winston, Publishers